Contents

National and regional listings, information and statistics

A-Z of Federation members, associates and subscribers

Advertisers

Cover design by Studio Eleven, www.studioeleven.uk.com

Advertising, Design and Production by Typecast Colour
T: 01892 838382   www.typecast.co.uk

Advertising Consultant Natalie Tuerena / Gareth Macfarlane T: 0845 226 0477

Published by the National Housing Federation, Lion Court, 25 Procter Street, London WC1V 6NY
T: 020 7067 1010   Fax: 020 7067 1011
E: info@housing.org.uk   www.housing.org.uk

© National Housing Federation 2013

ISBN 978 0 86297 576 0

This Directory has been prod... ...-managed sustainable forestry
programme and manufactured... ...has ISO 9001 quality and
ISO 14001 environmental acc... ...rocess. We would also like to
encourage you to please recyc...

Head Office

National Housing Federation
Lion Court
25 Procter Street
London WC1V 6NY
Tel: 020 7067 1010

E: info@housing.org.uk
W: www.housing.org.uk

Email us
bookshop@housing.org.uk
communications@housing.org.uk
events@housing.org.uk
marketing@housing.org.uk
membership@housing.org.uk
policy@housing.org.uk

 @natfednews
@yestohomes
@natfedfinance

 Find us on Facebook

 Join our LinkedIn networks

North

National Housing Federation
Manchester Office
City Point
701 Chester Road
Manchester M32 0RW
Tel: 0161 848 8132

E: north@housing.org.uk

 @Natfednorth

Derek Long	Assistant Director	derek.long@housing.org.uk
Monica Burns	Lead Manager, North East	monica.burns@housing.org.uk
Daniel Klemm	Lead Manager, North West	daniel.klemm@housing.org.uk
Rob Warm	Lead Manager, Yorkshire and Humberside	rob.warm@housing.org.uk
Gareth Bevan	Policy Officer	gareth.bevan@housing.org.uk
Anne Arnold	Communications Officer	anne.arnold@housing.org.uk
Rebecca Murphy	Events Officer	rebecca.murphy@housing.org.uk
Helen Collins	Administration Manager	helen.collins@housing.org.uk
Wendy Taylor	Office Administrator	wendy.taylor@housing.org.uk
Sophie Haigh	Office Administrator (Tuesdays, Wednesdays, Thursdays)	sophie.haigh@housing.org.uk

Midlands and South West

National Housing Federation
101 Victoria Street
Bristol BS1 6PU
Tel: 0117 929 7388

E: southwest@housing.org.uk
E: midlands@housing.org.uk

@natfedSW
@natfedwestmid
@natfedeastmid

Simon Nunn	Assistant Director	simon.nunn@housing.org.uk
Chris Hobson	Lead Manager, East Midlands	chris.hobson@housing.org.uk
Gemma Duggan	Lead Manager, West Midlands	gemma.duggan@housing.org.uk
Jenny Allen	Lead Manager, South West	jenny.allen@housing.org.uk
Catherine Brabner	Interim Lead Manager, South West	catherine.brabner@housing.org.uk
Peter Jones	Communications Officer	peter.jones@housing.org.uk
Veronica Cortes	Events Officer	veronica.cortes@housing.org.uk
Jean McCarthy	BSHP Officer	jean.mccarthy@housing.org.uk
Lesley Johnston	Administrator	lesley.johnston@housing.org.uk
Leah Jackson	Office Administrator	leah.jackson@housing.org.uk
Michelle Monks	Office Administrator	michelle.monks@housing.org.uk

London, South East and East of England

National Housing Federation
Lion Court
25 Procter Street
London WC1V 6NY
Tel: 020 7067 1046

E: london@housing.org.uk
E: southeast@housing.org.uk
E: eastofengland@housing.org.uk

@Londonnatfed
@natfedSE
@natfedeast

Kevin Williamson	Interim Assistant Director	kevin.williamson@housing.org.uk
Sharon West	PA to Assistant Director	sharon.west@housing.org.uk
Michelle Smith	Lead Manager, London	michelle.smith@housing.org.uk
Lizzie Clifford	Lead Manager, London	lizzie.clifford@housing.org.uk
Claire Astbury	Lead Manager, East of England	claire.astbury@housing.org.uk
Warren Finney	Lead Manager, South East	warren.finney@housing.org.uk
Rhona Brown	Policy Officer	rhona.brown@housing.org.uk
Clare Bevis Paredes	Communications Officer	clare.bevis@housing.org.uk
Violeta Reen	Administrator	violeta.reen@housing.org.uk

DAVID ORR – CHIEF EXECUTIVE
T: 020 7067 1021 E: david.orr@housing.org.uk

Executive Assistant – Beverley Harris
T: 020 7067 1022 E: beverleyharris@housing.org.uk

OPERATIONS
Director of Operations
Simon Charlick
T: 020 7067 1075
E: simon.charlick@housing.org.uk

Assistant Director – Finance and Business Systems
Jackie Cunningham
T: 020 7067 1106
E: jackie.cunningham@housing.org.uk

Head of Human Resources & Organisational Development
Chris White
T: 020 7067 1121
E: chris.white@housing.org.uk

Head of Governance & Company Secretary
Stephen Bull
T: 020 7067 1035
E: stephen.bull@housing.org.uk

Membership Manager
Paul Bayly
T: 020 7067 1036
E: paul.bayly@housing.org.uk

Head of Facilities
Lalita Paul
T: 020 7067 1124
E: lalita.paul@housing.org.uk

Head of My Home Finance
Tess Pendle
T: 020 7067 1043
E: tess.pendle@housing.org.uk

Head of ICT
Kalpesh Sonecha
T: 020 7067 1116
E: kalpesh.sonecha@housing.org.uk

COMMERCIAL SERVICES
Director of Commercial Services
Elaine Walder
T: 020 7067 1050
E: elaine.walder@housing.org.uk

Assistant Director – Marketing and Commercial Services
Adam Jones
T: 020 7067 1055
E: adam.jones@housing.org.uk

Head of Programme Management
Noreen Meehan
T: 020 7067 1175
E: noreen.meehan@housing.org.uk

CAMPAIGNS AND NEIGHBOURHOODS
Director of Campaigns and Neighbourhoods
Ruth Davison (job share)
E: ruth.davison@housing.org.uk
Gill Payne (job share)
T: 020 7067 1071
E: gill.payne@housing.org.uk

Assistant Director – Neighbourhoods
Helen Williams
T: 020 7067 1088
E: helen.williams@housing.org.uk

Head of Neighbourhoods
Rachel Fisher
T: 020 7067 1142
E: rachel.fisher@housing.org.uk

Assistant Director – Campaigns and Communications
Teresa Richardson
T: 020 7067 1026
E: teresa.richardson@housing.org.uk

Head of Campaigns and Public Affairs
Chloe Hardy
T: 020 7067 1030
E: chloe.hardy@housing.org.uk

Head of Media
Anna Brosnan
T: 020 7067 1028
E: anna.brosnan@housing.org.uk

Head of Member and Corporate Communications
Leanne Lawrence
T: 020 7067 1128
E: leanne.lawrence@housing.org.uk

Assistant Director (Regions) London, South East and East of England
Kevin Williamson
T: 020 7067 1087
E: kevin.williamson@housing.org.uk

Assistant Director (Regions) North
Derek Long
T: 0161 873 9441
E: derek.long@housing.org.uk

Assistant Director (Regions) Midlands and South West
Simon Nunn
T: 020 7067 1191
0117 952 9915
E: simon.nunn@housing.org.uk

Assistant Director – Research and Futures
Stuart Ropke
T: 020 7067 1103
E: stuart.ropke@housing.org.uk

Head of Investment Policy and Strategy
(position vacant)

the whole spectrum

The environment for housing and care providers is not getting any easier. And alongside political and financial challenges, there's always the question of where to find high quality advice you can trust. We're already well known for our work in governance and corporate strategy; mergers and partner selection; HR; recruitment; and performance management. Other services we offer, which you may not be aware of, include:

- **New business development** – bid writing, modelling, strategy analysis, sourcing opportunities
- **Financial and business planning** – viability review, capacity review, business plan validation
- **Strategic asset management** – portfolio analysis, stock rationalisation, property disposal
- **Resident scrutiny** – audit of resident involvement, development of scrutiny function, resident coaching, training programmes
- **Efficiency and value for money** – procurement support, shared services, service review, structure review
- **Mediation** – tenancy issues, neighbour disputes, property matters
- **PR and communications** – stakeholder perception survey, communications strategy, media training

Member statistics

Members by type

Type of Federation member	No. of members
Housing associations, trusts and societies (including voluntary transfers)	951
Co-operatives (primary and secondary)	54
Total no. of members	**1,011**

Members by sizeband

Sizeband (units owned, or managed for others)	No. of members	Total stock
10,000+	77	1,597,074
5,000-9,999	99	704,527
2,500-4,999	94	350,320
500-2,499	147	178,947
1-499	594	58,040
Total	**1,011**	**2,888,908**

Members by activity

Qualification	No. of members	No. of units
No management or development stock	182	0
No development programme (units owned, or managed for others only)	476	285,314
Over 500 units in development	59	87,513
Development programme	353	119,148
LCHO units in development	102	16,931

Members by region

Region	Code	No. of members based in region	No. of members that operate in region
North East	1	36	33
Yorkshire	2	63	47
North West	3	135	35
West Midlands	5	105	53
East Midlands	6	66	65
East of England	7	82	70
South West	8	112	50
South East	9	150	91
London	L	260	47
Other (Ireland)	-	2	

Data correct as at January 2013.

Risk Consulting   Insurance Services   Risk Transfer Solutions

intelligent
risk partnerships

acumus

intelligent risk partnerships

North West

Adactus HA Ltd
Adactus Housing Group
Aksa HA Ltd
Alpha (RSL) Ltd
Arawak Walton HA Ltd
Arcon HA
Arena Housing Group Ltd
Ashton Pioneer Homes Ltd
Assured Living HA
Bay HA Ltd
Beech HA Ltd
Beechwood Ballantyne
Bolton At Home Ltd
Bowlacre Home
Brampton Rural Housing Society
Calico Homes Ltd
Care HA
Chester & District Housing Trust
Chorley Community Housing Ltd
City of Liverpool YMCA
City South Manchester Housing Trust
City West Housing Trust
Cobalt Housing Ltd
Community Gateway Association Ltd
Contour Homes
Contour Property Services Ltd
Cosmopolitan HA Ltd
Cosmopolitan Housing Group Ltd
Creative Support Ltd
Crewe YMCA Foyer
Crosby HA
Derwent & Solway HA
Eastlands Homes Partnership Ltd
Eden HA Ltd
Eldonian Community Based HA Ltd
Equity HA Ltd
Equity Housing Group Ltd
Fairfield Moravian HA Ltd
Fairoak HA
Family HA (Birkenhead & Wirral) Ltd
First Choice Homes Oldham
Forum HA Ltd
Frontis
Gatesbield Quaker HA Ltd
Golden Gates Housing Trust Ltd
Great Places HA
Great Places Housing Group
Green Vale Homes Ltd
Halton Housing Trust
Halton YMCA Ltd
Helena Partnerships Ltd
Housing Pendle
Hyndburn Homes Ltd
Impact HA Ltd
Irwell Valley HA Ltd
Johnnie Johnson HA Ltd
Johnnie Johnson Housing Trust Ltd

Knowsley Housing Trust
Lake District HA Ltd
Leasowe Community Homes
Liverpool Housing Trust
Liverpool Jewish HA Ltd
Liverpool Mutual Homes Ltd
Longdendale Housing Society Ltd
Lowther & District HA Ltd
Lune Valley Rural HA Ltd
Lytham St Annes Lions Club HA Ltd
Lytham St Annes War Memorial HA Ltd
Manchester & District HA
Manchester Care & Repair Ltd
Manchester Jewish HA Ltd
Mitre HA Ltd
Mossbank Homes Ltd
Mosscare Housing Ltd
Muir Group HA Ltd
New Charter Homes Ltd
New Charter Housing Trust Ltd
New Foundations HA Ltd
New Fylde Housing Ltd
New Progress HA Ltd
North West Housing Services Ltd
One Vision Housing Ltd
Parkway Green Housing Trust
Partington HA
Peak Valley HA Ltd
Peaks & Plains Housing Trust
Pendleton Improved HA Ltd
People First HA Ltd
Pierhead HA Ltd
Pine Court HA Ltd
Places for People Homes Ltd
Places for People Individual Support Ltd
Plumlife Homes Ltd
Plus Dane (Cheshire) HA Ltd
Plus Dane (Merseyside) HA Ltd
Plus Dane Housing Group Ltd
Preston Care & Repair Ltd
Prestwich & North Western HA Ltd
Progress Care HA Ltd
Progress Housing Group Ltd
Provincial HA Ltd
Regenda Ltd
Ribble Valley Homes Ltd
Rochdale Boroughwide Housing
SLH Group
South Cheshire HS Ltd
South Lakes Housing
Southport Soroptimist HA Ltd
Southway Housing Trust
Spotland and Falinge HA Ltd
Springs Tenant Management Co-op Ltd
St Vincent's HA Ltd
Steve Biko HA
Symphony Housing Group

Terra Nova Developments Ltd
The Riverside Group Ltd
The St Michael's Housing Trust
The Villages HA Ltd
Trafford Housing Trust
Tung Sing HA Ltd
Twin Valley Homes Ltd
Two Castles HA Ltd
Venture HA Ltd
Villages Community HA Ltd

Warrington HA Ltd
Weaver Horizons Ltd
Weaver Vale Housing Trust
Weller Streets Housing Co-operative Ltd
Westfield HA Ltd
Willow Park Housing Trust
Wirral Methodist HA Ltd
Wirral Partnership Homes
Wulvern Housing
Your Housing Group

Yorkshire and Humberside

Accent Corporate Services Ltd
Accent Foundation Ltd
Accent Group Ltd
Action Housing & Support Ltd
Arches Housing Ltd
Boothferry HA Ltd
Broadacres HA Ltd
Broadacres Services Ltd
Chevin HA Ltd
Connect HA Ltd
Dyers Company HA Ltd
East Yorkshire HA Ltd
Family HA (York) Ltd
Foundation
Gipton Supported Independent Living Ltd
Grimsby, Cleethorpes & Humber Region YMCA
Harewood Housing Society Ltd
Harrogate Families HA Ltd
Harrogate Flower Fund Homes Ltd
Harrogate Neighbours HA Ltd
Headrow Ltd
Horton HA
Horton Housing Support Ltd
Hull Churches HA Ltd
Hull House Improvement Society Ltd
Hull Resettlement Project
Inclusion Housing CIC
Incommunities Group Ltd
Incommunities Ltd
Joseph Kaye's Almshouses
Joseph Rowntree Housing Trust
Leeds & Yorkshire HA Ltd

Leeds Federated HA Ltd
Leeds Housing Concern
Leeds Irish Health & Homes Ltd
Leeds Jewish HA Ltd
Manningham HA Ltd
Mary Morris International Residence Ltd
North Lincolnshire Homes Ltd
Padley HA Ltd
Pennine Housing 2000 Ltd
Pickering & Ferens Homes
Renaissance Social Housing Ltd
Renew Leeds Ltd
Sadeh Lok Housing Group Ltd
Shoreline Housing Partnership Ltd
South Yorkshire HA Ltd
Spenborough Flower Fund Homes Ltd
St Andrew Housing Co-operative Ltd
St Anne's Community Services
Staincliffe HA Ltd
Swinden HA Ltd
Tangram Housing Co-operative Ltd
Together Housing Group Ltd
Touchstone - Leeds Ltd
Unity HA Ltd
Wakefield and District Housing
YCH Developments Ltd
YH Residential Ltd
York HA Ltd
Yorkshire Coast Homes Ltd
Yorkshire Housing Ltd
Yorkshire Ladies Council (Hostels) Ltd

The Leading Housing Management Software Supplier in the UK

QL Housing   QL Financials   QL Business Intelligence   QL Personnel/Payroll

QL Housing & Financial Management Software is a truly integrated, flexible and highly functional software solution designed specifically to meet the needs of UK Social Housing Providers

For more information on Aareon UK and the complete QL Housing & Financials Product Suite
Contact us on 02476 323723 or visit www.aareon.co.uk

North East

700 Club
Aquila Way
Bernicia Group Ltd
Berwick Borough Housing
Byker Community Trust
Cestria Community HA
Cheviot HA Ltd
Coast & Country Housing Ltd
Darlington HA Ltd
Derwentside Homes Ltd
Durham Aged Mineworkers' Homes Association
Endeavour HA
Erimus Housing
Fabrick Housing Group Ltd
Four Housing Group
Gentoo Group Ltd
Gentoo Sunderland Ltd
Home Group Ltd

Housing Hartlepool Ltd
Isos Housing Ltd
livin
New Prospects Association Ltd
Norcare Ltd
North Star Housing Group Ltd
Probus Women's Housing Society Ltd
Railway HA and Benefit Fund
Red House Farm Housing Co-op Ltd
Square Building Trust Ltd
Tees Valley Housing Ltd
Teesdale HA Ltd
The North Eastern YWCA Trustees Ltd
Three Rivers HA Ltd
Tristar Homes Ltd
Tyne HA Ltd
Vela Group
Wansbeck Homes Ltd

West Midlands

Accord HA Ltd
Adullam Homes HA Ltd
Ashram HA
Aspire Group (Staffordshire) Ltd
Aspire Housing Ltd
BCOP (Broadening Choices for Older People)
BCS Associates Ltd
Birmingham Civic HA Ltd
Birmingham Co-operative Housing Services
Birmingham Jewish HA Ltd
Black Country Care Services Ltd
Black Country Housing Group Ltd
Blue Mountain HA Ltd
Boughey Roddam HA
Bournville Tenants Ltd
Bournville Village Trust
Bournville Works HS Ltd
Brighter Futures
Bromford Housing Group Ltd
Bromsgrove District Housing Trust
Bromsgrove Housing Initiatives Ltd
Caldmore Area HA Ltd
Castle Vale Community HA Ltd
CHOICES HA Ltd
Churches HA of Dudley & District (CHADD)
Coventry & Warwickshire YMCA
Dorcas Housing + Community Support Association Ltd
Empowering People Inspiring Communities Ltd
Evesham & Pershore HA Ltd
Family HA (Birmingham) Ltd
Festival Housing
Forward HA Ltd
Friendship Care and Housing
Fry Housing Trust
G3 Inspiring Individuals

Harborne Parish Lands Charity
Heantun Care HA Ltd
Heantun HA Ltd
Herefordshire Housing Ltd
Herefordshire Old Peoples HS Ltd
Hibiscus HA
Jephson HA Ltd
Jephson Homes HA Ltd
Kemble Housing Ltd
Lench's Trust
Lyng Community Association
Marches HA Ltd
Mercian HA Ltd
Meres and Mosses HA
Michael Blanning Trust HA Ltd
Midland Heart Ltd
Moorlands Housing
Nehemiah United Churches HA Ltd
New Outlook HA Ltd
Nexus (Midlands) HA (2005) Ltd
Old Ben Homes Ltd
Optima Community Association
Orbit Group Ltd
Orbit Heart of England
Rayner House and Yew Trees Ltd
Redditch Co-operative Homes
Redditch Friends HA
Redditch YMCA Ltd
Rooftop Homes Ltd
Rooftop Housing Group Ltd
Rotary Club of Dudley HA Ltd
Severnside Housing
Shropshire Association for Sheltered Housing Ltd
Shropshire Housing Ltd
Shropshire Rural HA Ltd

When it comes to protecting people and communities, we see the bigger picture

Streetwise is a web-based case management system that helps to protect people and the communities in which they live.

Designed and developed in-house, this hosted solution supports those working on the front-line to manage anti-social behaviour and pinpoint where help and support is most needed.

For more information call **0191 525 5000**
gentoogroup.com/streetwise

Sir Josiah Mason's Trust
Small Heath Park H Co-op Ltd
Solihull Care HA Ltd
South Shropshire HA
South Staffordshire HA
St Basils
St Peter's (Saltley) HA Ltd
Stafford and Rural Homes Ltd
Staffordshire HA Ltd
Stanhope Court (Worcester) HA Ltd
Starley Housing Co-operative Ltd
Stoke on Trent and North Staffordshire YMCA HA
Stoke-on-Trent Housing Society Ltd
Tamworth Cornerstone HA Ltd
The Community Housing Group
The Housing Plus Group Ltd

The Wrekin Housing Group Ltd
The Wrekin Housing Trust
Trent & Dove Housing
Trident Charitable HA Ltd
Trident HA Ltd
Walsall Housing Group Ltd
Warwickshire Rural HA Ltd
Waterloo HA Ltd
WATMOS Community Homes
Wednesfield HA Ltd
West Mercia Homes Ltd
Whitefriars Housing Group Ltd
WM Housing Group
Worcester Community Housing
Wyre Forest Community Housing Ltd
Wyre Forest Sheltered Housing Ltd

East Midlands

Acclaim Housing Group Ltd
Acis Group Ltd
Asra HA Ltd
Asra Housing Group Ltd
Asra Midlands HA Ltd
Belgrave Neighbourhood Co-operative HA Ltd
Boston Mayflower Ltd
Brunts Charity
Care & Repair England
Chesterfield Churches HA
Cossington Housing Co-operative Ltd
Dales Housing Ltd
Daventry & District Housing Ltd
de Montfort Housing Society Ltd
Derwent Living
East Midlands HA Ltd
East Midlands Housing Group
Enable HA Ltd
Family First Ltd
Forward Housing SW
Foundation HA Ltd
Framework HA
Futures Homescape Ltd
Futures Housing Group
Gedling Homes
Jesus Fellowship HA Ltd
Keystone Developments (LG) Ltd
Kirby Muxloe Free Church HA Ltd
Lace Housing Ltd
Leicester HA Ltd
Leicester Quaker HA Ltd
Leicestershire Rural HA Ltd
Lincolnshire Rural HA Ltd

Longhurst & Havelok Homes Ltd
Longhurst Group Ltd
Mansfield Road (Nottingham) Baptist HA Ltd
Maynard Co-operative HA Ltd
Methodist Homes HA
MHA
Midlands Rural Housing & Village Development Assn Ltd
Network for Change Ltd
New Linx Housing Trust
Northamptonshire Rural HA Ltd
Nottingham Community (2nd) HA Ltd
Nottingham Community HA Ltd
Nottingham Jewish HA Ltd
Nottinghamshire YMCA
Park Gardens Supported Housing Ltd
Peak District Rural HA Ltd
Rockingham Forest HA Ltd
Ross Walk Housing Co-operative Ltd
Seely Hirst House
Seven Locks Housing Ltd
South Northants Homes
Spire Homes (LG) Ltd
Spirita
Tamarisk Housing Ltd
The Leicester Young Mens Christian Association
The Trees Group
Thera Trust
Three Oaks Homes Ltd
Three Valleys Housing Ltd
Tuntum HA Ltd
Waterloo Housing Group Ltd
Wellingborough Homes Ltd
YMCA Derbyshire

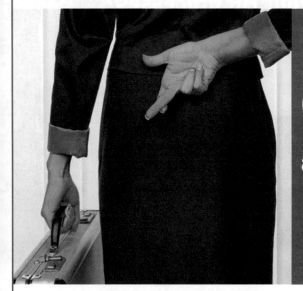

South West

1625 Independent People Ltd
Aashyana HA Ltd
Alliance Homes
Arcadia Housing Ltd
Aster Communities
Aster Group
Barnabas HA Ltd
Bath Centre for Voluntary Service Homes
BHSE
Bournemouth Churches HA (BCHA)
Bournemouth YMCA
Bristol Community Housing Foundation Ltd
Bristol Missing Link Ltd
Bristowe (Fair Rent) HA Ltd
Broadway Park HA Ltd
Brunel Care
Cirencester Housing Society Ltd
City of Exeter YMCA HA
Coastline Housing Ltd
Colebrook Housing Society Ltd
Cornerstone Housing Ltd
Cornwall CLT Ltd
Cornwall Rural HA Ltd
Curo
Devon & Cornwall Housing Ltd
Devon & Cornwall Leasehold Solutions Ltd
East Boro Housing Trust
Elim HA
Falcon Rural Housing Ltd
Fern Housing
German Lutheran HA Ltd
Gloucestershire Housing Society Ltd
Gloucestershire Rural HA Ltd
GreenSquare Group Ltd
Guinness Care & Support Ltd
Guinness HA Ltd
Hastoe Wyvern HA Ltd
Julian House
Kilmersdon Rural HA
King Alfred HA Ltd
King's Barton HA Ltd
Knightstone Charitable Housing Ltd
Knightstone HA Ltd
Langley House Trust
Locking Deanery HS Ltd
Magna HA Ltd
Magna Housing Group Ltd
Magna West Somerset HA Ltd
Marlborough & District HA Ltd
Merlin Housing Society Ltd
Mill Street Housing Society Ltd
North Devon Homes Ltd
Ocean Housing Group Ltd

Ocean Housing Ltd
Oxbode HA Ltd
Penwith HA Ltd
Plymouth Community Homes
Poole Old Peoples Welfare HS Ltd
Raglan HA Ltd
Red Devon Housing Ltd
Redland HA Ltd
Retired Baptist Ministers HS Ltd
Second Step HA Ltd
Self Help Community HA Ltd
Selwood Housing
Severn Vale Housing Society Ltd
SHAL Housing Ltd
Shape HA
Sidcot Friends HS Ltd
Signpost HA Ltd
Solon South West HA Ltd
Somer Community Housing Trust
Soroptimist (Poole) HA Ltd
South Devon Rural HA Ltd
South Western Housing Society Ltd
Southwold Young Peoples HA
Spectrum Housing Group Ltd
St Lawrence's Hospital Charity
St Michael Housing Society (Penzance) Ltd
St Minver CLT Ltd
St Petroc's Society
Stonechester HA Ltd
SWALLOW
Synergy Housing Ltd
Tamar Housing Society Ltd
Tarka Housing Ltd
Taunton Association for The Homeless
Teign Housing
The Gloucester Charities Trust
The Hallsands HS Ltd
The Parkview Society Ltd
Tor Homes
Two Rivers Housing
Two Rivers Initiatives Ltd
United HA Ltd
Watermoor House Residential Home
West Cornwall HA Ltd
West Devon Homes Ltd
West of England Friends HS Ltd
Westcountry HA Ltd
Westlea HA
Westward Housing Group Ltd
Wiltshire Rural HA Ltd
Worth CPT Ltd
Wyedean HA Ltd
Yarlington Housing Group

London

A2Dominion Group Ltd
Abeona Housing Co-op Ltd
Access Homes HA Ltd
Acme Artists Studios Ltd
Affinity Sutton
Affinity Sutton Homes
Affordable Christian HA Ltd
Afro-Caribbean HA Ltd
Agudas Israel HA Ltd
Apna Ghar HA Ltd
ARHAG HA Ltd
Arneway Housing Co-op Ltd
Bahay Kubo HA Ltd
Bancroft Tenant Management Co-operative Ltd
Bangla HA Ltd
Barnsbury HA Ltd
Beddington & Wallington HS Ltd
Bexley Churches HA Ltd
Birnbeck HA Ltd
Blenheim Gardens Resident Management Organisation
Bow Housing Society Ltd
Bramah House Ltd
Brandrams Housing Co-operative Ltd
Brixton Housing Co-op Ltd
Broadway
Brockley Tenants' Co-operative Ltd
Camberwell Housing Society Ltd
Camden Teacher Tenants Co-operative
Cass and Claredale Halls of Residence Association Ltd
Catalyst Housing Ltd
CBHA
CDS Co-operatives
Cedarmore HA Ltd
Central & Cecil
Centrepoint
Chapter 1
Charlton Triangle Homes Ltd
Chisel Ltd
Chislehurst & Sidcup HA
Christian Action (Enfield) HA Ltd
Christian Action Housing Special Projects Ltd
Church of England Pension Board
Circle
Circle Thirty Three Housing Trust Ltd
City YMCA, London
Clapham Park Homes
Clapton Park Management Organisation
Clissold Housing Co-operative Ltd
Co-op Homes (South) Ltd
Coin Street Secondary Housing Co-operative Ltd
Community Options Ltd
Community Trust Housing
Crown HA Ltd
Croydon Churches HA Ltd
Croydon Unitarian HA Ltd
Crystal Palace HA Ltd
Cyron Housing Co-operative Ltd

Denbigh Methodist HA Ltd
Deptford Housing Co-operative Ltd
Dolphin Square Charitable Foundation
Ducane HA Ltd
East Homes Ltd
East Living Ltd
East Potential
East Thames Group Ltd
EastendHomes Ltd
Ecco (Charitable) HA Ltd
Edward Henry House Co-operative Ltd
Ekarro Housing Co-operative Ltd
Ekaya HA Ltd
Eldon HA Ltd
Empty Homes Agency
Estonian House Ltd
Fairhazel Co-operative Ltd
Family Mosaic Home Ownership Ltd
Family Mosaic Housing
Field Lane Foundation
Forest HA Ltd
Forest YMCA
Foundation66
Gallions HA Ltd
Gateway HA Ltd
Genesis HA
Glebe HA Ltd
Greenwich Housing Society
Grenfell HA
Habinteg HA
Haig Homes
Haig Housing Trust
Haringey Association for Independent Living
Harlington Rectory HA Ltd
Harrison Housing
Harrow Churches HA
Hastoe HA Ltd
Haven Green HA Ltd
Heathview Tenants' Co-operative Ltd
Helix HA Ltd
Hendon Christian HA Ltd
Hestia Housing and Support
Hexagon HA Ltd
Hill Homes
Hillside Housing Trust
Home From Home HA Ltd
Homesdale (Woodford Baptist Homes) Ltd
Horniman HA Ltd
Hornsey (North London) YMCA HS Ltd
Hornsey Housing Trust Ltd
Housing & Community Association
Housing for Women
Hyde HA Ltd
Hyde Southbank Homes Ltd
Hyelm Group
Imani Housing Co-op Ltd
Inkerman HA

Innisfree HA
Inquilab HA Ltd
Irish Centre Housing Ltd
Islington & Shoreditch HA Ltd
Islington Community Housing Co-op Ltd
Jewish Community HA Ltd
Karin HA Ltd
Keniston HA Ltd
Kensington & Chelsea TMO Ltd
Kingston Upon Thames Churches HA Ltd
Kurdish HA Ltd
Ladybur Housing Co-op Ltd
Lambeth & Southwark HA Ltd
Lambeth Self Help HA Ltd
Larcombe HA Ltd
Lee HA
Leo Baeck HA Ltd
Lewisham Family Self Help Association Ltd
Lewisham Park HA Ltd
Lien Viet HA Ltd
Local Space Ltd
London & Quadrant Housing Trust
London Cyrenians Housing Ltd
London Housing Trust
London Strategic Housing Ltd
Longlife Housing Co-operative Ltd
Look Ahead Housing and Care Ltd
Mace Housing Co-op Ltd
Masonic HA
Mercers Company HA Ltd
Merton Priory Homes
Metropolitan
Metropolitan
Millat Asian HA Ltd
Mitali HA Ltd
Monmouth Road Housing Co-operative Ltd
Mount Carmel
Mulberry Housing Co-op United
Nacro Community Enterprises Ltd
National Council of YMCAs
Network Housing Group Ltd
Network Stadium HA Ltd
New Venture Housing Co-op Ltd
New World HA Ltd
Newlon Housing Trust
North Camden Housing Co-op Ltd
North London Muslim HA Ltd
Notting Hill Home Ownership HA Ltd
Notting Hill Housing Trust
Octavia Housing
Odu-Dua HA Ltd
Odyssey Care Ltd
Old Etonian HA Ltd
Old Ford HA
Old Oak HA Ltd
Omid HA Ltd
One Housing Group Ltd
Orchard Housing Society Ltd
Origin Housing Ltd

Orione Care
Outward
Park Hill Housing Co-op Ltd
Pathways
Peabody
Penge Churches HA
Peter Bedford HA Ltd
Phoenix Community HA (Bellingham & Downham) Ltd
Phoenix Futures
Pinner House Society Ltd
Places for People Group
Polish Citizen's Committee HA Ltd
Polish Retired Persons HA Ltd
Poplar HARCA
Providence Row HA
Quadrant-Brownswood Tenant Co-op Ltd
Quaker Housing Trust
RCHL
Refuge
Reside HA
Richmond Housing Partnership
Richmond Upon Thames Churches HT
Riverlink Housing Co-op Ltd
Ruskin Park House Ltd
Salvation Army HA
Scimitar HA Ltd
Scotscare
Seymour Housing Co-operative Ltd
Shenehom HA Ltd
Shepherds Bush Housing Group
Shian HA Ltd
Silverholme HA Ltd
Simba (Greenwich) HA Ltd
Single Homeless Project
SITRA
Soho HA Ltd
South London YMCA
South Mildmay Tenant Co-op Ltd
Southern Home Ownership Ltd
Southern Housing Group Ltd
Southwark & London Diocesan HA Ltd
Spitalfields HA Ltd
Springboard Two HA Ltd
St Christopher's Fellowship
St Ignatius HA Ltd
St Martin of Tours HA Ltd
St Mungo Community HA
St Vincents Family HA Ltd
Stoll
Stonewall HA Ltd
Stroud Green Housing Co-operative Ltd
Suffolk Estate Co-operative Ltd
Sunridge HA Ltd
Sutton Housing Society Ltd
Tally Ho Housing Co-op Ltd
Tamil Community HA Ltd
Tannery Arts Ltd
Teachers' HA Ltd
Thames Reach HA Ltd

Thames Valley Charitable HA Ltd
Thames Valley HA Ltd
The Friendly Almshouses
The Industrial Dwellings Society (1885) Ltd
The London Housing Foundation
The Richmond Fellowship
The Sheppard Trust
Thorlands Housing Management Society Ltd
Together: Working for Wellbeing
Tower Hamlets Community Housing Ltd
Turning Point
Twenty-Fifth Avenue Ltd
Victoria Park Homes (1965) Ltd
Viridian Housing

Walterton & Elgin Community Homes Ltd
Waltham Forest HA Ltd
Wandle HA Ltd
Waverley Eighth Co-operative HA
West Eleven Housing Co-op
West Hampstead Housing Co-operative Ltd
West London YMCA
Westlon HA
Westway HA Ltd
Willesden Green Housing Co-operative Ltd
Willow Housing and Care Ltd
Women's Pioneer Housing
Yarrow Housing
Zebra HA Ltd

South East

(The Lord Mayor of Portsmouth's) Coronation Homes
Ability HA
Accent Peerless Ltd
Advance Housing & Support Ltd
Agamemnon HA Ltd
Amicus Horizon Group Ltd
AmicusHorizon Ltd
Anchor Trust
Becket Trust HA Ltd
Berinsfield Community Business
Berkshire Women's Aid
BHT
Bledington Village HA Ltd
Bolney HA Ltd
Bracknell Forest Homes
Brighton & Hove Jewish HA Ltd
Brighton Lions Housing Society Ltd
Brighton Post & Tel Staff HA Ltd
Brighton YMCA
Broadhurst Welcome Home Community Ltd
Buckinghamshire HA Ltd
Burwash District HA for The Elderly Ltd
Cherchefelle HA Ltd
Chichester Greyfriars HA Ltd
Christ Church (St Leonards on Sea) House
Improvement Soc Ltd
Church of England Soldiers' Sailors' & Airmen's HA
Cottsway HA Ltd
Deddington HA Ltd
Dimensions UK Ltd
Dorking Charities
Dorking Residential Care Homes Ltd
Drum HA Ltd
Eddystone HA Ltd
Elmbridge Housing Trust Ltd
English Rural HA Ltd
Enham
Epsom & Ewell HA Ltd
Farnborough (War Memorial) HS Ltd
Fellowship Houses Trust
First Wessex

Five Villages Home Association Ltd
Franklands Village HA Ltd
God's Port Housing Society Ltd
Golding Homes
Grange Management (Southern) Ltd
Gravesend Churches HA Ltd
Grayshott & District HA Ltd
Greenoak HA Ltd
Guildford Sunset Homes
Hanover HA
Hassocks Housing Society Ltd
Hatton Housing Trust Ltd
Havant HA Ltd
Hawkridge HA Ltd
Heart of Medway HA Ltd
Henley & District Housing Trust Ltd
Holtspur HA Ltd
Holy Trinity (Guildford) HA Ltd
Housing 21
Housing Solutions Ltd
Island Cottages Ltd
Leatherhead United Charities
Ley Community Drug Services
Limpsfield & Oxted Cottage Society Ltd
Little Black Bag HA Ltd
Martlet Homes Ltd
mcch Society Ltd
MHS Homes Ltd
Moat Homes Ltd
Moat Housing Group
Mole Valley HA Ltd
Mount Green HA Ltd
MuirCroft HA Ltd
New Forest Villages HA Ltd
Ockley HA Ltd
Orbit South HA Ltd
Orchard (Weybridge) HA Ltd
Oriel Housing Ltd
Oxford Citizens HA Ltd
Oxford Overseas Students HA Ltd
Oxted Limpsfield & District HA Ltd

Paradigm Homes Charitable HA Ltd
Paradigm Housing Group Ltd
Paragon Community Housing Group
Peacehaven & Telscombe HA Ltd
Petersfield HA Ltd
Porchlight
Portal HA Ltd
Portsmouth Churches HA Ltd
Portsmouth Rotary HA Ltd
Prospect Housing and Support Services
Puttenham and Wanborough Housing Society Ltd
Radian Group Ltd
Radian Support Ltd
Raven Housing Trust Ltd
Red Kite Community Housing Ltd
Reigate Quaker HA Ltd
Ringwood & District Old People's Housing Society Ltd
Rockdale HA Ltd
Rogate & Terwick HA Ltd
Rosebery HA Ltd
Rosemary Simmons Memorial HA Ltd
Russet Homes
Sanctuary HA
Saxon Weald
Sentinel HA Ltd
Sherborne Close Housing Society Ltd
Shipbourne Housing Trust
Society of St James
Soha Housing Ltd
Southdown HA
Sovereign HA Ltd
St Johns College HA Ltd
St Lukes Housing Society Ltd
St Thomas's Housing Society Ltd

Surrey Federation Charitable HA
Sussex Central YMCA
Sussex Housing & Care
Sussex Oakleaf HA Ltd
Sussex Overseas HS Ltd
Swarthmore Housing Society Ltd
TCHG Foundation
TCHG Living Ltd
Thame & District HA Ltd
The ACT Foundation
The Guinness Partnership
The Radcliffe Housing Society Ltd
The Richard HA Ltd
The Royal Air Forces Association Housing Ltd
The Swaythling Housing Society Ltd
Thorngate Almshouse Trust
Town & Country Housing Group
Transform Housing and Support
Two Piers Housing Co-op Ltd
Two Saints Ltd
Uckfield & District HA Ltd
Vale of Aylesbury Housing Trust
Vectis HA Ltd
Warbleton HA Ltd
Wargrave on Thames HA Ltd
West Kent HA
Whitmore Vale HA Ltd
Winchester Working Mens HS Ltd
Windsor and District HA
Wokingham Area Housing Society Ltd
Worthing Homes Ltd
Wyndham HA Ltd
You

East of England

Accent Nene Ltd
Aldwyck Housing Group
Aldwyck Housing Group Ltd
Aragon HA Ltd
Argyle Street Housing Co-op Ltd
Ashwell HA Ltd
Axiom HA Ltd
B3 Living Ltd
Balkerne Gardens Trust Ltd
Bedford Citizens HA Ltd
Bedford Soroptimist HA Ltd
Billericay Co-operative Housing Society Ltd
bpha
Braintree Housing Society Ltd
Brentwood Housing Trust Ltd
Broadland HA Ltd
Care & Repair (East Cambridgeshire) Ltd
Cherry Tree HA Ltd
CHP
CHS Group

Colne Housing Society Ltd
Community Meeting Point
Corton House Ltd
Cotman HA Ltd
Cross Keys Homes Ltd
CWL Housing
Deepdale & Brancaster HS Ltd
Essex General HA Ltd
Estuary HA Ltd
Firbank Housing Society Ltd
Flagship Housing Group Ltd
Freebridge Community Housing
GFS Platform
Grand Union Housing Group Ltd
Granta Housing Society Ltd
Gretton Court Ltd
Hightown Praetorian and Churches HA Ltd
Holt & Neighbourhood HS Ltd
Housing Partnership (London) Ltd
Howard Cottage HA

straight talking on HR and recruitment

Recruiting the right people is a challenge. It can be time consuming and costly, and easy to make a mistake. Over the past eight years, we have worked with well over 200 housing associations, councils and ALMOs across the UK to recruit nearly 600 executives, interim managers and Board members. With a first time success rate of 95%, we will help you maximise value for money in your recruitment, and achieve the results you seek.

Our support in the field of human resources and recruitment doesn't stop there. Our team of experienced consultants offers a comprehensive range of services. We will listen, work with you and bring solutions across a variety of projects, including:

- Board training and development
- Disciplinary / grievance support
- Salaries and equal pay review
- Equality and inclusion review
- Organisational development
- Outsourced HR services
- Training programmes
- Workforce planning
- Executive coaching

Hundred Houses Society Ltd
Janes Housing Society Ltd
Luminus Group
Luminus Homes
Luton Community Housing Ltd
MacIntyre HA Ltd
Maldon HA Ltd
Minster General HA Ltd
North Hertfordshire Homes Ltd
Norwich Housing Society Ltd
Oak Foundation
Ogilby Housing Society Ltd
Orwell HA Ltd
Pine Ridge HA Ltd.
Purleigh Old People's HA Ltd
Rickmansworth Churches HA Ltd
Riversmead HA Ltd
Rochford HA
Roddons HA
Romford YMCA Ltd
Saffron Housing Trust Ltd

South Anglia Housing Ltd
St Martins Housing Trust
Suffolk Housing Society Ltd
Swan HA
The Abbeyfield Society
The Cambridge Pringle Group Ltd
The Cambridgeshire Cottage HS Ltd
The Havebury Housing Partnership
The King Street Housing Society Ltd
The Margery Maplethorpe Trust
The Papworth Trust
Theydon Trusts Ltd
Thrive Homes Ltd
Umbrella Housing Group Ltd
Victory Housing Trust
Watford Community Housing Trust
Waveney & Yare HA Ltd
Welwyn Garden City HA Ltd
Wherry HA Ltd
Witham HA Ltd
YMCA Norfolk

Regional committees

Our regional committees help ensure there is effective two-way communication between the Federation and its members.

North West

Members in the North West are currently considering how to increase engagement through approaches such a wider and more inclusive Chief Executives Forum. This more inclusive forum provides an opportunity to be challenged and to share information, expertise and knowledge on issues of importance for housing associations in the North West. For further information contact Daniel Klemm at Daniel.klemm@housing.org.uk

Chair

Ian Munro	New Charter Housing Trust

Vice Chair

Rob Young	Helena Partnerships

Members

Ken Perry	Plus Dane Housing Group
Jim Lunney	Johnnie Johnson Housing Trust
Cym D'Souza	Arawak Walton Housing Assocation
Matthew Gardiner	Trafford Housing Trust
Bob Taylor	Knowsley Housing Trust
Michelle Gregg	Your Housing Group
Philip Gandy	Symphony Housing Group
Jacqui De-Rose	Progress Housing Group
Carol Matthews	The Riverside Group
Jon Lord	Bolton at Home
Hugh Owen	The Riverside Group
Steve Coffey	Liverpool Mutual Homes
Cath Green	First Choice Homes Oldham
John Eccles	Your Housing Group (Board Member Support Group (Chair))

North East

The North East Regional Committee has decided to invite all chief executives of housing associations in the North East to their quarterly meetings. For further information contact Monica Burns at monica.burns@housing.org.uk

Chair

Paul Fiddaman	Cestria Community Housing Association

Vice Chair

Geraldine Wilcox	Derwentside Homes

Members

Iain Sim	Coast and Country Housing
Maurice Condie	Tyne Housing Association
Alison Thain	Tees Valley Housing
Keith Loraine	Isos Housing
Angela Lockwood	Endeavour Housing Association
Ian Porter	Gentoo Sunderland
Mike Axe	Three Rivers Housing Association
Colin Steel	livin
Paul Tanney	Four Housing Group
Graham Darby	Home Group
Cath Purdy	Vela Group

Yorkshire and Humberside

Following discussions with the members, it has been agreed to move to a wider, more inclusive Chief Executives Forum. This group is open to all housing association chief executives in the region, and acts as a place where chief executives can share information, challenges and expertise on the issues that matter to them. This group is chaired by Tom Miskell and meets every two months. For further information contact Rob Warm at rob.warm@housing.org.uk

Chair

Tom Miskell	Together Housing Group

Vice Chair

Geraldine Howley	Incommunities

Members

Tony Stacey	South Yorkshire HA
Jenny Brierley	Connect HA
Sheila Bamford	Horton HA
Ansar Ali	Manningham HA
Gordon Perry	Accent Group
Tony Bramley	Shoreline Housing Partnership
Mervyn Jones	Yorkshire Housing
Kevin Dodd	Wakefield & District Housing
Shaun Tymon	Yorkshire Coast Homes
Geoff Butler	Pennine Housing 2000
Helen Spencer	Together Housing Group

West Midlands (2012)

At the time of going to print, elections were being held, so the membership will change. Confirmation of new members of the West Midlands committees will be confirmed in March 2013 – check our website for more details. For further information contact Elizabeth Humphreys at elizabeth.humphreys@housing.org.uk

Chair

Dr Chris Handy OBE	Accord Housing Association

Vice Chair

Diane Lea	Staffordshire Housing Association

Members

Andy Ballard	Herefordshire Housing (Co-optee)
Sarah Boden	Severnside Housing
Mike Brown	Bromsgrove District Housing Trust
Jon Crockett (Co-optee)	Heantun Housing Association
Ron Dougan	Trent & Dove Housing
Colin Hudson (Co-optee)	Mercian HA
Simon Kimberley	Optima Community Association
Michelle Musgrave	Midland Heart
Danielle Oum (Co-optee)	Family HA (Birmingham)
Guy Weston	Festival Housing Group
Boris Worrall	Orbit Group
Anne Goymer (Co-optee)	Aster Living

East Midlands (2012)

At the time of going to print, elections were being held, so the membership will change. Confirmation of new members of the East Midlands committees will be confirmed in March 2013 – check our website for more details. For further information contact Chris Hobson at chris.hobson@housing.org.uk

Chair

Lindsey Williams	Futures Housing Group

Vice Chair

Julie Doyle	Spire Homes (Longhurst Group)

Members

Jackie King-Owen	Enable Housing Association
Richard Renwick MBE	Tuntum Housing Association
Bob Walder	Longhurst Group
Gerald Taylor	Dales Housing
Mike Andrews	Nottingham Community Housing Association
Chan Kataria	East Midlands Housing Group
Peter McCormack	Derwent Living
David Willis	Wellingborough Homes
Matt Cooney	LHA-ASRA Group
Alan Humphreys	Grand Union Housing Group
Lynn Clayton (co-optee)	Gedling Homes
Jenny Danson (co-optee)	Metropolitan
Carl Larter (co-optee)	Midland Heart

South West (2012/2013)

For further information contact Catherine Brabner at catherine.brabner@housing.org.uk

Chair

Nick Horne	Arcadia Housing

Vice Chair

John Brace	Aster Group

Members

Alistair Allender	Elim Housing Association
Karen Ayling	Westcountry Housing Association
Ann Cornelius	GreenSquare Group
Paul Crawford	Devon and Cornwall Housing Group
Victor Da Cunha	Curo Group
Oona Goldsworthy	Bristol Community Housing Foundation
Peter Moore	Cornwall Rural Housing Association
Barbara Shaw	Westward Housing
Jitinder Takhar	Spectrum Housing Group
Clive Turner	Plymouth Community Homes

London

For further information contact Michelle Smith at michelle.smith@housing.org.uk or Lizzie Clifford at lizzie.clifford@housing.org.uk

Chair

Sara Thakkar	Wandle Housing Association

Members

Anabel Palmer	Southern Housing Group (Vice Chair)

See page 63 for A-Z listings of Federation members

My Home
Energy Switch

My Home Energy SWITCH

My Home Energy Switch is an energy supply financial inclusion service from the National Housing Federation. This **FREE** service is for social housing tenants and housing associations to help them:

- **Save tenants money** – make sure your tenants are on the lowest available tariff with this free, impartial online or telephone comparison and switching service.

- **Simplify your void property process** – reduce the void period by letting My Home Energy Switch close off all issues related to energy supply and meter maintenance quickly and efficiently.

- **Reduce business costs** – check and switch the energy supply to your corporate properties to ensure you're getting the best deal.

Contact our team today to find out more on **0800 0014 706** or visit
www.myhomeenergyswitch.org.uk.

Rod Cahill	Catalyst Housing
Sheron Carter	Gateway Housing Association
Elizabeth Clarson	Housing for Women
Paul Doe	Shepherds Bush Housing Group
Mark Hayes	Christian Action (Enfield) Housing Association
Grahame Hindes	Octavia Housing
Jeremy Kape	Affinity Sutton
Caroline Tiller	Central & Cecil Housing Trust
Mike Wilkins	Ducane Housing Association

South East

For further information contact Warren Finney at warren.finney@housing.org.uk

Chair

| Geeta Nanda | Thames Valley Housing Association |

Vice Chair

| Andrea Smith | Radian Group |

Members

Catherine Dixson	GreenSquare Group
Vivien Knibbs	Orbit South Housing Association
Wayne Morris	Spectrum Housing Group
Ann Santry	Sovereign Housing Association
David Standfast	Saxon Weald
Peter Stringer	Golding Homes
Raj Upadhyaya	Guinness Partnership
Raife West	Havant Housing Association

East of England

For further information contact Claire Astbury at claire.astbury@housing.org.uk

Chair

| Mick Leggett | Cross Keys Homes Ltd |

Vice Chair

| Paul Durkin | Estuary Housing Association Ltd |

Members

Vanessa Connolly	Bedford Citizens HA Ltd
David Bogle	Hightown Praetorian & Churches HA Ltd
Ian Winslet	Suffolk Housing Society Ltd
Chris Jackson	Hundred Houses Society Ltd
Tina Barnard	Watford Community Housing Trust
Karen Mayhew	The Havebury Housing Partnership
Adam Ronaldson	Saffron Housing Trust Ltd
Alan Lewin	Axiom Housing Association Ltd
David McQuade	Flagship Housing Group
Craig Glasper	The King Street Housing Society Ltd

Practitioner groups

Our practitioner groups bring our members together to organise events, raise awareness of issues, and share good practice and expertise. Chairs and contacts listed below correct as at January 2013.

North West

Adaptations	Paula McGlynn	Wirral Partnership Homes
Asset Management	Vinny Thornton	St Vincent's Housing Association
Board Member Support	John Eccles	Your Housing Group
Care and Support Provider Forum	Donna Kelly	Liverpool Housing Trust
Community Housing Associations North West (smaller HAs)	Chris Allen	Forum Housing Association
Development	Claire Griffiths	Plus Dane
Finance	Viv Cross	Plus Dane
Health and Safety	John Bailey	Helena Partnerships
Home Ownership	Carol Lavender	The Riverside Group
Housing Management (Welfare Reform)	Tony Kiely	Plus Dane
Human Resources	Marie Wild	MWA People Solutions
Income Management	Melanie Price	Great Places
IT	Colin Arnold	Wirral Partnership Homes
Social Impact Group	Gwen Crawford	Bolton at Home
Sustainability	Tom Rock	City South Manchester Housing Trust
Worklessness	Louise Harris	Knowsley Housing Trust
Federation contact	Wendy Taylor	wendy.taylor@housing.org.uk

North East

Asset Management	David Pye	Derwentside Homes
Board Members' Executive	Mike Clark	Vela Group
Care and Support	Helen Neal	Fabrick Housing Group
Development	Martin Hawthorne	Fabrick Housing Group
Employment and Skills	Tracy O'Neill	Coast and Country Housing
Finance	Andrew Malcolm	Fabrick Housing Group
Financial Inclusion (FINCAN)	Victoria MacKay-Parkin	Gentoo Group
Governance and Data Protection	Martin Warhurst	Cestria
Homelessness	Monica Burns	monica.burns@housing.org.uk
Housing Management	Paul Stephens	Cestria
	Colin Steel	livin
Media	Graeme King	ISOS Housing
Repairs and Maintenance	John Turner	Gentoo Group
Resident Engagement	David Jones	Cestria
Rural	Monica Burns	monica.burns@housing.org.uk
Social Enterprise	Phillip Curran	Derwentside Homes
Welfare Reform	Monica Burns	monica.burns@housing.org.uk
Federation contact	Sophie Haigh	sophie.haigh@housing.org.uk

Yorkshire and Humberside

Asset Management	Peter Ross	Broadacres HA
Board Members' Forum	Geoff Butler	Together Housing Group
Care and Support	Kate Spencer	York HA
Design and Standards	Sonia Whetham	Accent Group
	Helen Forman	HCA

My Home
Contents Insurance

My Home
Contents Insurance

How many of your tenants and leaseholders have home contents insurance?

Imagine if the worst was to happen ...

In our experience, take up of insurance is significantly higher when tenants get a full understanding of how insuring their home contents can benefit them. This is where you come in.

My Home Contents Insurance Scheme
The National Housing Federation, in conjunction with Jardine Lloyd Thompson Tenant Risks, provides you with **My Home** Contents Insurance. **My Home** is an affordable and flexible scheme, designed to protect your tenants against a whole range of risks.

It's easy and simple for you:

Peace of mind that your tenants are fully protected

• A scheme designed to be affordable and flexible

• No cost to you as a member

• Provision of full marketing support and growth plan

• Full product training and ongoing support

• Bespoke scheme options 'with rent' or 'arm's length' available.

For further information on the scheme and how it could benefit you, and your tenants, **call 0113 203 5823/5843, or email MyHome@jltgroup.com**

 business for neighbourhoods

JLT

Development	Andy Gamble	Accent Group
	Ged Walsh	Yorkshire Housing
Finance	Darren Cooper	LJHA
	Sean Flynn	Connect HA
Housing Management / Welfare Reform	Rob Warm	rob.warm@housing.org.uk
SP Provider Forum	John Hill	Foundation
Worklessness	Helen Wordsworth	Wakefield and District Housing
Federation contact	Helen Collins	helen.collins@housing.org.uk

North East & Yorkshire and Humberside

Health and Safety	Barbara McAuley	livin
Low Cost Home Ownership	Andrew Serbert	Incommunities
Small Housing Associations	Paul Dolan	Sadeh Lok
Human Resources	Megan Henderson	Leeds Federated HA
Federation contact	Helen Collins	helen.collins@housing.org.uk

Northern (NE, NW & Y and H)

Training Group	Ian Stone	Incommunities
Federation contact	Helen Collins	helen.collins@housing.org.uk

West Midlands

Board Members Forum	Mike Ager	Heantun Housing Association
Care and Support Forum	Mick Gallagher	Bromford Group
Central Home Ownership	Bob Deol	Mercian Housing Association
Midlands Continuous Improvement	Kathryn Webster	East Midlands Housing Group
Finance	Andy Howarth	Worcester Community Housing
Northern Financial Inclusion Group	Elizabeth Humphreys	elizabeth.humphreys@housing.org.uk
Employment and Skills	(Rotating Chair)	
HAMMAR (Housing Asset Management, Maintenance And Regeneration)	Wayne Gethings	Wrekin Housing Trust
Housing Services	Jula Brady	St Basils
HR Forum	Helen Watkins	Housing Plus
Investment	Alan Yates	Accord Group
Midland Network for Resident Involvement	Chris Pinson-Bradley	Heantun Housing
Rural Development	Paul Sutton	Shropshire Housing Group
Smaller Housing Association	Elizabeth Humphreys	elizabeth.humphreys@housing.org.uk
Social Enterprise Group	Steve Woods	Adullam Homes Housing Association
Federation contact	Leah Jackson	leah.jackson@housing.org.uk

East Midlands

Care and Support	Jackie King-Owen	Enable HA
Central Home Ownership	Bob Deol	Mercian Housing Association
Chairs Forum	(Rotating chair)	
Continuous Improvement	Kathryn Webster	East Midlands Housing Group
Development	Jim Patman	East Midlands Housing Group
Finance	Rob Griffiths	Longhurst Group
Financial Inclusion	Peter Cowley	Nottingham Community HA
Governance and Legal Compliance	Joanne Tilley	East Midlands Housing Association

HAMMAR (Housing Asset Management, Maintenance And Regeneration)	Steve Grocock	Trent and Dove
Midland Network for Resident Involvement	Chris Pinson-Bradley	Heantun Housing
Small and BME Housing Association Benchmarking	Nikki Chawda	Foundation HA
Social Enterprise Forum	Antony Baines	Futures
Yorkshire and East Midlands Diversity Discussion Forum	Hannah Mason	Housing Diversity Network
Federation contact	Leah Jackson	leah.jackson@housing.org.uk

South West

Communities Network	Molly Holmes	Sanctuary Housing
Development	Nikki Tillett	The Guinness Partnership
	Wendy Lewis	Knightstone Housing Association
Governance Network	Lucy Rickson	Westward Housing Group
View the group's website	http://swgovernancenetwork.wordpress.com/	
Home Ownership	Amy MacKay	Aster Group
HAMMAR (Housing Asset Management, Maintenance And Regeneration)	Stephen Chalmers	
Incomes and Inclusion	Jim Bruckel	Yarlington Housing Group
Personnel and Training Officers' Group (PATOG)	Ria Bristow	Selwood Housing
Rural Housing Development	Peter Moore	Cornwall Rural HA
Smaller Housing Association	Gill Shell	Wiltshire Rural Housing Association
Social Enterprise Forum	Paul Smith	Aster Group
Supported Housing Forum	Myriam Kniveton	
Sustainability South	Alex Roberts	Aster Group
Federation contact	Leah Jackson	leah.jackson@housing.org.uk

London

Development	Kerry Heath	Hexagon
Environment	Tessa Barraclough	Peabody
Finance	Phil Newsam	Hexagon Housing
Home Ownership	Simon Scott	Origin Housing Association
Housing Management	(Vacant Chair)	
Leased Accommodation	Nick Caprara	Genesis Housing
London Supported Housing Forum	Chris Hampson	Look Ahead Housing and Care
Federation contact	Violeta Reen	violeta.reen@housing.org.uk

We are also pleased to support:

G320 Committee	John Delahunty	Innisfree Housing Association
Housing Financial Inclusion	Jahanara Hussain	Hyde Housing

South East

Finance	Julie Layton	Advance Housing and Support LTD
HAMMAR (Housing Asset Management, Maintenance And Regeneration)	Tav Sahota	Greensquare Group
Housing Management	Deborah Pike	Rosebery Housing Association
Home Ownership	Tim Willcocks	Radian Group
SE20	Karen MacDonald	Radian Group
Smaller Housing Associations Forum	Diana Kingdon	Greenoak Housing Association
Supported Housing Forum	Raife West	Havant Housing Association
Sustainability South	Alex Roberts	Aster Group
Federation contact	Violeta Reen	violeta.reen@housing.org.uk

East of England

Care and Support	Clare Lawrance	Colne Housing Society Ltd
Development	Fiona Coulson	Circle Housing Group
Equality and Diversity	Sean Kent	Freebridge Community Housing
Finance	Chris Wyer (Interim Chair)	Orwell Housing Association
Asset Management	Peter Scott (Co-ordinator)	
HR Forum	Stuart Tinkler	Saffron Housing Trust Ltd
Neighbourhood Management	Sue Philp	Suffolk Housing Society Ltd
Social Enterprise and Employment Group	Claire Astbury (Co-ordinator)	claire.astbury@housing.org.uk
Federation contact	Violeta Reen	violeta.reen@housing.org.uk

Communications networks

Our communications networks provide a forum for PR and communications professionals from the Federation's member organisations. The networks aim to:

- Increase awareness of affordable housing, and help member organisations raise their profile through participation in Federation media and campaign activities

- Share expertise and good practice with fellow communication professionals within the sector

- Assist communication professionals to meet their training and support needs.

North

Chair (and contact)	Anne Arnold	anne.arnold@housing.org.uk

West Midlands

Chair	Sarah Clee	Midland Heart
Vice Chair	Alex Roberts	Bromford Group
Federation contact	Peter Jones	peter.jones@housing.org.uk

East Midlands

Chair 1	Alison Bessey	Waterloo Housing Group
Chair 2	Mel Grant	Longhurst Group
Vice Chair	Lou Rudkin	Nottingham Community Housing Association
Federation contact	Peter Jones	peter.jones@housing.org.uk

Conferences and events 2013

Our conferences give you the chance to network with colleagues and engage with government ministers and representatives. Book now at www.housing.org.uk/events or call 020 7067 1066.

Dates for your diary 2013

25 – 26 Feb	Leaders Forum and Exhibition	Grange Tower Bridge Hotel, London
7 Mar	Communications and Marketing Conference and Exhibition	Grange Tower Bridge Hotel, London
19 Mar	Housing Association National Accountancy Awards	Hilton, Coventry
20 – 21 Mar	Housing Finance Conference and Exhibition	University of Warwick, Coventry
21 May	Affordable Home Ownership and Intermediate Housing Conference and Exhibition	Grange Tower Bridge Hotel, London
18 June	Resident Employment and Skills	The Gallery Suites, NEC, Birmingham
4 – 5 July	Asset Management and Maintenance Conference and Exhibition	University of Warwick, Coventry
4 – 5 July	Housing Development Conference and Exhibition	University of Warwick, Coventry
9 – 10 July	Housing Care and Support Conference and Exhibition	The Palace Hotel, Manchester
18 – 20 Sept	Annual Conference and Social Housing Exhibition	ICC, Birmingham

South West

Chair	Rebecca O'Neil	Selwood Housing
Vice Chair	Vanessa Gray	Westward Housing Group
Federation contact	Peter Jones	peter.jones@housing.org.uk

London

Chair	Lilah Woods	Gallions HA
Federation contact	Clare Bevis Paredes	clare.bevis@housing.org.uk

South East

Chair	Lisa Morris	AmicusHorizon
Vice Chair	Carol Levin	Paradigm Housing
Federation contact	Clare Bevis Paredes	clare.bevis@housing.org.uk

East of England

Chair	Rachael Trezise	Saffron HT
Vice Chair	Sarah Walker	Grand Union Housing Group
Federation contact	Clare Bevis Paredes	clare.bevis@housing.org.uk

Don't miss out on the publications below, available from our website. Download, purchase, or get more information at www.housing.org.uk/publications

Providing an alternative pathway
- Our report aimed at local commissioners of health and social care tells the real stories of five people who receive integrated care, housing and support.

Count us in
- Our research and practice review profiles the work housing associations are carrying out across England to help tenants cut their energy use.

Homeless bound?
- Uses research from local authorities, housing associations and central government data to build a picture of homelessness in London, the South East and East of England.

Communications for smaller housing associations
- Illustrates how smaller housing associations can communicate effectively, whatever their resources.

Code of conduct 2012
- Expanded and updated code guidance designed to help organisations achieve the highest standards of conduct.

Building futures
- Shows that every year housing associations in England help around eight million people by investing in a range of services.

On the pulse
- Features analysis of current health and care priorities and explores how housing associations can work with health and social care commissioners.

Federation News: sign up
- Subscribe and get the Federation's free monthly newsletter delivered straight to your inbox.

The Bulletin*
- Quarterly magazine produced to keep members up to date with policy and campaigning work.

*Member only

The following is a list of Federation group structures. The parent organisation is shown first in **bold** followed by the subsidiaries.

Accent Group Ltd
Accent Corporate Services Ltd
Accent Foundation Ltd
Accent Nene Ltd
Accent Peerless Ltd

Acclaim Housing Group Ltd
Dales Housing Ltd
Seven Locks Housing Ltd

Accord Housing Association Ltd
Ashram HA
Birmingham Co-operative Housing Services
Caldmore Area HA Ltd
Fry Housing Trust
Redditch Co-operative Homes

Adactus Housing Group
Adactus HA Ltd
Beech HA Ltd
Chorley Community Housing Ltd

Affinity Sutton
Aashyana HA Ltd
Affinity Sutton Homes
Grange Management (Southern) Ltd

AmicusHorizon Ltd
Amicus Horizon Group Ltd
Crystal Palace HA Ltd

Arcadia Housing Ltd
Knightstone HA Ltd

Arena Housing Group Ltd
Headrow Ltd
Leasowe Community Homes
Tung Sing HA Ltd

Aspire Group (Staffordshire) Ltd
Aspire Housing Ltd

Aspire Housing Ltd
Stoke-on-Trent Housing Society Ltd

Asra Housing Group Ltd
Asra HA Ltd
Family First Ltd
Leicester HA Ltd

Aster Group
Aster Communities
Synergy Housing Ltd

Bernicia Group Ltd
Cheviot HA Ltd
Wansbeck Homes Ltd

Black Country Housing Group Ltd
BCS Associates Ltd
Black Country Care Services Ltd

Broadacres Housing Association Ltd
Broadacres Services Ltd

Bromsgrove District Housing Trust
Bromsgrove Housing Initiatives Ltd

Christian Action (Enfield) HA Ltd
Christian Action Housing Special Projects Ltd

Circle
Circle Thirty Three Housing Trust Ltd
Mercian HA Ltd
Merton Priory Homes
Mole Valley HA Ltd
Old Ford HA
Roddons HA
Russet Homes
South Anglia Housing Ltd
Wherry HA Ltd

Cosmopolitan Housing Group Ltd
Chester & District Housing Trust
Cosmopolitan HA Ltd

Devon & Cornwall Housing Ltd
Devon & Cornwall Leasehold Solutions Ltd
Penwith HA Ltd
Tor Homes

East Midlands Housing Group
East Midlands HA Ltd
Foundation HA Ltd
Midlands Rural Housing & Village Development Assn Ltd
Three Oaks Homes Ltd
Three Valleys Housing Ltd

East Thames Group Ltd
East Homes Ltd
East Living Ltd
East Potential

Equity Housing Group Ltd
Equity HA Ltd
Provincial HA Ltd

Fabrick Housing Group Ltd
Erimus Housing
Norcare Ltd
Tees Valley Housing Ltd

Family Mosaic Housing
Charlton Triangle Homes Ltd
Family Mosaic Home Ownership Ltd
Old Oak HA Ltd

Four Housing Group
Berwick Borough Housing
Three Rivers HA Ltd

Futures Housing Group
Daventry & District Housing Ltd
Futures Homescape Ltd

Genesis HA
Springboard Two HA Ltd

Gentoo Group Ltd
Gentoo Sunderland Ltd

Grand Union Housing Group Ltd
Aragon HA Ltd
MacIntyre HA Ltd
South Northants Homes

Great Places Housing Group
Great Places HA
Plumlife Homes Ltd
Terra Nova Developments Ltd

GreenSquare Group Ltd
Oxford Citizens HA Ltd
Westlea HA

Hastoe Housing Association Ltd
Hastoe Wyvern HA Ltd

Heantun HA Ltd
Heantun Care HA Ltd

Hexagon HA Ltd
Horniman HA Ltd

Lion Court Conference Centre

Lion Court Conference Centre boasts some of the most well-equipped meeting and conference facilities in London.

Situated in Holborn, conveniently close to the City and West End of London with Holborn tube only two minutes' walk away, the centre has 22 meeting rooms including a lecture theatre with fixed seating and compact, fitted writing shelves for 80 people.

The Conference Centre can provide a range of menus catering for every event from large to small including breakfast, lunch, snacks and a range of hot and cold beverages.

Collectively this makes Lion Court Conference Centre one of the most sought after venues in London.

How to book

Email us at **sales@lion-court.com** or call us on **020 7067 1126**.

At least 48 hours' notice is required although it is advisable to book early in order for us to meet all your requirements.

We would be delighted to show you around at a convenient time for you, allowing you to experience the ambience of the conference centre and see first hand what we can offer you. To arrange a viewing please contact us on the details below.

25 Procter Street, London WC1V 6NY
Tel: 020 7067 1126
Fax: 020 7067 1127
E: sales@lion-court.com
W: www.lion-court.com

Hightown Praetorian and Churches HA Ltd
Community Meeting Point

Horton HA
Horton Housing Support Ltd

Hyde HA Ltd
Hillside Housing Trust
Hyde Southbank Homes Ltd
Martlet Homes Ltd
Minster General HA Ltd

Incommunities Group Ltd
Incommunities Ltd

Irwell Valley Housing Association Ltd
Pendleton Improved HA Ltd

Islington & Shoreditch HA Ltd
Lien Viet HA Ltd

Jephson Homes HA Ltd
Jephson HA Ltd
Marches HA Ltd

Johnnie Johnson Housing Trust Ltd
Johnnie Johnson HA Ltd

Knightstone Housing Association Ltd
Knightstone Charitable Housing Ltd

Longhurst Group Ltd
Friendship Care and Housing
Keystone Developments (LG) Ltd
Longhurst & Havelok Homes Ltd
Spire Homes (LG) Ltd

Luminus Group
Luminus Homes
Oak Foundation

Magna Housing Group Ltd
Magna HA Ltd
Magna West Somerset HA Ltd

Manchester & District HA
Partington HA

Metropolitan
Clapham Park Homes
Granta Housing Society Ltd
Metropolitan
Spirita

MHA
Methodist Homes HA

MHS Homes Ltd
Heart of Medway Housing Association Ltd

Moat Homes Ltd
Moat Housing Group

Mosscare Housing Ltd
Mossbank Homes Ltd

Network Housing Group Ltd
Community Trust Housing
London Strategic Housing Ltd
Mitali HA Ltd
Network Stadium Housing Association Ltd
Riversmead HA Ltd
Willow Housing and Care Ltd

New Charter Housing Trust Ltd
Aksa HA Ltd
Gedling Homes
New Charter Homes Ltd

Newlon Housing Trust
Access Homes HA Ltd
Outward

North Star Housing Group Ltd
Endeavour HA
Teesdale HA Ltd

Notting Hill Housing Trust
Notting Hill Home Ownership HA Ltd

Nottingham Community HA Ltd
Nottingham Community (2nd) HA Ltd

Ocean Housing Group Ltd
Ocean Housing Ltd

One Vision Housing Ltd
Pine Court HA Ltd

Orbit Group Ltd
Orbit Heart of England
Orbit South HA Ltd

Paradigm Housing Group Ltd
Paradigm Homes Charitable HA Ltd

Paragon Community Housing Group
Elmbridge Housing Trust Ltd
Richmond Upon Thames Churches HT

Peabody
CBHA

Places for People Group
Cotman HA Ltd
Places for People Homes Ltd
Places for People Individual Support Ltd

Plus Dane Housing Group Ltd
Plus Dane (Cheshire) HA Ltd
Plus Dane (Merseyside) HA Ltd

Progress Housing Group Ltd
New Fylde Housing Ltd
New Progress HA Ltd
Progress Care HA Ltd

Radian Group Ltd
Drum HA Ltd
Oriel Housing Ltd
Portal HA Ltd
Radian Support Ltd
The Swaythling Housing Society Ltd
Windsor and District HA

Richmond Housing Partnership
Co-op Homes (South) Ltd

Rooftop Housing Group Ltd
Evesham & Pershore Housing Association Ltd
G3 Inspiring Individuals
Rooftop Homes Ltd

Rosemary Simmons Memorial HA Ltd
Fellowship Houses Trust

Sanctuary HA
Asra Midlands HA Ltd
Rochford HA

Housing **exhibitions** 2013

The National Housing Federation's successful series of conferences and exhibitions provide expert coverage of fundamental issues of importance to decision-makers in the sector and attract 6,000 attendees annually.

The following exhibitions are confirmed for 2013:

Leaders' Forum and Exhibition 2013
Grange Tower Bridge Hotel, London

Communications and Marketing Conference and Exhibition 2013
Grange Tower Bridge Hotel, London

Housing Finance Conference and Exhibition 2013
University of Warwick, Coventry

Social Enterprise Conference and Exhibition 2013
Inmarsat Conference Centre, London

HR in Housing Conference and Exhibition 2013
Inmarsat Conference Centre, London

Affordable Home Ownership and Intermediate Housing Conference and Exhibition 2013
Inmarsat Conference Centre, London

Community Land Trusts Annual Conference and Exhibition 2013
Burlington Hotel, Birmingham

Asset Management and Maintenance Conference and Exhibition 2013
Mead Gallery, University of Warwick, Coventry

Housing Development Conference and Exhibition 2013
Mead Gallery, University of Warwick, Coventry

Housing Care and Support Conference and Exhibition 2013
The Palace Hotel, Manchester

Social Housing Exhibition 2013 the National Housing Federation Annual Conference
International Convention Centre, Birmingham
www.socialhousingexhibition.com

Conference and Exhibition for Smaller Housing Associations 2013
Inmarsat Conference Centre, London

IT in Housing Conference and Exhibition 2013
Olympia Conference Centre, London
www.itinhousingexhibition.co.uk

For more information please contact
Foremarke Exhibitions on
020 8877 8899 or
housing@foremarke.uk.com

Foremarke
EXHIBITIONS

10 years of excellence

iN business for neighbourhoods

Shropshire Housing Ltd
Meres and Mosses HA
South Shropshire HA

Southern Housing Group Ltd
Southern Home Ownership Ltd

Staffordshire Housing Association Ltd
Blue Mountain HA Ltd

Symphony Housing Group
Beechwood Ballantyne
Cobalt Housing Ltd
Contour Homes
Contour Property Services Ltd
Hyndburn Homes Ltd
Liverpool Housing Trust
Peak Valley HA Ltd
Ribble Valley Homes Ltd

Thames Valley HA Ltd
Thames Valley Charitable HA Ltd

The Community Housing Group
Wyre Forest Community Housing Ltd
Wyre Forest Sheltered Housing Ltd

The Guinness Partnership
Guinness Care & Support Ltd
Guinness HA Ltd

The Housing Plus Group Ltd
South Staffordshire HA

The London Housing Foundation
Bramah House Ltd

The Riverside Group Ltd
The St Michael's Housing Trust

The Villages Housing Association Ltd
Villages Community Housing Association Ltd

The Wrekin Housing Group Ltd
CHOICES HA Ltd
The Wrekin Housing Trust

Thera Trust
Forward Housing SW

Together Housing Group Ltd
Chevin HA Ltd
Green Vale Homes Ltd
Harewood Housing Society Ltd
Housing Pendle
Pennine Housing 2000 Ltd
Twin Valley Homes Ltd

Town & Country Housing Group
TCHG Foundation
TCHG Living Ltd

Trident HA Ltd
Trident Charitable Housing Association Ltd

Two Rivers Housing
Two Rivers Initiatives Ltd

Vela Group
Housing Hartlepool Ltd
Tristar Homes Ltd

Waterloo Housing Group Ltd
de Montfort Housing Society Ltd
New Linx Housing Trust
Waterloo HA Ltd

Weaver Vale Housing Trust
Weaver Horizons Ltd

Westward Housing Group Ltd
Tarka Housing Ltd
Westcountry HA Ltd

WM Housing Group
Kemble Housing Ltd
Nexus (Midlands) Housing Association (2005) Ltd
Optima Community Association
West Mercia Homes Ltd
Whitefriars Housing Group Ltd

Yorkshire Coast Homes Ltd
YCH Developments Ltd

Yorkshire Housing Ltd
YH Residential Ltd

Your Housing Group
Arena Housing Group Ltd
Derwent & Solway HA
Frontis
Manchester & District HA
Moorlands Housing
Tung Sing HA Ltd

See page 63 for A-Z listings of Federation members **53**

The following is a list of subsidiary and parent organisations. The subsidiary is shown in the first column with the parent organisation shown opposite.

Subsidiary	Parent
Aashyana HA Ltd	Affinity Sutton
Accent Corporate Services Ltd	Accent Group Ltd
Accent Foundation Ltd	Accent Group Ltd
Accent Nene Ltd	Accent Group Ltd
Accent Peerless Ltd	Accent Group Ltd
Access Homes HA Ltd	Newlon Housing Trust
Adactus HA Ltd	Adactus Housing Group
Affinity Sutton Homes	Affinity Sutton
Aksa HA Ltd	New Charter Housing Trust Ltd
Aldwyck Housing Group	Aldwyck Housing Group Ltd
Amicus Horizon Group Ltd	AmicusHorizon Ltd
Aragon HA Ltd	Grand Union Housing Group Ltd
Arena Housing Group Ltd	Your Housing Group
Ashram HA	Accord HA Ltd
Aspire Housing Ltd	Aspire Group (Staffordshire) Ltd
Asra HA Ltd	Asra Housing Group Ltd
Asra Midlands HA Ltd	Sanctuary HA
Aster Communities	Aster Group
BCS Associates Ltd	Black Country Housing Group Ltd
Beech HA Ltd	Adactus Housing Group
Beechwood Ballantyne	Symphony Housing Group
Berwick Borough Housing	Four Housing Group
Birmingham Co-operative Housing Services	Accord HA Ltd
Black Country Care Services Ltd	Black Country Housing Group Ltd
Blue Mountain HA Ltd	Staffordshire HA Ltd
Bramah House Ltd	The London Housing Foundation
Broadacres Services Ltd	Broadacres HA Ltd
Bromsgrove Housing Initiatives Ltd	Bromsgrove District Housing Trust
Caldmore Area HA Ltd	Accord HA Ltd
CBHA	Peabody
Charlton Triangle Homes Ltd	Family Mosaic Housing
Chester & District Housing Trust	Cosmopolitan Housing Group Ltd
Chevin HA Ltd	Together Housing Group Ltd
Cheviot HA Ltd	Bernicia Group Ltd
CHOICES HA Ltd	The Wrekin Housing Group Ltd
Chorley Community Housing Ltd	Adactus Housing Group
Christian Action Housing Special Projects Ltd	Christian Action (Enfield) HA Ltd
Circle Thirty Three Housing Trust Ltd	Circle
Clapham Park Homes	Metropolitan
Co-op Homes (South) Ltd	Richmond Housing Partnership
Cobalt Housing Ltd	Symphony Housing Group
Community Meeting Point	Hightown Praetorian and Churches HA Ltd
Community Trust Housing	Network Housing Group Ltd
Contour Homes	Symphony Housing Group
Contour Property Services Ltd	Symphony Housing Group
Cosmopolitan HA Ltd	Cosmopolitan Housing Group Ltd
Cotman HA Ltd	Places for People Group
Crystal Palace HA Ltd	AmicusHorizon Ltd
Dales Housing Ltd	Acclaim Housing Group Ltd
Daventry & District Housing Ltd	Futures Housing Group
de Montfort Housing Society Ltd	Waterloo Housing Group Ltd
Derwent & Solway HA	Your Housing Group
Devon & Cornwall Leasehold Solutions Ltd	Devon & Cornwall Housing Ltd
Drum HA Ltd	Radian Group Ltd

See page 63 for A-Z listings of Federation members

Located at the National Housing Federation's headquarters in Lion Court Conference Centre, the Leadership Lounge is an exclusive membership lounge.

It is conveniently close to central London, with Holborn tube station (Central and Piccadilly lines) only two minutes' walk away.

The lounge provides a unique, comfortable and well equipped environment for all your business needs. For more information including membership rates please contact us:

- Exclusive use of a stylish, private and contemporary lounge
- Membership available at competitive rates
- Small meeting rooms available up to two hours per day
- Free Wi-Fi access
- Availability to host own events
- Complimentary hot beverages

The Leadership Lounge, 25 Procter Street, London WC1V 6NY
Tel: 020 7067 1192
E: leadershiplounge@housing.org.uk

Subsidiary	Parent
East Homes Ltd	East Thames Group Ltd
East Living Ltd	East Thames Group Ltd
East Midlands HA Ltd	East Midlands Housing Group
East Potential	East Thames Group Ltd
Elmbridge Housing Trust Ltd	Paragon Community Housing Group
Endeavour HA	North Star Housing Group Ltd
Equity HA Ltd	Equity Housing Group Ltd
Erimus Housing	Fabrick Housing Group Ltd
Evesham & Pershore HA Ltd	Rooftop Housing Group Ltd
Family First Ltd	Asra Housing Group Ltd
Family Mosaic Home Ownership Ltd	Family Mosaic Housing
Fellowship Houses Trust	Rosemary Simmons Memorial HA Ltd
Forward Housing SW	Thera Trust
Foundation HA Ltd	East Midlands Housing Group
Friendship Care and Housing	Longhurst Group Ltd
Frontis	Your Housing Group
Fry Housing Trust	Accord HA Ltd
Futures Homescape Ltd	Futures Housing Group
G3 Inspiring Individuals	Rooftop Housing Group Ltd
Gedling Homes	New Charter Housing Trust Ltd
Gentoo Sunderland Ltd	Gentoo Group Ltd
Grange Management (Southern) Ltd	Affinity Sutton
Granta Housing Society Ltd	Metropolitan
Great Places HA	Great Places Housing Group
Green Vale Homes Ltd	Together Housing Group Ltd
Guinness Care & Support Ltd	The Guinness Partnership
Guinness HA Ltd	The Guinness Partnership
Harewood Housing Society Ltd	Together Housing Group Ltd
Hastoe Wyvern HA Ltd	Hastoe HA Ltd
Headrow Ltd	Arena Housing Group Ltd
Heantun Care HA Ltd	Heantun HA Ltd
Heart of Medway HA Ltd	MHS Homes Ltd
Hillside Housing Trust	Hyde HA Ltd
Horniman HA Ltd	Hexagon HA Ltd
Horton Housing Support Ltd	Horton HA
Housing Hartlepool Ltd	Vela Group
Housing Pendle	Together Housing Group Ltd
Hyde Southbank Homes Ltd	Hyde HA Ltd
Hyndburn Homes Ltd	Symphony Housing Group
Incommunities Ltd	Incommunities Group Ltd
Jephson HA Ltd	Jephson Homes HA Ltd
Johnnie Johnson HA Ltd	Johnnie Johnson Housing Trust Ltd
Keystone Developments (LG) Ltd	Longhurst Group Ltd
Knightstone Charitable Housing Ltd	Knightstone HA Ltd
Knightstone HA Ltd	Arcadia Housing Ltd
Knowsley Housing Trust	First Ark Group
Leasowe Community Homes	Arena Housing Group Ltd
Leicester HA Ltd	Asra Housing Group Ltd
Lien Viet HA Ltd	Islington & Shoreditch HA Ltd
Liverpool Housing Trust	Symphony Housing Group
London Strategic Housing Ltd	Network Housing Group Ltd
Longhurst & Havelok Homes Ltd	Longhurst Group Ltd
Luminus Homes	Luminus Group
MacIntyre HA Ltd	Grand Union Housing Group Ltd
Magna HA Ltd	Magna Housing Group Ltd
Magna West Somerset HA Ltd	Magna Housing Group Ltd
Manchester & District HA	Your Housing Group
Marches HA Ltd	Jephson Homes HA Ltd
Martlet Homes Ltd	Hyde HA Ltd

See page 63 for A-Z listings of Federation members

Federation subscribers

The new way to engage with the social housing sector

Sign up to our exciting scheme, offering a range of benefits to organisations wishing to provide products and services to the social housing sector. The scheme provides an ideal platform to gain access to the sector by presenting organisations with an opportunity to:

- Use the Federation subscriber logo and obtain a listing on our website
- Demonstrate their commitment to the sector
- Network with our housing association members
- Build upon their knowledge of the work of housing associations
- Raise their profile within the social housing sector
- Gain access to the Directory of members plus exclusive mailing lists
- Receive discounted rates for conferences, publications and training

Further information email kuljit.karir@housing.org.uk

www.housing.org.uk

Advertise in the Directory

The Directory offers a unique opportunity to increase your profile in the sector.

- Used by budget holders controlling over 95% of housing association stock.
- Over 5,000 copies are distributed FREE each year with free online access for over 150,000 staff.
- All advertisers in the book are included in the online directory in a categorised section.

Contact us on 0845 226 0477 to book your space for 2014 and take advantage of our special offers, or email us:

Gareth Macfarlane garethm@media-shed.co.uk
Natalie Tuerena natt@media-shed.co.uk

www.nhfdirectory.co.uk

Subsidiary and parent organisations

Subsidiary	Parent
Mercian HA Ltd	Circle
Meres and Mosses HA	Shropshire Housing Ltd
Merton Priory Homes	Circle
Methodist Homes HA	MHA
Metropolitan	Metropolitan
Midlands Rural Housing & Village Development Assn Ltd	East Midlands Housing Group
Minster General HA Ltd	Hyde HA Ltd
Mitali HA Ltd	Network Housing Group Ltd
Moat Housing Group	Moat Homes Ltd
Mole Valley HA Ltd	Circle
Moorlands Housing	Your Housing Group
Mossbank Homes Ltd	Mosscare Housing Ltd
Network Stadium HA Ltd	Network Housing Group Ltd
New Charter Homes Ltd	New Charter Housing Trust Ltd
New Fylde Housing Ltd	Progress Housing Group Ltd
New Linx Housing Trust	Waterloo Housing Group Ltd
New Progress HA Ltd	Progress Housing Group Ltd
Norcare Ltd	Fabrick Housing Group Ltd
Notting Hill Home Ownership HA Ltd	Notting Hill Housing Trust
Nottingham Community (2nd) HA Ltd	Nottingham Community HA Ltd
Oak Foundation	Luminus Group
Ocean Housing Ltd	Ocean Housing Group Ltd
Old Ford HA	Circle
Old Oak HA Ltd	Family Mosaic Housing
Optima Community Association	WM Housing Group
Orbit Heart of England	Orbit Group Ltd
Orbit South HA Ltd	Orbit Group Ltd
Oriel Housing Ltd	Radian Group Ltd
Outward	Newlon Housing Trust
Oxford Citizens HA Ltd	GreenSquare Group Ltd
Paradigm Homes Charitable HA Ltd	Paradigm Housing Group Ltd
Parkway Green Housing Trust	Wythenshawe Community Housing Group
Partington HA	Manchester & District HA
Peak Valley HA Ltd	Symphony Housing Group
Pendleton Improved HA Ltd	Irwell Valley HA Ltd
Pennine Housing 2000 Ltd	Together Housing Group Ltd
Penwith HA Ltd	Devon & Cornwall Housing Ltd
Pine Court HA Ltd	One Vision Housing Ltd
Places for People Homes Ltd	Places for People Group
Places for People Individual Support Ltd	Places for People Group
Plumlife Homes Ltd	Great Places Housing Group
Plus Dane (Cheshire) HA Ltd	Plus Dane Housing Group Ltd
Plus Dane (Merseyside) HA Ltd	Plus Dane Housing Group Ltd
Portal HA Ltd	Radian Group Ltd
Progress Care HA Ltd	Progress Housing Group Ltd
Provincial HA Ltd	Equity Housing Group Ltd
Radian Support Ltd	Radian Group Ltd
Redditch Co-operative Homes	Accord HA Ltd
Ribble Valley Homes Ltd	Symphony Housing Group
Richmond Upon Thames Churches HT	Paragon Community Housing Group
Riversmead HA Ltd	Network Housing Group Ltd
Rochford HA	Sanctuary HA
Roddons HA	Circle
Rooftop Homes Ltd	Rooftop Housing Group Ltd
Russet Homes	Circle
Seven Locks Housing Ltd	Acclaim Housing Group Ltd
Signpost HA Ltd	Spectrum Housing Group Ltd
South Anglia Housing Ltd	Circle
South Northants Homes	Grand Union Housing Group Ltd
South Shropshire HA	Shropshire Housing Ltd
South Staffordshire HA	The Housing Plus Group Ltd

Subsidiary and parent organisations

Subsidiary	Parent
Southern Home Ownership Ltd	Southern Housing Group Ltd
Spire Homes (LG) Ltd	Longhurst Group Ltd
Spirita	Metropolitan
Springboard Two HA Ltd	Genesis HA
Stoke-on-Trent Housing Society Ltd	Aspire Housing Ltd
Synergy Housing Ltd	Aster Group
Tarka Housing Ltd	Westward Housing Group Ltd
TCHG Foundation	Town & Country Housing Group
TCHG Living Ltd	Town & Country Housing Group
Tees Valley Housing Ltd	Fabrick Housing Group Ltd
Teesdale HA Ltd	North Star Housing Group Ltd
Terra Nova Developments Ltd	Great Places Housing Group
Thames Valley Charitable HA Ltd	Thames Valley HA Ltd
The St Michael's Housing Trust	The Riverside Group Ltd
The Swaythling Housing Society Ltd	Radian Group Ltd
The Wrekin Housing Trust	The Wrekin Housing Group Ltd
Three Oaks Homes Ltd	East Midlands Housing Group
Three Rivers HA Ltd	Four Housing Group
Three Valleys Housing Ltd	East Midlands Housing Group
Tor Homes	Devon & Cornwall Housing Ltd
Trident Charitable HA Ltd	Trident HA Ltd
Tristar Homes Ltd	Vela Group
Tung Sing HA Ltd	Your Housing Group
Twin Valley Homes Ltd	Together Housing Group Ltd
Two Rivers Initiatives Ltd	Two Rivers Housing
Villages Community HA Ltd	The Villages HA Ltd
Wansbeck Homes Ltd	Bernicia Group Ltd
Waterloo HA Ltd	Waterloo Housing Group Ltd
Weaver Horizons Ltd	Weaver Vale Housing Trust
West Mercia Homes Ltd	WM Housing Group
Westcountry HA Ltd	Westward Housing Group Ltd
Westlea HA	GreenSquare Group Ltd
Wherry HA Ltd	Circle
Whitefriars Housing Group Ltd	WM Housing Group
Willow Housing and Care Ltd	Network Housing Group Ltd
Willow Park Housing Trust	Wythenshawe Community Housing Group
Windsor and District HA	Radian Group Ltd
Wyre Forest Community Housing Ltd	The Community Housing Group
Wyre Forest Sheltered Housing Ltd	The Community Housing Group
YCH Developments Ltd	Yorkshire Coast Homes Ltd
YH Residential Ltd	Yorkshire Housing Ltd

New members 2012

Blenheim Gardens Resident Management Organisation
Gentoo Art of Living
Red Kite Community Housing Ltd
Tamarisk Housing Limited

Name changes 2012

Old name	New name
First Choice Homes Oldham Ltd	First Choice Homes Oldham
Arena Housing Group Ltd	Your Housing Group
Harvest Housing Group	Your Housing Group
Evesham and Pershore HA Ltd	Evesham & Pershore Housing Association Ltd

Key to abbreviations and symbols

Abbreviations

Whenever possible, the full name of each member is given. However in some cases it has been necessary to abbreviate.

Occasionally the name of the organisation is abbreviated as follows:

CHS	Co-operative Housing Society
HA	Housing Association
HS	Housing Society
HT	Housing Trust
Soc or S	Society

Organisational status

The symbol here indicates the legal status of the member. The key for the symbols is as follows:

○	charitable HA
☆	charitable company
■	non-charitable HA
❑	charitable trust
✪	not-for-profit company
▼	co-ownership society
★	co-operative society
●	self-build association
▲	other

Senior officers

The designation of the senior officials of each member can vary:

Ch refers to the chair, however styled, of the organisation's main board or management committee

Sec is the secretary; in some cases the post may be held by a board member, in others by a paid staff member

CE refers to the most senior staff member: the Chief Executive or Director, but in some organisations Manager, Secretary/Manager, Co-ordinator or another job title

Regions

This refers to the Federation's region or regions in which the member's head office is based. The member's main region will be stated first – this is the region in which the association has its registered office. If other regions are stated, the member has over 50 units in ownership in each area.

Subsidiaries and groups

Where a member has a subsidiary organisation, ie, another housing organisation in Federation membership under its control, the subsidiary(ies) will appear within the normal alphabetical listing as well as being shown at the end of the 'parent' entry.

Each subsidiary association will also state its parent association.

Symbols

▰	Over 10,000 units in management
◰	Over 5,000 units in management
VTHO	Voluntary transfer housing organisation
500	Over 500 units in development
▣	A development programme (rent or LCHO)
⚷	Low cost home ownership (LCHO) scheme
⧍	Over 250 full-time staff employed
🤝	Care and support provided
♻	Group structure
⌂	Black and minority ethnic association

Owned and managed

These are the total number of homes that the Federation member owns or manages.

These rental totals **(Rt)** are broken down into general needs **(GN)**, supported housing **(Sup)**, and older people **(OP)**. The following information is listed separately from the rent totals: shared ownership **(SO)**, non-social owned **(NSO)**, total new and re-lets **(Tot lets)** and general needs bedspaces **(GN bs)**.

Development total

These are the total number of homes that the member has in development. The total number of homes is broken down by new build acquired **(NBA)** and new build completed **(NBC)**.

Rental totals **(Rt)** are broken down into general needs **(GN)**, supported **(Sup)** and older people **(OP)** and excludes low cost home ownership **(LCHO)**.

700

700 Club
☆ Charitable Company
TSA Reg ✗ 🐝
Head Office, Grange Centre, Grange Road Baptist Church, Darlington, County Durham, DL1 5NH
T 01325 366397
E 700club@700club.org.uk
W www.700club.org.uk
CE Dr John Elliston
Sec Mrs Yvonne Beattie
Ch Mrs Lee Vasey
Total Staff 28
Region North East
Tenant Type % Family 3% **Single** 97%

1625 Independent People Ltd
○ Charitable HA
TSA Reg ✗ 🐝
Kingsley Hall, 59 Old Market Street, Bristol, Avon, BS2 0ER
T 0117 317 8800
E enquiries@1625ip.co.uk
W www.1625ip.co.uk
CE Dominic Wood
Ch Mr Stephen Lodge
Total Staff 75
Region South West
Tenant Type % Single 100%

Aa

A2Dominion Group Ltd
○ Charitable HA
TSA Reg ✓
🔲 🔲 🔲 🔲 🔲 🔲 🐝
15th Floor, Capital House, 25 Chapel Street, London, Greater London, NW1 5WX
T 020 8825 1000
E info@a2dominion.co.uk
W www.a2dominion.co.uk
CE Mr Darrell J Mercer
Sec Ms Zoe Ollerearnshaw
Ch Mr Derek Joseph
Total Staff 859
Regions London + South East
Owned or managed 34878
Rt 23934 **GN** 20835 **Sup** 2136 **OP** 963 **SO** 7865 **NSO** 3079 **Tot lets** 2415 **GN bs** 20783
Tenant Type % Family 45% **Older** 16% **Single** 39%
Development Total 1066
Rt 1268 **GN** 1234 **OP** 34 **LCHO** 609
NBC 1066

Aashyana HA Ltd
○ Charitable HA
TSA Reg ✓ 🔑 👤 🏠
2 Pritchard Street, St Paul's, Bristol, Avon, BS2 8RH
T 0117 939 3911
E housing@aashyana.co.uk
W www.aashyana.co.uk
CE Lewin Dumper
Ch Shaheen Chaudry
Total Staff 1
Region South West
Owned or managed 164
Rt 156 **GN** 156 **SO** 8 **Tot lets** 23
GN bs 0
Tenant Type % Family 88%
Older 5% **Single** 7%
Parent Association Affinity Sutton

Abeona Housing Co-op Ltd
★ Co-operative Society
TSA Reg ✓
30 Fleet Road, London, Greater London, NW3 2QS
T 020 7482 2138
E info@abeona.org
W www.abeona.org
Sec Ms Elaine Scanlane
Ch Ms Annie Thierl
Total Staff 3
Region London
Owned or managed 44
Rt 44 **GN** 44
Tenant Type % Family 10%
Single 90%

Ability HA
☆ Charitable Company
TSA Reg ✓ 🔑 🐝
The Coach House, Gresham Road, Staines, Middlesex, TW18 2AE
T 01784 490910
E info@ability-housing.co.uk
W www.ability-housing.co.uk
CE Mr David Williams
Sec Ms Donna Marshall
Ch Mr John Daley
Total Staff 190
Regions South East + London, South West, East of England
Owned or managed 616
Rt 603 **GN** 220 **Sup** 383 **SO** 5 **NSO** 8 **Tot lets** 0 **GN bs** 0
Tenant Type % Family 22%
Older 3% **Single** 75%

Accent Corporate Services Ltd
■ Non-Charitable HA
TSA Reg ✓ 👤
Charlestown House, Acorn Park Industrial Estate, Charlestown, Shipley, West Yorkshire, BD17 7SW
T 01274 717500
E apsenquiries@accentgroup.org
W www.accentgroup.org
CE Mr Gordon Perry
Sec Mr Matthew Sugden
Ch Ms Gwyneth Sarker
Total Staff 162
Region Yorkshire & Humberside
Parent Association
Accent Group Ltd

Accent Foundation Ltd
○ Charitable HA
TSA Reg ✓ 🔲 🔲 🔲 🔲 🔑 👤 👤
Charlestown House, Acorn Park Industrial Estate, Charlestown, Shipley, West Yorkshire, BD17 7SW
T 01274 717500
W www.accentgroup.org
CE Ms Claire Stone
Sec Mr Matthew Sugden
Ch Mr Peter Caffrey
Total Staff 295
Regions Yorkshire & Humberside + London, South East, North East, North West
Owned or managed 12851
Rt 11370 **GN** 9063 **Sup** 373 **OP** 1934 **SO** 1388 **NSO** 93 **Tot lets** 1470
GN bs 9063
Tenant Type % Family 36%
Older 19% **Single** 35%
Development Total 327
NBA 208 **NBC** 119
Parent Association
Accent Group Ltd

Accent Group Ltd
○ Charitable HA
TSA Reg ✓ 👤
Charlestown House, Acorn Park Industrial Estate, Charlestown, Shipley, West Yorkshire, BD17 7SW
T 01274 717500
W www.accentgroup.org
CE Mr Gordon Perry
Sec Mr Matthew Sugden
Ch Ms Gwyneth Sarker
Total Staff 0
Region Yorkshire & Humberside
Subsidiary Association(s) Accent Corporate Services Ltd; Accent Foundation Ltd; Accent Nene Ltd; Accent Peerless Ltd

Accent Nene Ltd
○ Charitable HA
TSA Reg ✓ 🏠 🔑 🐾 🔥
Manor House, 57 Lincoln Road, Peterborough, Cambridgeshire, PE1 2RR
T 01733 295400
E info@accentnene.org
W www.accentnene.org
CE Andrew Williams
Sec Andrew Williams
Ch Mr Roger Davis
Total Staff 90
Regions East of England + East Midlands
Owned or managed 4141
Rt 3596 GN 2984 Sup 23 OP 589 SO 447 NSO 98 Tot lets 253
 GN bs 2840
Tenant Type % Family 56%
Older 23% Single 21%
Development Total 12
Rt 67 GN 67 NBA 6 NBC 6
Parent Association
Accent Group Ltd

Accent Peerless Ltd
○ Charitable HA
TSA Reg ✓ 🚚 🏠 🔑 🐾 🔥
Station House, 1 Pembroke Broadway, Camberley, Surrey, GU15 3XD
T 01276 852900
E enquiries@accentpeerless.co.uk
W www.accentpeerless.co.uk
CE Mr Gordon Perry
Sec Mr Richard Williams
Ch Mr Geoff Heath
Total Staff 66
Region South East
Owned or managed 4025
Rt 3645 GN 3339 Sup 60 OP 246 SO 368 NSO 12 Tot lets 287
GN bs 2861
Tenant Type % Family 45%
Older 15% Single 40%
Development Total 22
 NBA 11 NBC 11
Parent Association
Accent Group Ltd

Access Homes HA Ltd
■ Non-Charitable HA
TSA Reg ✓ 🔑 🔥
Newlon House, 4 Daneland Walk, Hale Village, London, Greater London, N17 9FE
T 020 7613 8074
E info@newlon.org.uk
W www.newlon.org.uk
CE Mr Mike Hinch
Sec Ms Rita Akushie
Ch Mr Steve Akeju
Total Staff 0

Region London
Owned or managed 229
Rt 40 GN 40 SO 189 Tot lets 0
GN bs 0
Tenant Type % Family 60%
Older 10% Single 30%
Parent Association
Newlon Housing Trust

Acclaim Housing Group Ltd
✪ Not-for-Profit Company
TSA Reg ✓ 🔥
Scholes Mill, Old Coach Road, Tansley, Matlock, Derbyshire, DE4 5FY
T 01629 761540
E info@acclaim-group.co.uk
W www.acclaim-group.co.uk
CE Mr Gerald Taylor
Sec Mr Mike Finister-Smith
Ch Valerie Hammond
Total Staff 25
Region East Midlands
Subsidiary Association(s) Dales Housing Ltd; Seven Locks Housing Ltd

Accord HA Ltd
○ Charitable HA
TSA Reg ✓ 📱 🏠 🔑 ♦ 🐾 🔥
178 Birmingham Road, West Bromwich, West Midlands, B70 6QG
T 0300 111 7000
E customerfirst@accordgroup.org.uk
W www.caldmoreaccordha.org.uk
CE Dr Christopher Handy OBE
Sec Mr Lakhbir Jaspal
Ch Mr Akshay Parikh
Total Staff 967
Region West Midlands
Owned or managed 5722
Rt 4549 GN 3793 Sup 116 OP 640 SO 1162 NSO 11 Tot lets 547
GN bs 3358
Tenant Type % Family 61%
Older 27% Single 12%
Development Total 43
Rt 513 GN 513 LCHO 121 NBA 32 NBC 11
Subsidiary Association(s) Ashram HA; Birmingham Co-operative Housing Services; Caldmore Area HA Ltd; Fry Housing Trust; Redditch Co-operative Homes

Acis Group Ltd
☆ Charitable Company
TSA Reg ✓ 📱 🏠 🔑 🐾
Acis House, Bridge Street, Gainsborough, Lincolnshire, DN21 1GG
T 01427 678000
E info@acisgroup.co.uk
W www.acisgroup.co.uk

CE Ms Valerie Waby
Sec Mr Russ Blenkinsop
Ch Rodney Must
Total Staff 123
Regions East Midlands + Yorkshire & Humberside
Owned or managed 5335
Rt 5102 GN 4853 Sup 15 OP 234 SO 217 NSO 16 Tot lets 790
GN bs 4756
Tenant Type % Family 32%
Older 42% Single 26%
Development Total 157
NBA 82 NBC 75

Acme Artists Studios Ltd
○ Charitable HA
TSA Reg ✗
44 Copperfield Road,, Bow, London, Greater London, E3 4RR
T 020 8981 6811
E mail@acme.org.uk
W www.acme.org.uk
CE Mr Jonathan Harvey
Sec Mr Jonathan Harvey
Ch Mr David Panton
Total Staff 13
Region London

Action Housing & Support Ltd
☆ Charitable Company
TSA Reg ✓ 🐾
6 Genesis Business Park, Sheffield Road, Rotherham, South Yorkshire, S60 1DX
T 01709 821251
E info@actionhousinguk.org
W www.actionhousinguk.org
CE Mr Steve Owen
Sec Jill Thompson
Ch Mr Gwilym Griffith
Total Staff 162
Regions Yorkshire & Humberside + East Midlands
Owned or managed 207
Rt 207 GN 6 Sup 201
Tenant Type % Family 5% Single 95%

Adactus HA Ltd
○ Charitable HA
TSA Reg ✓ 📱 🏠 🔑 ♦ 🔥
Turner House, 56 King Street, Leigh, Lancashire, WN7 4LJ
T 01942 608715
E info@adactushousing.co.uk
W www.adactushousing.co.uk
CE Mr Paul Lees
Sec Mr Brian Moran
Ch Olwen Baker
Total Staff 275
Region North West
Owned or managed 8659
Rt 8365 GN 7160 Sup 353 OP 852 SO 294 Tot lets 815 GN bs 5715

Tenant Type % Family 38%
Older 21% Single 41%
Development Total 259
Rt 257 GN 257 LCHO 39 NBA 158
NBC 101
Parent Association
Adactus Housing Group

Adactus Housing Group
■ Non-Charitable HA
TSA Reg ✓ ✦ ♦
Turner House, 56 King Street, Leigh,
Lancashire, WN7 4LJ
T 01942 608715
E info@adactushousing.co.uk
W www.adactushousing.co.uk
CE Mr Paul Lees
Sec Mr Brian Moran
Ch Mr Alan Cain
Total Staff 269
Region North West
Subsidiary Association(s) Adactus
HA Ltd; Beech HA Ltd; Chorley
Community Housing Ltd

Adullam Homes HA Ltd
○ Charitable HA
TSA Reg ✓ 🐦
Walter Moore House,
34 Dudley Street, West Bromwich,
West Midlands, B70 9LS
T 0121 500 2828
E info@adullam.org.uk
W www.adullam.org.uk
CE Mr Trevor Palfreyman
Sec Mr Trevor Palfreyman
Ch Mrs Anne Bishop
Total Staff 213
Regions West Midlands + East
Midlands, North West
Owned or managed 791
Rt 791 GN 7 Sup 784
Tenant Type % Family 1% Single 99%

Advance Housing & Support Ltd
○ Charitable HA
TSA Reg ✓ 🖻 ♦ ✦ 🐦
2 Witan Way, Witney, Oxfordshire,
OX28 6FH
T 01993 772885
E info@advanceuk.org
W www.advanceuk.org
CE Mr Tim Cooper
Sec Mrs Julie Layton
Ch Mrs Helen Baker
Total Staff 508
Regions South East + London, South
West, East Midlands, West Midlands,
East of England
Owned or managed 1981
Rt 1389 GN 4 Sup 1385 SO 568
NSO 24 Tot lets 185 GN bs 4
Tenant Type % Family 6% Older

10% Single 84%
Development Total 17
Rt 26 Sup 26 LCHO 37 NBA 11
NBC 6

Affinity Sutton
■ Non-Charitable HA
TSA Reg ✓ ♦ 🐦 ♦
Level 6, 6 More London Place,
London, Greater London, SE1 2DA
T 0300 100 0303
W www.affinitysutton.com
CE Mr Keith Exford
Sec Mrs Clare Miller
Ch Mr Neil Goulden
Total Staff 1498
Region London
Subsidiary Association(s) Aashyana
HA Ltd; Affinity Sutton Homes;
Grange Management (Southern) Ltd

Affinity Sutton Homes
○ Charitable HA
TSA Reg ✓ 🖥 🖵 🚐 🖻 🔑 ♦
Level 6, 6 More London Place,
London, Greater London, SE1 2DA
T 0300 100 0303
W www.affinitysutton.com
Sec Mrs Clare Miller
Ch Mr Mike Herring
Total Staff 0
Regions London + South East,
South West, East Midlands,
West Midlands, East of England,
Yorkshire & Humberside,
North East, North West
Owned or managed 51157
Rt 45610 GN 40923 Sup 831
OP 3856 SO 5056 NSO 491
Tot lets 4082 GN bs 39522
Development Total 2028
Rt 1989 GN 1989 LCHO 1025
NBA 1102 NBC 926
Parent Association Affinity Sutton

Affordable Christian HA Ltd
○ Charitable HA
TSA Reg ✗ 🔑
8 Belmont Hill, Lewisham, London,
Greater London, SE13 5BD
T 020 8318 4432
E info@achal.org.uk
W www.achal.org.uk
CE Mr Jim Gilbourne
Sec Mrs Judi Feasey
Ch Mr Robert Lantsbury
Total Staff 3
Region London
Owned or managed 24
Rt 10 GN 10 SO 14 Tot lets 0
GN bs 0
Tenant Type % Family 64%
Single 36%

Afro-Caribbean HA Ltd
○ Charitable HA
TSA Reg ✗ 🐦 🏠
324 Bensham Lane, Thornton Heath,
Surrey, CR7 7EQ
T 020 8689 9535
W www.afrohousing.org
CE Erskine Odongo
Sec Erskine Odongo
Ch Mr Cons Matata
Total Staff 5
Region London
Tenant Type % Family 55%
Single 45%

Agamemnon HA Ltd
○ Charitable HA
TSA Reg ✓
H M S Nelson, Portsmouth,
Hampshire, PO1 3HH
T 023 9282 2021
E caroline.barnes@agamemnon.org.uk
W www.agamemnonha.org
CE Mr Peter Tidd
Sec Mr Peter Tidd
Ch Commodore Tom Morton
Total Staff 16
Region South East
Owned or managed 190
Rt 190 OP 190
Tenant Type % Older 100%

Agudas Israel HA Ltd
○ Charitable HA
TSA Reg ✓ 🔑 🐦 🏠
206 Lordship Road, London,
Greater London, N16 5ES
T 020 8802 3819
E info@aihaltd.co.uk
CE Mrs Ita Symons, MBE
Sec Mrs Ita Symons, MBE
Ch Mr M. Berger
Total Staff 140
Regions London + North West
Owned or managed 587
Rt 520 GN 430 Sup 34 OP 56 SO 48
NSO 19 Tot lets 0 GN bs 5
Tenant Type % Family 75%
Older 15% Single 10%

Aksa HA Ltd
○ Charitable HA
TSA Reg ✓ 🖻 🐦 ♦ 🏠
249 Cavendish Street, Ashton-
Under-Lyne, Lancashire, OL6 7AT
T 0161 620 2992
E info@aksahousing.co.uk
W www.aksahousing.co.uk
CE Mr Ian Munro
Sec Mr Martin Frost
Ch Georgia Parker
Total Staff 0
Region North West
Owned or managed 720

Rt 720 **GN** 720
Tenant Type % Family 88% **Older**
5% **Single** 7%
Development Total 30
Rt 52 **GN** 52 **NBA** 30
Parent Association New Charter
Housing Trust Ltd

Aldwyck Housing Group
○ Charitable HA
TSA Reg ✓ ◊
6 Houghton Hall Business Park,
Porz Avenue, Houghton Regis,
Dunstable, Bedfordshire, LU5 5UZ
T 01582 869100
W www.aldwyck.co.uk
CE Mr Harj Singh
Sec Mr Peter Jeffery
Ch Mr Harj Singh
Total Staff 0
Region East of England
Owned or managed 221
Rt 71 **Sup** 71 **NSO** 150
Tenant Type % Family 6% **Single** 94%
Parent Association Aldwyck Housing
Group Ltd

Aldwyck Housing Group Ltd
■ Non-Charitable HA
TSA Reg ✓
■ ▢ ▦ ▢ ✱ ◆ ☜
6 Houghton Hall Business Park,
Porz Avenue, Houghton Regis,
Dunstable, Bedfordshire, LU5 5UZ
T 01582 869100
E info@aldwyck.co.uk
W www.aldwyck.co.uk
CE Mr Harj Singh
Sec Mr Peter Jeffery
Ch Mr Greg Lomax
Total Staff 453
Regions East of England + London,
South East, East Midlands
Owned or managed 10002
Rt 7771 **GN** 6609 **Sup** 809 **OP** 353
SO 1572 **NSO** 659 **Tot lets** 609
GN bs 6324
Tenant Type % Family 60%
Older 5% **Single** 35%
Development Total 522
Rt 710 **GN** 600 **Sup** 50 **OP** 60
LCHO 250 **NBA** 310 **NBC** 212

Alliance Homes
○ Charitable HA
TSA Reg ✓ ▢ ▦ ▢ ✱ ◆ ☜
40 Martingale Way,
Portishead, BS20 7AW
T 0300120120
E customerservices@alliancehomes.
org.uk
W www.alliancehomes.org.uk
CE Mr Clive Bodley
Sec Mr Darren Hartley

Ch Mr Chris Perry
Total Staff 290
Region South West
Owned or managed 6623
Rt 6105 **GN** 4924 **Sup** 85 **OP** 1096
SO 512 **NSO** 6 **Tot lets** 482
GN bs 4924
Tenant Type % Family 38%
Older 42% **Single** 16%
Development Total 16
Rt 91 **GN** 91 **NBA** 16

Alpha (RSL) Ltd
✪ Not-for-Profit Company
TSA Reg ✓ ▢ ✱ ☜
Thursby House, 1 Thursby Road,
Croft Business Park, Bromborough,
Wirral, Merseyside, CH62 3PW
T 0151 346 1598
E enquiries@alpha-homes.co.uk
W www.alpha-homes.co.uk
CE Mr John Agass
Sec Mr Ian McCall
Ch Mr Philip Halliday
Total Staff 35
Regions North West +
West Midlands, North East
Owned or managed 787
Rt 774 **OP** 774 **SO** 13 **Tot lets** 193
GN bs 774
Tenant Type % Older 100%
Development Total 173
NBA 173

Amicus Horizon Group Ltd
✪ Not-for-Profit Company
TSA Reg ✓ ◊
Grosvenor House, 125 High Street,
Croydon, Surrey, CRO 9XP
T 01795 431134
E info@amicushorizon.org.uk
W www.amicushorizon.org.uk
CE Paul Hackett
Sec Ms Jane Lester
Ch Mr Will Tuckley
Total Staff 0
Region South East
Parent Association
AmicusHorizon Ltd

AmicusHorizon Ltd
○ Charitable HA
TSA Reg ✓ ■ ▢ ▢ ✱ ◆ ☜ ◊
Grosvenor House, 125 High Street,
Croydon, CRO 9XP
T 0800 121 6060
E contactus@amicushorizon.org.uk
W www.amicushorizon.org.uk
CE Steve Walker
Sec Mrs Alison Wignall
Ch Lord Falconer of Thoroton QC
Total Staff 892
Regions South East + London
Owned or managed 27811

Rt 24073 **GN** 21795 **Sup** 649
OP 1629 **SO** 3673 **NSO** 65
Tot lets 2654 **GN bs** 20692
Development Total 197
NBA 132 **NBC** 65
Subsidiary Association(s)
Amicus Horizon Group Ltd;
Crystal Palace HA Ltd

Anchor Trust
☆ Charitable Company
TSA Reg ✓ ■ ▢ ▢ ✱ ◆ ☜
2nd Floor, 25 Bedford Street,
London, Greater London, WC2E 9ES
T 020 7759 9100
E enquiries@anchor.org.uk
W www.anchor.org.uk
CE Mrs Jane Ashcroft
Sec Mr David Edwards
Ch Mr Aman Dalvi, OBE
Total Staff 9143
Regions South East + London,
South West, East Midlands,
West Midlands, East of England,
Yorkshire & Humberside,
North East, North West
Owned or managed 30139
Rt 23060 **GN** 91 **OP** 22969 **SO** 6752
NSO 327 **Tot lets** 3925 **GN bs** 91
Tenant Type % Older 100%
Development Total 56
NBA 28 **NBC** 28

Apna Ghar HA Ltd
○ Charitable HA
TSA Reg ✓ ☜ ⌂
1 Olympic Way, Wembley,
Middlesex, HA9 0NP
T 020 8795 5405
E agha@apnaghar.org.uk
W www.agha.org.uk
CE Mr Jai Dosanjh
Sec Mr Jai Dosanjh
Ch Ms Noreen Sumra
Total Staff 12
Region London
Owned or managed 269
Rt 269 **GN** 242 **Sup** 27
Tenant Type % Family 91%
Older 8% **Single** 1%

Aquila Way
☆ Charitable Company
TSA Reg ✗ ☜
573 Durham Road, Low Fell,
Gateshead, NE9 5EY
T 0191 491 5700
E info@aquilaway.org
W www.aquilaway.org
CE Ms Nancy Doyle
Sec Ms Nancy Doyle
Ch Mr Paul Merton
Total Staff 48
Region North East

Owned or managed 27
Rt 27 Sup 27
Tenant Type % Family 40%
Single 60%

Aragon HA Ltd
■ Non-Charitable HA
TSA Reg ✓ ▯ ▧ⱽᵀᴴᴼ ▢ ⚷ ➳ ◊
Katherine's House, Dunstable Street,
Ampthill, Bedfordshire, MK45 2JP
T 0300 123 5544
E enquiry@aragon-housing.co.uk
W www.aragon-housing.co.uk
CE Ms Aileen Evans
Sec Ms Aileen Evans
Ch Mr Richard Hughes
Total Staff 133
Regions East of England + South
East, East Midlands
Owned or managed 6846
Rt 6491 GN 4635 Sup 142 OP 1714
SO 340 NSO 15 Tot lets 715
GN bs 4563
Tenant Type % Family 56%
Older 36% Single 8%
Development Total 497
 NBA 307 NBC 190
Parent Association Grand Union
Housing Group Ltd

Arawak Walton HA Ltd
○ Charitable HA
TSA Reg ✓ ⚷ ➳ ◊
Margaret House, 23 Manor Street,
Manchester, M12 6HE
T 0161 272 6094
W www.arawakwalton.com
CE Ms Cym D'Souza
Sec Ms Cym D'Souza
Ch Jayne Gouldthorpe
Total Staff 25
Region North West
Owned or managed 946
Rt 930 GN 823 OP 107 SO 16
Tot lets 48 GN bs 0
Tenant Type % Family 76%
Older 11% Single 13%

Arcadia Housing Ltd
■ Non-Charitable HA
TSA Reg ✓ ◊
2 Station Road, Worle, Weston-
Super-Mare, Somerset, BS22 6AP
T 01934 524300
E info@arcadiahousing.co.uk
W www.arcadiahousing.co.uk
CE Mr Nick Horne
Sec Miss Charlotte Ferris
Ch Mrs Delyth Lloyd-Evans
Total Staff 68
Region South West
Subsidiary Association(s)
Knightstone HA Ltd

Arches Housing Ltd
○ Charitable HA
TSA Reg ✓ ▢ ⚷ ◊
122 Burngreave Road, Sheffield,
South Yorkshire, S3 9DE
T 0114 228 8100
E info@archeshousing.org.uk
W www.archeshousing.org.uk
CE Mr Brian Summerson
Sec Mr Brian Summerson
Ch Mr Tariq Zaman
Total Staff 18
Region Yorkshire & Humberside
Owned or managed 1023
Rt 931 GN 877 Sup 54 SO 92
Tot lets 124 GN bs 0
Tenant Type % Family 65%
Older 12% Single 23%
Development Total 30
Rt 54 GN 54 LCHO 6 NBA 16
NBC 14

Arcon HA
○ Charitable HA
TSA Reg ✓ ▢ ⚷
12 Lloyd Street, Manchester,
Lancashire, M2 5ND
T 0161 214 4120
E enquiries@arcon.org.uk
W www.arcon.org.uk
CE Mr Peter Schilizzi
Sec Mr Peter Schilizzi
Ch Ms Dora Blake
Total Staff 22
Regions North West +
East Midlands
Owned or managed 1183
Rt 1059 GN 1059 SO 84 NSO 40
Tot lets 92 GN bs 958
Tenant Type % Family 30%
Older 40% Single 30%
Development Total 70
NBA 65 NBC 5

Arena Housing Group Ltd
○ Charitable HA
TSA Reg ✓ ▣ ▯ ▢ ⚷ ➳ ◊
Your Housing Group, Thomson
House, Faraday Street, Birchwood
Park, Warrington, WA3 6GA
T 01925 236400
W www.yourhousinggroup.co.uk
CE Mr Brian Cronin
Sec Mrs Bronwen Rapley
Ch Mrs Kathy Cowell
Total Staff 0
Regions North West +
Yorkshire & Humberside
Owned or managed 11439
Rt 10143 GN 7640 Sup 741 OP 1762
SO 1296 Tot lets 2089 GN bs 7245
Tenant Type % Family 60%
Older 25% Single 15%
Development Total 356
Rt 674 GN 525 OP 149 LCHO 52

NBA 201 NBC 155
Parent Association
Your Housing Group
Subsidiary Association(s)
Headrow Ltd; Leasowe Community
Homes; Tung Sing HA Ltd

Argyle Street Housing Co-op Ltd
★ Co-operative Society
TSA Reg ✓
3 Fletcher's Terrace, Cambridge,
Cambridgeshire, CB1 3LU
T 01223 411615
W www.ash.coop
Ch Mr Richard Rippin
Total Staff 2
Region East of England
Owned or managed 84
Rt 84 GN 84
Tenant Type % Family 7% Single 93%

ARHAG HA Ltd
○ Charitable HA
TSA Reg ✓ ▢ ⚷ ➳ ◊
Unit B, Ground Floor, Mary Brancker
House, 54-74 Holmes Road, Kentish
Town, London, Greater London,
NW5 3AQ
T 020 7424 7370
E contact@arhag.co.uk
W www.arhag.co.uk
CE Mr Dorian Leatham
Ch Mr Barrington Billings
Total Staff 22
Region London
Owned or managed 738
Rt 727 GN 714 Sup 13 SO 11 Tot
lets 47 GN bs 0
Tenant Type % Family 55% Older
5% Single 40%
Development Total 30
NBC 30

Arneway Housing Co-op Ltd
★ Co-operative Society
TSA Reg ✓ ◊
The Designworks, Park Parade,
Harlesden, Greater London,
NW10 4HT
T 020 8965 5537
E info@arnewayhousing.co.uk
W www.arnewayhousing.co.uk
CE Duncan Aitkins
Sec Sharon Zacs
Ch Mr Peter Akanbi
Total Staff 1
Region London
Owned or managed 65
Rt 65 GN 65
Tenant Type % Family 13% Older 5%
Single 82%

Ashram HA

○ Charitable HA
TSA Reg ✓ 🏠 🔑 🤝 ◊ 🏘
2nd Floor, Fairgate House,
205 Kings Road, Tyseley, Birmingham,
West Midlands, B11 2AA
T 0300 111 7000
E customerfirst@accordgroup.org.uk
W www.ashramha.org.uk
Sec Ms Joanne Easton
Ch Mr Ghulam Shabar
Total Staff 79
Region West Midlands
Owned or managed 1139
Rt 1106 GN 971 Sup 26 OP 109
SO 33 Tot lets 32 GN bs 0
Tenant Type % Family 75%
Older 10% Single 15%
Development Total 57
NBA 57
Parent Association Accord HA Ltd

Ashton Pioneer Homes Ltd

✪ Not-for-Profit Company
TSA Reg ✓
Margaret House, Margaret Street,
Ashton-Under-Lyne, Lancashire,
OL6 7TH
T 0161 343 8128
E aph@ashtonpioneerhomes.co.uk
W www.ashtonpioneerhomes.co.uk
CE Tony Berry
Sec Tony Berry
Ch Cllr Warren Bray
Total Staff 40
Region North West
Owned or managed 921
Rt 921 GN 921
Tenant Type % Family 24% Older
8% Single 68%

Ashwell HA Ltd

○ Charitable HA
TSA Reg ✓
Pioneer House, Norton Way
South, Letchworth Garden City,
Hertfordshire, SG6 1NY
T 01462 683307
Sec Mrs Alison Murray
Ch Mrs Hilary Cooke
Total Staff 0
Region East of England
Owned or managed 10
Rt 10 GN 10
Tenant Type % Family 70%
Older 10% Single 20%

Aspire Group (Staffordshire) Ltd

✪ Not-for-Profit Company
TSA Reg ✓ ◊
Kingsley, The Brampton,
Newcastle Under Lyme,
Staffordshire, ST5 0QW
CE Ms Sinéad Butters
Sec Mr Paul Medford
Ch Brian Tomkins
Total Staff 0
Region West Midlands
Subsidary Association(s)
Aspire Housing Ltd

Aspire Housing Ltd

■ Non-Charitable HA
TSA Reg ✓ 🏠 🤝 🏠 🔑 ◆ 🤝 ◊
Kingsley, The Brampton,
Newcastle-Under-Lyme,
Staffordshire, ST5 0QW
T 01782 854850
E enquiries@aspirehousing.org.uk
W www.aspirehousing.co.uk
CE Ms Sinéad Butters
Sec Mr Paul Medford
Ch Mrs Philippa Holland
Total Staff 406
Regions West Midlands +
North West
Owned or managed 9177
Rt 8862 GN 8245 Sup 22 OP 595
SO 309 NSO 6 Tot lets 878
GN bs 7761
Tenant Type % Family 35%
Older 55% Single 10%
Development Total 117
Rt 69 GN 69 LCHO 43 NBA 77
NBC 40
Parent Association Aspire Group
(Staffordshire) Ltd
Subsidary Association(s) Stoke-on-
Trent Housing Society Ltd

Asra HA Ltd

○ Charitable HA
TSA Reg ✓ 🏠 🔑 🤝 ◊
3 Bede Island Road,
Leicester, LE2 7EA
T 0116 257 6700
E enquiries@asra.org.uk
W www.asra.org.uk
CE Mr Matt Cooney
Sec Martin Lewis
Ch Mr Aman Dalvi
Total Staff 0
Regions East Midlands + London,
South East, East of England
Owned or managed 3441
Rt 3252 GN 2762 Sup 25 OP 465
SO 189 Tot lets 404 GN bs 2491
Tenant Type % Family 67%
Older 25% Single 8%
Development Total 144

NBA 82 NBC 62
Parent Association Asra Housing
Group Ltd

Asra Housing Group Ltd

■ Non-Charitable HA
TSA Reg ✓ ◆ ◊
3 Bede Island Road, Leicester,
Leicestershire, LE2 7EA
T 0116 257 6700
E enquiries@asra.org.uk
W www.asra.org.uk
CE Mr Matt Cooney
Sec Mr Matt Cooney
Ch Jaffer Kapasi OBE
Total Staff 532
Region East Midlands
Tenant Type % Family 66%
Older 17% Single 17%
Subsidary Association(s) Asra HA
Ltd; Family First Ltd; Leicester
HA Ltd

Asra Midlands HA Ltd

○ Charitable HA
TSA Reg ✓ 🔑 🤝 ◊ 🏘
78 Burleys Way, Leicester,
Leicestershire, LE1 3BD
T 01905 334000
E midlands@sanctuary-housing.co.uk
W www.sanctuary-housing.co.uk
CE Mr David Bennett
Sec Mr Craig Moule
Ch Mr Narendra Waghela
Total Staff 83
Region East Midlands
Owned or managed 858
Rt 856 GN 552 Sup 35 OP 269 SO 2
Tot lets 0 GN bs 0
Tenant Type % Family 56%
Older 33% Single 11%
Parent Association Sanctuary HA

Assured Living HA

✪ Not-for-Profit Company
TSA Reg ✓
c/o Ashbridge Independent School,
Lindle Lane, Hutton, CHAPEL LANE,
Preston, Lancashire, PR4 4AQ
T 01772 610894
E grace.carr@assuredlivingha.co.uk
Ch Mr Russell Atkinson
Total Staff 3
Region North West
Owned or managed 38
Rt 38 Sup 38
Tenant Type % Older 12%
Single 88%

Aster Communities
○ Charitable HA
TSA Reg ✓ ■ □ 500 ▣ ♪ ◊
Sarsen Court, Horton Avenue,
Cannings Hill, Devizes, SN10 2AZ
T 01380 720027
W www.astercommunities.co.uk
CE Jo Savage
Sec Carolyn Filmore
Ch Mr John McGibbon
Total Staff 191
Regions South West + South East
Owned or managed 17479
Rt 15751 GN 13783 Sup 213
OP 1755 SO 1564 NSO 164
Tot lets 1758 GN bs 13476
Tenant Type % Family 46%
Older 27% Single 27%
Development Total 561
Rt 704 GN 660 OP 44 LCHO 234
NBA 337 NBC 224
Parent Association Aster Group

Aster Group
■ Non-Charitable HA
TSA Reg ✓ ◊
Sarsen Court, Horton Avenue,
Devizes, SN10 2AZ
T 01380 726001
E info@aster.co.uk
W www.aster.co.uk
CE Mr Bjorn Howard
Sec Mrs Carolyn Filmore
Ch Mr Mel Cook
Total Staff 120
Region South West
Subsidiary Association(s)
Aster Communities; Synergy
Housing Ltd

Axiom HA Ltd
○ Charitable HA
TSA Reg ✓ ▣ ♪ 🤝
Axiom House, Maskew Avenue,
Peterborough, Cambridgeshire,
PE1 2SX
T 01733 347135
E enquiries@axiomha.org.uk
W www.axiomha.org.uk
CE Mr Alan Lewin
Sec Mrs Louise Platt
Ch Mr David Fowler
Total Staff 170
Regions East of England +
East Midlands
Owned or managed 2173
Rt 2097 GN 1349 Sup 242 OP 506
SO 75 NSO 1 Tot lets 654
GN bs 1349
Tenant Type % Family 63%
Older 24% Single 13%
Development Total 3
Rt 132 GN 96 Sup 36 LCHO 8
NBA 3

Bb

B3 Living Ltd
○ Charitable HA
TSA Reg ✓ 🚐YTHO ▣ ♪
17 Amwell Street, Hoddesdon,
Hertfordshire, EN11 8TS
T 01992 453700
E enquiry@b3living.org.uk
W www.b3living.org.uk
CE Mr John Giesen
Sec Ken Goodsell
Ch Ms Sandra Royer
Total Staff 166
Region East of England
Owned or managed 4421
Rt 3587 GN 2788 Sup 13 OP 786
SO 726 NSO 108 Tot lets 351
GN bs 2766
Tenant Type % Family 50%
Older 22% Single 28%
Development Total 27
Rt 109 GN 109 LCHO 36 NBA 14
NBC 13

Bahay Kubo HA Ltd
○ Charitable HA
TSA Reg ✗ 🏠
1st Floor, 129 St. John's Way,
London, Greater London, N19 3RQ
T 020 7281 4477
E info@bahaykubo.org.uk
W www.bahaykubo.org.uk
CE Emma Bibal
Sec Mrs Estela Nalden
Ch Alvin Ellaga-Oliva
Total Staff 0
Region London
Tenant Type % Family 60%
Single 40%

Balkerne Gardens Trust Ltd
○ Charitable HA
TSA Reg ✓ 🤝
Parsley House, Balkerne Gardens,
Colchester, Essex, C01 1PR
T 01206 543517
E admin@bgtrust.org
W www.balkernegardens.org.uk
CE Mrs Amanda Westbrook
Sec Mrs Amanda Westbrook
Ch Dr Nicholas Dixon
Total Staff 183
Region East of England
Owned or managed 69
Rt 69 OP 69
Tenant Type % Older 100%

Bancroft Tenant Management Co-operative Ltd
★ Co-operative Society
TSA Reg ✗
12 Wickford Street, Bethnal Green,
London, Greater London, E1 5QN
T 020 7265 8343
E enquiries@bancroftmc.org.uk
CE Mr Lockhart Murdoch
Sec Mr Abdul Quddus
Ch Mr Kona Miah
Total Staff 9
Region London
Tenant Type % Family 85%
Single 15%

Bangla HA Ltd
○ Charitable HA
TSA Reg ✓ 🏠
243 Lower Clapton Road, London,
Greater London, E5 8EG
T 020 8985 1124
E info@banglaha.org.uk
W www.banglaha.org.uk
CE Mr Bashir Uddin
Sec Mr Bashir Uddin
Ch Mr Mohammed A Nazim Rahman
Total Staff 5
Region London
Owned or managed 256
Rt 256 GN 256
Tenant Type % Family 76%
Older 12% Single 12%

Barnabas HA Ltd
○ Charitable HA
TSA Reg ✗ 🤝
14 Newton Road, Yeovil,
Somerset, BA20 1NF
T 01935 477286
E admin@barnabashousing.com
CE Mrs Mary Firth
Sec Mrs Linda Jones
Total Staff 0
Region South West
Tenant Type % Family 25%
Single 75%

Barnsbury HA Ltd
○ Charitable HA
TSA Reg ✓
60 Morland Mews, Islington,
London, N1 1HN
T 020 7704 2324
E ziggy@barnsbury.org
W www.barnsbury.org
CE Ms Ziggy Crawford
Sec Ms Ziggy Crawford
Ch Andrew Mountney
Total Staff 8
Region London
Owned or managed 238
Rt 238 GN 238

Tenant Type % Family 48%
Older 23% Single 29%

Bath Centre for Voluntary Service Homes
○ Charitable HA
TSA Reg ✓ 👓
Top Floor, Greystones, Hayesfield Park, Bath, Avon, BA2 4QE
T 01225 330534
E co.secretary.bcvs.homes@live.co.uk
W www.bcvshomes.co.uk
Sec Ms Patricia Perkins
Ch Mr B Pettit
Total Staff 55
Region South West
Owned or managed 47
Rt 47 Sup 47
Tenant Type % Older 100%

Bay HA Ltd
○ Charitable HA
TSA Reg ✗ 👓
72-74 Alexandra Road, Blackpool, Lancashire, FY1 6HW
T 01253 403044
E paul.bayha@btconnect.com
CE Paul Greenwood
Sec Viv Eaves
Ch Ms S Lucas
Total Staff 19
Region North West
Owned or managed 30
Rt 30 Sup 30
Tenant Type % Single 100%

BCOP (Broadening Choices for Older People)
☆ Charitable Company
TSA Reg ✓ 👓
Imperial Court, 40B, First Floor, Kings Norton Business Centre, Pershore Road South, Birmingham, West Midlands, B30 3ES
T 0121 459 7670
E general@bcop.org.uk
W www.bcop.org.uk
CE Mr Marcus Fellows
Ch Mrs Diane Gagnon
Total Staff 160
Region West Midlands
Owned or managed 195
Rt 195 GN 150 Sup 45
Tenant Type % Older 100%

BCS Associates Ltd
✪ Not-for-Profit Company
TSA Reg ✗ 👓 ♨
134 High Street, Blackheath, West Midlands, B65 0EE
T 0121 561 1969
W www.bcha.co.uk
CE Ms Sandra Spence
Ch Mr Richard Newby
Total Staff 0
Region West Midlands
Parent Association Black Country Housing Group Ltd

Becket Trust HA Ltd
○ Charitable HA
TSA Reg ✓
Birches, Penshurst, Tonbridge, Kent, TN1 8DL
T 01892 870349
Sec Sarah Crookenden
Ch Jeremy Leathers
Total Staff 0
Region South East
Owned or managed 8
Rt 8 GN 8
Tenant Type % Family 67%
Older 33%

Beddington & Wallington HS Ltd
○ Charitable HA
TSA Reg ✗
The Cedars, 21 Bond Gardens, Wallington, Surrey, SM6 7LW
Sec Mrs Marilyn Gordon-Jones
Ch Mr John Rees
Total Staff 0
Region London
Tenant Type % Older 100%

Bedford Citizens HA Ltd
○ Charitable HA
TSA Reg ✓ 👓
Bedford Charter House, 1a Kimbolton Road, Bedford, Bedfordshire, MK40 2PU
T 01234 321400
E enquiries@bchal.org
W www.bchal.org
CE Mrs Vanessa Connolly
Sec Mrs Vanessa Connolly
Ch Richard Wilkinson
Total Staff 97
Region East of England
Owned or managed 198
Rt 198 GN 88 OP 110
Tenant Type % Family 3%
Older 93% Single 4%

Bedford Soroptimist HA Ltd
○ Charitable HA
TSA Reg ✗
22 Roseby Way, Bedford, MK41 9RP
T 01234 401475
Ch Miss Rita Beaumont
Total Staff 0
Region East of England
Owned or managed 2
Rt 2 GN 2
Tenant Type % Single 100%

Beech HA Ltd
■ Non-Charitable HA
TSA Reg ✓ 🏠 🔑 ♨
Turner House, 56 King Street, Leigh, Lancashire, WN7 4LJ
T 01942 608715
E info@adactushousing.co.uk
W www.adactushousing.co.uk
CE Mr Paul Lees
Sec Mr Brian Moran
Ch Olwen Baker
Total Staff 0
Region North West
Owned or managed 1076
Rt 408 GN 270 OP 138 SO 668
Tot lets 87 GN bs 245
Tenant Type % Family 18%
Older 47% Single 43%
Development Total 8
NBA 8
Parent Association
Adactus Housing Group

Beechwood Ballantyne
○ Charitable HA
TSA Reg ✓ 🏢 👓 ♨
Manor House, Beechwood Drive, Beechwood, Prenton, Merseyside, CH43 7ZU
T 0151 606 6262
E info@bbcha.org.uk
W www.bbcha.org.uk
CE Mr Andy Hall
Sec Mr Andy Hall
Ch Ms Breda Dutton
Total Staff 18
Region North West
Owned or managed 829
Rt 829 GN 683 Sup 146
Tenant Type % Family 40%
Older 20% Single 40%
Parent Association Symphony Housing Group

Belgrave Neighbourhood Co-operative HA Ltd
★ Co-operative Society
TSA Reg ✓ 👓 🏠
131 Loughborough Road, Leicester, Leicestershire, LE4 5LQ
T 0116 257 6800
W www.belgravecoop.org.uk

CE Mr Sanjay Manon
Sec Mr Kishor Samani
Ch Mr Shantilal Makwana
Total Staff 0
Region East Midlands
Owned or managed 374
Rt 374 GN 354 OP 20
Tenant Type % Family 76% Older 6%
Single 18%

Berinsfield Community Business
✪ Not-for-Profit Company
TSA Reg ✗
6 Dorchester House,
Wimblestraw Road, Berinsfield,
Oxfordshire, OX10 7LZ
T 01865 343715
E enqs@bcomb.co.uk
W www.bcomb.co.uk
CE Mr Mark Williams
Sec Mr Mark Williams
Ch Mr Alan Gray
Total Staff 8
Region South East
Owned or managed 320
Rt 320 GN 320
Tenant Type % Family 75%
Older 10% Single 15%

Berkshire Women's Aid
☆ Charitable Company
TSA Reg ✗ 🤝
PO Box 413, Reading,
Berkshire, RG1 8XL
T 0118 950 0182
W www.berkshirewomensaid.org.uk
Sec Ms Judith Thurlow
Ch Ms Janette Cooper
Total Staff 43
Region South East
Tenant Type % Family 65%
Single 35%

Bernicia Group Ltd
■ Non-Charitable HA
TSA Reg ✓ ◊
Beaminster Way East, Kingston Park,
Newcastle Upon Tyne,
Tyne And Wear, NE3 2ER
T 0844 800 3800
E info@bernicia.com
W www.bernicia.com
CE Mr Bill Heads
Sec Mr Bill Heads
Ch Ian Armstrong
Total Staff 0
Region North East
Subsidiary Association(s) Cheviot
HA Ltd; Wansbeck Homes Ltd

Berwick Borough Housing
○ Charitable HA
TSA Reg ✓ 📋 🔧 🤝 ◊
1 Windmill Way North, Ramparts
Business Park, Berwick-Upon-Tweed,
Northumberland, TD15 1TA
T 0800 461451
E contact@berwickboroughhousing.
co.uk
W www.berwickboroughhousing.
co.uk
CE Mr Paul Tanney
Sec Mr Mike Axe
Ch Brian Fishwick
Total Staff 35
Region North East
Owned or managed 2124
Rt 1932 GN 1858 OP 74 SO 192
Tot lets 170 GN bs 1824
Parent Association
Four Housing Group

Bexley Churches HA Ltd
○ Charitable HA
TSA Reg ✓
The Thames Innovation Centre, 2
Veridion Way, Erith, Kent, DA18 4AL
T 020 8320 1085
E becha@bexleychurchesha.org.uk
W www.becha.org.uk
CE Mr Graham Horton
Sec Mr Graham Horton
Ch Mr Graham Horton
Total Staff 6
Region London
Owned or managed 137
Rt 137 GN 134 Sup 3
Tenant Type % Family 65%
Older 14% Single 21%

BHSE
○ Charitable HA
TSA Reg ✓ 🤝
Woodlands, 11 Stourwood Avenue,
Southbourne, Bournemouth, Dorset,
BH6 3QD
T 01202 430848
E info@bhse.org.uk
W www.bhse.org.uk
CE Mr Steven Hayes
Sec Mr Steven Hayes
Ch Mr Michael R Barrow
Total Staff 10
Region South West
Owned or managed 202
Rt 202 OP 202
Tenant Type % Older 100%

BHT
❏ Charitable Trust
TSA Reg ✓ 🤝
144 London Road, Brighton,
East Sussex, BN1 4PH
T 01273 645400
E enquiries@bht.org.uk
W www.bht.org.uk
CE Mr Andy Winter
Sec Ms Kate Watson
Ch Mr Patrik Allen
Total Staff 221
Region South East
Owned or managed 729
Rt 729 GN 414 Sup 315
Tenant Type % Family 10%
Older 10% Single 80%

Billericay Co-operative Housing Society Ltd
■ Non-Charitable HA
TSA Reg ✗
40 The Lock Building, 72 High Street,
London, Greater London, E15 2QB
T 020 8534 0383
E Appleby.Wood@btinternet.com
Sec Mr Richard Oswald
Ch Mr Lyndon Johnston
Total Staff 0
Region East of England
Tenant Type % Family 35%
Older 65%

Birmingham Civic HA Ltd
○ Charitable HA
TSA Reg ✓
230-232 Wheelwright Road,
Erdington, Birmingham, West
Midlands, B24 8EH
T 0121 382 5105
E bcha@bcivic.co.uk
W www.bcivic.co.uk
CE Mr Geoffrey Round
Sec Mr Geoffrey Round
Ch Mr Robert Ian Stuart
Total Staff 9
Region West Midlands
Owned or managed 217
Rt 217 GN 217
Tenant Type % Family 46%
Older 13% Single 41%

Birmingham Co-operative Housing Services
★ Co-operative Society
TSA Reg ✓ ◊
Fairgate House, 205 Kings Road,
Tyseley, Birmingham, West Midlands,
B11 1AA
T 0121 764 3807
E info@bchs.org.uk
W www.bchs.org.uk
CE Mr Carl Taylor
Sec Miss Frances Broomhall

Ch Margaret Cope
Total Staff 13
Region West Midlands
Owned or managed 98
Rt 98 **GN** 98
Tenant Type % Family 55%
Older 10% **Single** 35%
Parent Association Accord HA Ltd

Birmingham Jewish HA Ltd
■ Non-Charitable HA
TSA Reg ✓ 🦅 🏠
Bill Steiner Suite, 1 River Brook
Drive, Stirchley, Birmingham, West
Midlands, B30 2SH
T 0121 459 3819
E admin@bjha.co.uk
CE Mr Irving Myers
Sec Heather Hockley
Total Staff 1
Region West Midlands
Owned or managed 42
Rt 42 **GN** 8 **OP** 34
Tenant Type % Older 90%
Single 10%

Birnbeck HA Ltd
■ Non-Charitable HA
TSA Reg ✓ 🦅
Birnbeck Court, 850 Finchley Road,
Temple Fortune, London, Greater
London, NW11 6BB
T 020 8201 8484
E johnsilverman@btconnect.com
CE Mr John Silverman
Sec Mr John Silverman
Ch Mr Liam Colgan
Total Staff 1
Regions London + South East,
South West, West Midlands,
East of England
Owned or managed 165
Rt 165 **GN** 82 **Sup** 83
Tenant Type % Family 47%
Older 15% **Single** 38%

Black Country Care Services Ltd
✪ Not-for-Profit Company
TSA Reg ✗ 👁
c/o 134 High Street, Black Heath,
West Midlands, B65 0EE
T 0121 561 1961
E connellm@bcha.co.uk
W www.bcha.co.uk
CE Ms Sandra Spence
Ch Mr Richard Newby
Total Staff 0
Region West Midlands
Parent Association Black Country
Housing Group Ltd

Black Country Housing Group Ltd
✪ Not-for-Profit Company
TSA Reg ✓ 🅿 🔑 🦅 👁
134 High Street, Blackheath,
West Midlands, B65 0EE
T 0121 561 1969
E marketing@bcha.co.uk
W www.bcha.co.uk
CE Ms Sandra Spence
Sec Amanda Tomlinson
Ch Mr Peter Bilson
Total Staff 223
Region West Midlands
Owned or managed 1905
Rt 1773 **GN** 1484 **Sup** 60 **OP** 229
SO 132 **Tot lets** 205 **GN bs** 1446
Tenant Type % Family 70%
Older 14% **Single** 17%
Development Total 61
NBA 41 **NBC** 20
Subsidiary Association(s) BCS
Associates Ltd; Black Country Care
Services Ltd

Bledington Village HA Ltd
■ Non-Charitable HA
TSA Reg ✗
The Old Vicarage, Main Street,
Bledington, Chipping Norton,
Oxfordshire, OX7 6UX
T 01608 658525
E info@glosha.co.uk
W www.glosha.co.uk
Ch Mr Anthony Windsor
Total Staff 0
Region South East
Owned or managed 8
Rt 8 **GN** 8
Tenant Type % Older 100%

Blenheim Gardens Resident Management Organisation
TSA Reg ✗
Blenheim Gardens Estate
Management, 24 Prague Place,
Brixton, London, SW2 5ED
T 020 7926 0158
E dhowcroft@lambeth.gov.uk
CE Mr Danny Howcroft
Sec Anne Jones
Ch Mr Eamon Maguire
Total Staff 0
Region London
Tenant Type % Family 35%
Older 10% **Single** 55%

Blue Mountain HA Ltd
○ Charitable HA
TSA Reg ✗ 🦅 👁 🏠
308 London Road, Stoke-On-Trent,
Staffordshire, ST4 5AB
T 01782 572288
E mailbox@blue-mountain.org.uk

W www.blue-mountain.org.uk
CE Mrs Diane Lea
Sec Mr Frank Hammond
Ch Ms Rhian Hughes
Total Staff 0
Region West Midlands
Tenant Type % Family 40%
Single 60%
Parent Association Staffordshire
HA Ltd

Bolney HA Ltd
○ Charitable HA
TSA Reg ✓
Bookers Farmhouse, Foxhole Lane,
Bolney, Haywards Heath,
West Sussex, RH17 5NB
T 01444 881320
E timh@rhwclutton.co.uk
Sec Tim Hutchings
Ch Tim Hutchings
Total Staff 0
Region South East
Owned or managed 14
Rt 14 **GN** 14
Tenant Type % Family 15%
Older 65% **Single** 20%

Bolton At Home Ltd
☆ Charitable Company
TSA Reg ✓ ■ 🖥 👁 🔑 👤 🦅
1-3 The Courtyard, St Peter's
Business Park, Off Calvin Street,
Bolton, Lancashire, BL1 8PB
T 01204 335656
E info@boltonathome.org.uk
W www.boltonathome.org.uk
CE Jon Lord
Sec Mrs Sharon Taylor
Ch Ms Tracy Woods
Total Staff 1094
Region North West
Owned or managed 18300
Rt 18024 **GN** 15221 **Sup** 67 **OP** 2736
SO 276 **Tot lets** 1837 **GN bs** 15204
Development Total 23
NBA 14 **NBC** 9

Boothferry HA Ltd
○ Charitable HA
TSA Reg ✗ 🦅
Cornerstones, 1 Airmyn Road,
Goole, North Humberside,
DN14 6XA
T 01405 768207
E boothferryhousingassociation@
yahoo.co.uk
Sec Mr Richard J Watson
Ch Miss Susan Garner
Total Staff 20
Region Yorkshire & Humberside
Owned or managed 10
Rt 10 **Sup** 10
Tenant Type % Single 100%

Boston Mayflower Ltd
☆ Charitable Company
TSA Reg ✓
Friars House, Quaker Lane, Boston,
Lincolnshire, PE21 6BZ
T 01205 318500
E mail@bostonmayflower.org.uk
W www.bostonmayflower.org.uk
CE Mr Murray Macdonald
Sec Mr Murray Macdonald
Ch Mr Steve Harriott
Total Staff 172
Regions East Midlands + East of
England, Yorkshire & Humberside
Owned or managed 4768
Rt 4555 GN 3662 Sup 20 OP 873
SO 194 NSO 19 Tot lets 424
GN bs 3662
Tenant Type % Family 42%
Older 38% Single 20%
Development Total 3
NBA 3

Boughey Roddam HA
○ Charitable HA
TSA Reg ✓
Merewood, Springfields, Newport,
Shropshire, TF10 7EZ
T 01952 814628
E bougheyroddamha@btinternet.com
CE Mr Stuart Barber
Ch Eva Allan
Total Staff 0
Region West Midlands
Owned or managed 39
Rt 39 GN 39
Tenant Type % Older 100%

Bournemouth Churches HA (BCHA)
○ Charitable HA
TSA Reg ✓
St Swithuns House,
21 Christchurch Road,
Bournemouth, Dorset, BH1 3NS
T 01202 410500
E enquiries@bcha.org.uk
W www.bcha.org.uk
CE Mr Martin Hancock
Sec Mr Philip Baker
Ch Graham Exon
Total Staff 509
Region South West
Owned or managed 1237
Rt 1191 GN 510 Sup 630
OP 51 NSO 46
Tenant Type % Family 15%
Single 85%
Development Total 210
NBA 152 NBC 58

Bournemouth YMCA
☆ Charitable Company
TSA Reg ✓
Delta House, 56 Westover Road,
Bournemouth, Dorset, BH1 2BS
T 01202 290451
E enquiries@bournemouthymca.org.uk
W www.bournemouthymca.org.uk
CE Mr Blair Crawford
Sec Mr Blair Crawford
Ch Mr Andrew Dobbins
Total Staff 94
Region South West
Owned or managed 97
Rt 97 Sup 97
Tenant Type % Single 100%

Bournville Tenants Ltd
★ Co-operative Society
TSA Reg ✗
Estate Office, Oak Tree Lane,
Birmingham, West Midlands,
B30 1UB
T 0121 472 3831
CE Steven Bridgman
Sec Mrs Ann Ryan
Ch Steven Bridgman
Total Staff 0
Region West Midlands
Owned or managed 90
Rt 90 GN 83 OP 7
Tenant Type % Family 80%
Older 20%

Bournville Village Trust
❑ Charitable Trust
TSA Reg ✓
Estate Office, Oak Tree Lane,
Birmingham, West Midlands,
B30 1UB
T 0121 472 3831
E estateoffice@bvt.org.uk
W www.bvt.org.uk
CE Mr Peter Roach
Sec Mr Paul Haywood
Ch Mr Roger Cadbury
Total Staff 320
Region West Midlands
Owned or managed 3515
Rt 3273 GN 2946 Sup 49 OP 278
SO 105 NSO 137 Tot lets 282
GN bs 2946
Tenant Type % Family 55%
Older 37% Single 8%
Development Total 174
NBA 115 NBC 59

Bournville Works HS Ltd
○ Charitable HA
TSA Reg ✓
Estate Office, Oak Tree Lane,
Birmingham, West Midlands,
B30 1UB
T 0121 449 9129
E enquiries@bwhs-ltd.co.uk
W www.bwhs.org.uk
CE Mr Sam Chatterley
Sec Sandra Chapman
Ch Mr Sam Chatterley
Total Staff 1
Region West Midlands
Owned or managed 314
Rt 314 GN 314
Tenant Type % Family 50%
Older 30% Single 20%

Bow Housing Society Ltd
○ Charitable HA
TSA Reg ✓
Bow House, 23 - 24 Bolingbroke
Grove, Wandsworth Common,
London, Greater London, SW11 6EN
T 020 7228 2421
E bow@housing.myzen.co.uk
W www.bowhouse.org.uk
CE Mr Ray Cole
Sec Mr Ray Cole
Ch Mr Graham Smith
Total Staff 4
Region London
Owned or managed 18
Rt 18 OP 18
Tenant Type % Older 90%
Single 10%

Bowlacre Home
○ Charitable HA
TSA Reg ✗
Elson Drive, Stockport Road,
Stockport, Cheshire, SK14 5EZ
T 0161 368 8481
E info@bowlacre.org
W www.bowlacre.org
CE Mr Robert W Smith
Sec Mrs Marilyn Smith
Ch Mr Robert W Smith
Total Staff 35
Region North West
Owned or managed 12
Rt 12 OP 12
Tenant Type % Family 30%
Older 100% Single 70%

bpha
○ Charitable HA
TSA Reg ✓
Pilgrims House, Horne Lane,
Bedford, Bedfordshire, MK40 1NY
T 01234 791000
E info@bpha.org.uk
W www.bpha.org.uk
CE Mr John Cross
Ch Mr Stephen Hallett
Total Staff 319
Regions East of England + South
East, South West, East Midlands
Owned or managed 16890
Rt 10520 GN 9394 Sup 615 OP 511
SO 3836 NSO 2534 Tot lets 1331
GN bs 9144
Tenant Type % Family 59%
Older 23% Single 18%
Development Total 1226
NBA 699 NBC 527

Bracknell Forest Homes
○ Charitable HA
TSA Reg ✓
Berkshire Court, Western Road,
Bracknell, Berkshire, RG12 1RE
T 01344 382800
E bfh@bracknellforesthomes.org.uk
W www.bracknellforesthomes.org.uk
CE Ms Caroline Titley
Ch Mr Dermot McRoberts
Total Staff 236
Region South East
Owned or managed 6677
Rt 5586 GN 5180 Sup 27 OP 379
SO 1091 Tot lets 337 GN bs 5167
Development Total 8
NBA 8

Braintree Housing Society Ltd
■ Non-Charitable HA
TSA Reg ✗
7 Bridge Street, Halstead,
Essex, CO9 1HU
T 01787 474123
E rent@hims.uk.com
W www.hims.uk.com
Sec P I Haylock
Ch J E Hunnable
Total Staff 0
Region East of England
Tenant Type % Family 27%
Older 24% Single 49%

Bramah House Ltd
✪ Not-for-Profit Company
TSA Reg ✗
5th Floor, 57a Great Suffolk Street,
London, Greater London, SE1 0BB
T 020 7934 0177
E info@ficltd.co.uk

W www.lhf.org.uk
CE Mr Donald Wood
Sec Mr Derek Joseph
Ch Mr Donald Wood
Total Staff 0
Region London
Parent Association The London
Housing Foundation

Brampton Rural Housing Society
○ Charitable HA
TSA Reg ✗
Estate Office, The Old Brewery,
Craw Hall, Brampton,
Cumbria, CA8 1TR
T 01697 72323
E ruralhousing@unicombox.co.uk
Sec Miss Julie Whitlock
Ch Mr John Holland
Total Staff 4
Region North West
Owned or managed 163
Rt 163 GN 163
Tenant Type % Family 51%
Older 36% Single 13%
Development Total 10
Rt 4 GN 4 NBA 10

Brandrams Housing Co-operative Ltd
★ Co-operative Society
TSA Reg ✓
Flat 1, Brandrams Wharf,
127-131 Rotherhithe Street, London,
Greater London, SE16 4NF
T 01424 752381
W www.cch.coop/coops/brandrams.
html
Sec Ms Helena Birkenshaw
Ch Mr Richard Bartrum
Total Staff 0
Region London
Owned or managed 50
Rt 50 GN 50
Tenant Type % Single 100%

Brentwood Housing Trust Ltd
○ Charitable HA
TSA Reg ✓
The Lodge, 28 St Thomas Road,
Brentwood, Essex, CM14 4DB
T 01277 225084
E val@brentwoodhousingtrust.co.uk
CE Mrs Val Fulcher
Sec Mrs Val Fulcher
Ch Mr Christopher Giles
Total Staff 5
Regions East of England + London
Owned or managed 183
Rt 170 GN 170 NSO 13
Tenant Type % Family 52%
Older 13% Single 35%

Brighter Futures
○ Charitable HA
TSA Reg ✓
Unit 5, Whittle Court, Town Road
Business Quarter, Stoke-On-Trent,
Staffordshire, ST1 2QE
T 01782 683168
E info@brighter-futures.org.uk
W www.brighter-futures.org.uk
CE Mrs Gill Brown
Sec Ms Lisa Stephenson
Ch Mr Mike Wolfe
Total Staff 197
Region West Midlands
Owned or managed 218
Rt 218 GN 11 Sup 207
Tenant Type % Single 100%

Brighton & Hove Jewish HA Ltd
○ Charitable HA
TSA Reg ✓
61 Furze Croft, Hove,
East Sussex, BN3 1PD
T 01273 738463
E edwin.prince@ssesurf.co.uk
Sec Mr Edwin Prince
Ch Mr Ivor Collins
Total Staff 2
Region South East
Owned or managed 25
Rt 25 GN 25
Tenant Type % Older 90%
Single 10%

Brighton Lions Housing Society Ltd
○ Charitable HA
TSA Reg ✓
Lions Gate, 95 Rowan Avenue,
Hove, East Sussex, BN3 7JZ
T 01273 738416
E brightonlionshousing@btconnect.
com
W www.brightonlionshousing.com
Sec Mr Brian Slater
Ch Mr William C Catchpole
Total Staff 4
Region South East
Owned or managed 116
Rt 116 GN 116
Tenant Type % Older 100%

Brighton Post & Tel Staff HA Ltd
○ Charitable HA
TSA Reg ✗
Ashdown House, 7 Knoyle Road,
Brighton, East Sussex, BN1 6RB
T 07730 734667
Sec Mrs Paula Waterman
Ch Mr Rick Clifford
Total Staff 0
Region South East
Tenant Type % Older 100%

Brighton YMCA
☆ Charitable Company
TSA Reg ✓ 🕶
Steine House, 55 Old Steine,
Brighton, BN1 1NX
T 01273 220900
E generalenquiries@brightonymca.
co.uk
W www.ymca.org.uk
CE Mr John Osborne
Sec Mr John Osborne
Ch Mr Peter Field, JP
Total Staff 68
Region South East
Owned or managed 281
Rt 281 Sup 281
Tenant Type % Single 100%

Bristol Community Housing Foundation Ltd
○ Charitable HA
TSA Reg ✓ 🕿 🔑
400 Filton Avenue, Horfield, Bristol,
Avon, BS7 0LJ
T 0845 130 1804
E info@bchf.co.uk
W www.bchf.co.uk
CE Ms Oona Goldsworthy
Sec Joanna Makinson
Ch Ms Patsy Hudson
Total Staff 18
Region South West
Owned or managed 720
Rt 684 GN 684 SO 36 Tot lets 46
GN bs 700
Tenant Type % Family 70%
Older 27% Single 3%
Development Total 46
Rt 97 GN 97 LCHO 15 NBC 46

Bristol Missing Link Ltd
○ Charitable HA
TSA Reg ✗ 🕶
Link House, 5 Queen Square,
Bristol, Avon, BS1 4JQ
T 0117 925 1811
E enquiries@missinglinkhousing.co.uk
W www.missinglinkhousing.co.uk
CE Ms Carol Metters
Sec Ms Carol Metters
Ch Ms Suzanne Allan
Total Staff 0
Region South West
Tenant Type % Family 15%
Single 85%

Bristowe (Fair Rent) HA Ltd
■ Non-Charitable HA
TSA Reg ✓
Sixth Floor, One Redcliff Street,
Bristol, Avon, BS1 6NP
T 0117 945 2500
E djacobs@milsted-langdon.co.uk
CE Mr Stephen Rosser

Sec Sian Narracott
Ch Mr Stephen Rosser
Total Staff 0
Region South West
Owned or managed 63
Rt 63 GN 63
Tenant Type % Family 50%
Older 25% Single 25%

Brixton Housing Co-op Ltd
★ Co-operative Society
TSA Reg ✓
90 Railton Road, London,
Greater London, SE24 0LD
T 020 7733 9034
E bhc_homes@btconnect.com
CE Ms Glenda Persaud
Sec Ms Leona Mitchell
Ch Mr Andrew Matheson
Total Staff 0
Region London
Owned or managed 86
Rt 86 GN 86
Tenant Type % Family 18%
Single 82%

Broadacres HA Ltd
○ Charitable HA
TSA Reg ✓ 🖵 🕿 🕿 🔑 ♦ 🕶 ◊
Broadacres House, Mount View,
Standard Way Industrial Park,
Northallerton, North Yorkshire,
DL6 2YD
T 01609 767900
E INFO@BROADACRES.ORG.UK
W www.broadacres.org.uk
CE Stephen Towers
Sec Mr Guru Naidoo
Ch Rev Brian Mayne
Total Staff 295
Regions Yorkshire & Humberside +
North East
Owned or managed 5381
Rt 5207 GN 4905 Sup 201 OP 101
SO 131 NSO 43 Tot lets 519
GN bs 4856
Tenant Type % Family 73%
Older 4% Single 23%
Development Total 240
Rt 565 GN 540 Sup 10 OP 15
LCHO 75 NBA 174 NBC 66
Subsidiary Association(s)
Broadacres Services Ltd

Broadacres Services Ltd
✪ Not-for-Profit Company
TSA Reg ✓ ◊
Broadacres House, Standard Way,
Northallerton, North Yorkshire,
DL6 2YD
T 01609 767923
E info@broadacres.org.uk
W www.broadacres.org.uk
CE Stephen Towers

Sec Mr Guru Naidoo
Ch Mr Anthony Twiggs
Total Staff 0
Region Yorkshire & Humberside
Parent Association
Broadacres HA Ltd

Broadhurst Welcome Home Community Ltd
○ Charitable HA
TSA Reg ✗
221 Sycamore Road, Farnborough,
Hampshire, GU14 6RQ
T 01252 519317
Sec Mrs S Mead
Ch Dr Olive O'Dowd-Booth
Total Staff 0
Region South East
Tenant Type % Single 100%

Broadland HA Ltd
○ Charitable HA
TSA Reg ✓ 🕿 🔑
NCFC, Jarrold Stand, Carrow Road,
Norwich, Norfolk, NR1 1HU
T 0303 303 0003
E enq@broadlandhousing.org
W www.broadlandhousing.org
CE Mr Michael Newey, BSc
FRICS MCIH
Sec Mrs Anna Simpson, MA FCA
Ch Baroness Hollis of Heigham
Total Staff 237
Region East of England
Owned or managed 4947
Rt 4727 GN 3971 Sup 162 OP 594
SO 135 NSO 85 Tot lets 500
GN bs 3898
Tenant Type % Family 54%
Older 16% Single 30%
Development Total 209
NBA 113 NBC 96

Broadway
☆ Charitable Company
TSA Reg ✗ 🕶
3rd Floor, 15 Half Moon Court,
London, Greater London, EC1A 7HF
T 020 7089 9500
E broadway@broadwaylondon.org
W www.broadwaylondon.org
CE Mr Howard Sinclair
Sec Ms Helen Giles
Ch Sir Leigh Lewis
Total Staff 240
Region London
Tenant Type % Single 100%

Broadway Park HA Ltd
○ Charitable HA
TSA Reg ✓ 🔑
423-425 Ashley Road, Parkstone,
Poole, Dorset, BH14 0AX
T 01202 735422
E enquiries@bpha.co.uk
W www.bpha.co.uk
CE Mrs Fiona Ferenczy
Sec Mrs Fiona Ferenczy
Total Staff 4
Region South West
Owned or managed 204
Rt 140 GN 140 SO 48 NSO 16
Tot lets 0 GN bs 0
Tenant Type % Family 85%
Older 5% Single 10%

Brockley Tenants' Co-operative Ltd
★ Co-operative Society
TSA Reg ✓
249 Lewisham Way, Brockley,
London, SE4 1XF
T 020 8691 5898
E management@brockley.coop
W www.brockley.coop
CE Mr Jeremy Hopkin
Sec Ms Geraldine Chambers
Ch Ms Maggie Martin
Total Staff 4
Region London
Owned or managed 162
Rt 162 GN 162
Tenant Type % Family 44%
Older 6% Single 50%

Bromford Housing Group Ltd
■ Non-Charitable HA
TSA Reg ✓
■ ⬜ 🚌 ⬚ 🔑 ♦ 🤝 ◊
1 Exchange Court, Brabourne
Avenue, Wolverhampton Business
Park, Wolverhampton, West
Midlands, WV10 6AU
T 0330 123 4034
E info@bromford.co.uk
W www.bromford.co.uk
CE Mr Mick Kent
Sec Ms Philippa Jones
Ch Mr Anthony Crawford
Total Staff 1119
Regions West Midlands + South
East, South West, East Midlands
Owned or managed 26855
Rt 23256 GN 21445 Sup 960
OP 851 SO 3288 NSO 311
Tot lets 3129 GN bs 21208
Tenant Type % Family 52%
Older 18% Single 30%
Development Total 895
Rt 931 GN 905 Sup 26 LCHO 416
NBA 507 NBC 388

Bromsgrove District Housing Trust
☆ Charitable Company
TSA Reg ✓ 🚌 🔑 🤝 ◊
Buntsford Court, Buntsford Gate,
Bromsgrove, Worcestershire,
B60 3DJ
T 0800 085 0160
E info@bdht.co.uk
W www.bdht.co.uk
CE Mr Mike Brown
Sec Mr Mark Robertson
Ch Mr John Morgan
Total Staff 131
Region West Midlands
Owned or managed 3466
Rt 3305 GN 2398 Sup 18 OP 889
SO 161 Tot lets 318 GN bs 2176
Tenant Type % Family 41%
Older 51% Single 8%
Subsidiary Association(s)
Bromsgrove Housing Initiatives Ltd

Bromsgrove Housing Initiatives Ltd
○ Charitable HA
TSA Reg ✓ ⬚ 🔑 ◊
Buntsford Court, Unit 2,
The Courtyard, Buntsford Drive,
Bromsgrove, Worcestershire,
B60 3DJ
T 01527 557557
W www.bdht.co.uk
CE Mr Mike Brown
Sec Mr Mark Robertson
Ch Mr Stephen Gabriel
Total Staff 0
Region West Midlands
Owned or managed 271
Rt 216 GN 195 Sup 5 OP 16 SO 55
Tot lets 9 GN bs 9
Tenant Type % Family 55%
Older 32% Single 13%
Development Total 83
Rt 34 GN 34 LCHO 12 NBC 83
Parent Association Bromsgrove
District Housing Trust

Brunel Care
☆ Charitable Company
TSA Reg ✓ 🔑 ♦ 🤝
3-8 Redcliffe Parade West,
Bristol, Avon, BS1 6SL
T 0117 914 4200
E info@brunelcare.org.uk
W www.brunelcare.org.uk
CE Ms Helen Joy
Sec Mr Tim Jenkinson
Ch Mr James Magness
Total Staff 972
Region South West
Owned or managed 1085
Rt 1058 GN 8 OP 1050 SO 27
Tot lets 141 GN bs 8
Tenant Type % Older 100%

Brunts Charity
❏ Charitable Trust
TSA Reg ✓
Brunts Chambers, 2 Toothill Lane,
Mansfield, Nottinghamshire,
NG18 1NJ
T 01623 623055
Sec Mrs H Williams
Ch Mr K F Williams
Total Staff 9
Region East Midlands
Owned or managed 156
Rt 156 GN 156
Tenant Type % Older 100%

Buckinghamshire HA Ltd
○ Charitable HA
TSA Reg ✓ 🏠 🔑
Unit 4, Stokenchurch Business Park,
Ibstone Road, Stokenchurch,
High Wycombe, Buckinghamshire,
HP14 3FE
T 01494 480340
E info@bucksha.co.uk
W www.buckshousing.co.uk
CE Mr Keith Dobson
Sec Mr Keith Dobson
Ch Paul Ricketts
Total Staff 12
Region South East
Owned or managed 425
Rt 414 GN 396 Sup 4 OP 14 SO 11
Tot lets 32 GN bs 0
Tenant Type % Family 36%
Older 35% Single 29%
Development Total 1
Rt 14 GN 14 NBA 1

Burwash District HA for The Elderly Ltd
○ Charitable HA
TSA Reg ✗
St Anthony's, High Street, Burwash,
Etchingham, East Sussex, TN19 7EN
T 01435 883443
Sec Mr R E Burn
Ch Mr W A Kingston
Total Staff 0
Region South East
Owned or managed 13
Rt 13 OP 13
Tenant Type % Older 100%

Byker Community Trust
○ Charitable HA
TSA Reg ✓
23 Raby Cross, Byker,
Newcastle Upon Tyne, NE6 2FF
T 0191 278 8617
E philip.ambrose@bykerct.co.uk
W www.bykercommunitytrust.org
CE Ms J Haley
Sec Mrs Joanne Noble-Nesbitt
Ch Mr P Roberts

Total Staff 5
Region North East
Owned or managed 1803
Rt 1803 **GN** 1693 **OP** 110
Tenant Type % Family 64%
Older 18% **Single** 18%

Cc

Caldmore Area HA Ltd
○ Charitable HA
TSA Reg ✓
18 Caldmore Green, Caldmore, Walsall, West Midlands, WS1 3RL
T 01922 614505
E webmaster@caldmorehousing.co.uk
W www.caldmorehousing.co.uk
CE Mr Mike Hew
Sec Mr Sam Dhadwar
Ch Ms Joanne Keatley
Total Staff 159
Region West Midlands
Owned or managed 2126
Rt 2025 **GN** 1577 **Sup** 138 **OP** 310
SO 101 **Tot lets** 543 **GN bs** 1310
Tenant Type % Family 50%
Older 12% **Single** 38%
Development Total 246
NBA 164 **NBC** 82
Parent Association Accord HA Ltd

Calico Homes Ltd
✪ Not-for-Profit Company
TSA Reg ✓
Centenary Court, Croft Street, Burnley, Lancashire, BB11 2ED
T 0800 169 2407
E contact@calico.org.uk
W www.calico.org.uk
CE Mr Michael Birkett
Sec Mr Steven Brook
Ch Lesley Burrows
Total Staff 336
Region North West
Owned or managed 4604
Rt 4495 **GN** 3274 **Sup** 64 **OP** 1157
SO 82 **NSO** 27 **Tot lets** 700
GN bs 3254
Tenant Type % Family 28%
Older 36% **Single** 36%
Development Total 10
NBA 10

Camberwell Housing Society Ltd
○ Charitable HA
TSA Reg ✓
Troy Town Flats, Nigel Road, Peckham Rye, London, Greater London, SE15 4NS
T 020 7732 1816
E camberwellhousing@btconnect.com
CE Ms Agnes Onayemi
Sec Ms Agnes Onayemi
Ch Gerald Golder
Total Staff 3
Region London
Owned or managed 65
Rt 65 **OP** 65
Tenant Type % Older 100%

Camden Teacher Tenants Co-operative
★ Co-operative Society
TSA Reg ✗
2-4 Ospringe Road, London, Greater London, NW5 2JE
T 020 7267 5509
E chair@cttc.org.uk
Sec Mr Joseph McKenzie
Ch Mr Simon Gould
Total Staff 0
Region London
Tenant Type % Family 55%
Single 45%

Care & Repair (East Cambridgeshire) Ltd
○ Charitable HA
TSA Reg ✗
11b Churchgate Street, Soham, Ely, Cambridgeshire, CB7 5DS
T 01353 723777
E info@careandrepair-ecambs.co.uk
W www.careandrepair-ecambs.co.uk
CE Mrs Yvonne Thresh
Ch Mr Roderick Mair
Total Staff 0
Region East of England

Care & Repair England
○ Charitable HA
TSA Reg ✗
The Renewal Trust Business Centre, 3 Hawksworth Street, Nottingham, Nottinghamshire, NG3 2EG
T 0115 950 6500
E info@careandrepair-england.org.uk
W www.careandrepair-england.org.uk
CE Mrs Sue Adams
Sec Ms Maria Brenton
Ch Mr Peter Archer
Total Staff 5
Region East Midlands

Care HA
✪ Not-for-Profit Company
TSA Reg ✓
Stanley Grange, Roach Road, Samlesbury, Preston, Lancashire, PR5 0RB
T 0845 437 7367
E Matthew.eddisford@careha.org.uk
CE Mr Matthew Eddisford
Ch Mr David Ward
Total Staff 1
Region North West
Owned or managed 78
Rt 78 **Sup** 78
Tenant Type % Single 100%

Cass and Claredale Halls of Residence Association Ltd
○ Charitable HA
TSA Reg ✗
Sir John Cass Hall, 150 Well Street, London, Greater London, E9 7LQ
T 020 8533 2529
E cass@cassandclaredale.co.uk
W www.cassandclaredale.co.uk
CE Mr Allan Hilton
Sec Mr Chris Plumley
Ch Mr Michael Goodswen
Total Staff 48
Region London
Owned or managed 377
NSO 377
Tenant Type % Single 100%

Castle Vale Community HA Ltd
○ Charitable HA
TSA Reg ✓
11 High Street, Castle Vale, Birmingham, B35 7PR
T 0121 748 8100
E enquiries@cvcha.org.uk
W www.cvcha.org.uk
CE Mr Peter Richmond
Sec Mr Ian Evans
Ch Ms Sheila Arthurs
Total Staff 108
Region West Midlands
Owned or managed 2426
Rt 2400 **GN** 2272 **OP** 128 **NSO** 26
Tenant Type % Family 68%
Older 20% **Single** 12%
Development Total 9
NBA 5 **NBC** 4

Catalyst Housing Ltd
○ Charitable HA
TSA Reg ✓
Ealing Gateway, 26-30 Uxbridge Road, London, Greater London, W5 2AU
T 020 8832 3334

See page 62 for key to symbols and abbreviations

E csc.queries@chg.org.uk
W www.chg.org.uk
CE Mr Rod Cahill
Sec Ms Maggie Pratt
Ch Mr Richard Brown
Total Staff 558
Regions London + South East, East of England
Owned or managed 16818
Rt 12774 **GN** 12106 **Sup** 80 **OP** 588 **SO** 4004 **NSO** 40 **Tot lets** 1827 **GN bs** 10916
Tenant Type % Family 58%
Older 23% **Single** 19%
Development Total 1394
Rt 2328 **GN** 2328 **LCHO** 1067 **NBC** 1394

CBHA
☆ Charitable Company
TSA Reg ✓ 🏠 🔑 🦇 ⌂
433-443 High Road, Leytonstone, London, Greater London, E11 4JU
T 020 7922 8500
E services@cbha.org.uk
W www.cbha.org.uk
CE Gary De Ferry
Sec Ms Susan Hickey
Ch Ms Debbie Griggs
Total Staff 43
Region London
Owned or managed 1504
Rt 1428 **GN** 1373 **OP** 55 **SO** 76
Tot lets 75 **GN bs** 1373
Tenant Type % Family 61%
Older 30% **Single** 9%
Development Total 71
NBA 40 **NBC** 31
Parent Association Peabody

CDS Co-operatives
★ Co-operative Society
TSA Reg ✓ 🏠 🔑
3 Marshalsea Road, London, Greater London, SE1 1EP
T 020 7397 5711
E enquiries@cds.coop
W www.cds.coop
CE Ms Orla Gallagher
Sec Mr Stephen Brown
Ch Maureen Stables
Total Staff 46
Regions London + South East, East of England
Owned or managed 3112
Rt 2854 **GN** 2854 **SO** 218 **NSO** 40
Tot lets 32 **GN bs** 690
Tenant Type % Family 69%
Older 8% **Single** 23%
Development Total 1
NBC 1

Cedarmore HA Ltd
○ Charitable HA
TSA Reg ✓ 🦇
267 Southlands Road, Bickley, Kent, BR1 2EG
T 020 8468 7778
E coordinator@cedarmoreha.fsnet.co.uk
Sec Mrs Judith Meerloo
Ch Mr Roy Kemp
Total Staff 75
Region London
Owned or managed 51
Rt 48 **OP** 48 **NSO** 3
Tenant Type % Older 100%

Central & Cecil
○ Charitable HA
TSA Reg ✓ 🏠 ♦ 🦇
266 Waterloo Road, London, SE1 8RQ
T 020 7922 5300
E enquiries@ccht.org.uk
W www.ccht.org.uk
CE Mrs Caroline Tiller
Sec Mrs Caroline Tiller
Ch Mr Nick Moore
Total Staff 553
Regions London + South East, West Midlands, East of England
Owned or managed 2095
Rt 2095 **GN** 241 **Sup** 467 **OP** 1387
Tenant Type % Family 4% **Older** 89% **Single** 6%
Development Total 100
NBA 50 **NBC** 50

Centrepoint
☆ Charitable Company
TSA Reg ✓ 🦇
Central House,
25 Camperdown Street, London, Greater London, E1 8DZ
T 0845 466 3400
E info@centrepoint.org
W www.centrepoint.org.uk
CE Mr Seyi Obakin
Sec Ms Maxine Edney
Ch Michael O'Higgins
Total Staff 212
Regions London + North East
Owned or managed 467
Rt 467 **GN** 37 **Sup** 430
Tenant Type % Single 1%

Cestria Community HA
○ Charitable HA
TSA Reg ✓ 🏢 🏠 🔑
Bowes Offices, Lambton Park, Chester Le Street, County Durham, DH3 4AN
T 0191 385 1900
E enquiries@cestria.org
W www.cestria.org

CE Mr Paul Fiddaman
Sec Mr Martin Warhurst
Ch Mr David Butler
Total Staff 153
Region North East
Owned or managed 4226
Rt 4203 **GN** 2954 **OP** 1249 **SO** 23
Tot lets 355 **GN bs** 2946
Development Total 2
NBA 2

Chapter 1
☆ Charitable Company
TSA Reg ✓ ♦ 🦇
2 Exton Street, London, Greater London, SE1 8UE
T 020 7593 0470
E mail@ch1.org.uk
W www.ch1.org.uk
CE Mr Geoff Hawkins
Sec Mr Geoff Hawkins
Ch Mr Rob Taylor
Total Staff 344
Regions London + South East, South West, West Midlands, North West
Owned or managed 724
Rt 724 **GN** 191 **Sup** 533
Tenant Type % Family 10%
Single 90%

Charlton Triangle Homes Ltd
☆ Charitable Company
TSA Reg ✓ 🏠 🔑 ⌂
9-10 Cedar Court, Fairlawn, Charlton, London, Greater London, SE7 7EH
T 020 8319 8870
E cth@familymosaic.co.uk
W www.charltontriangle.org.uk
CE Mr Andrew Kimmance
Sec Mr Andrew Kimmance
Ch Mr Mark Adams
Total Staff 12
Region London
Owned or managed 1154
Rt 1005 **GN** 1005 **SO** 149
Tot lets 79 **GN bs** 1005
Tenant Type % Family 100%
Development Total 11
NBA 11
Parent Association
Family Mosaic Housing

Cherchefelle HA Ltd
○ Charitable HA
TSA Reg ✓ 🦇
Enterprise Court, 3 Mill Street, Redhill, Surrey, RH1 6PA
T 01737 244312
E mail@cfha.org.uk
W www.cherchefelle.org.uk
CE Mr Martin Bellinger
Sec Mr Martin Bellinger

Ch Mr Roy Woodward
Total Staff 102
Region South East
Owned or managed 212
Rt 212 **Sup** 176 **OP** 36
Tenant Type % **Family** 1% **Older** 56%
Single 43%

Cherry Tree HA Ltd
○ Charitable HA
TSA Reg ✓ 🐾
Orchard Villa, Porters Park Drive,
Shenley, Radlett, Hertfordshire,
WD7 9DS
T 01923 850580
E dave.press@cherrytreeha.org.uk
W www.cherrytreeha.co.uk
CE Mr David Press
Sec Mr David Press
Ch Ms Caroline McCaffrey
Total Staff 17
Regions East of England + London
Owned or managed 76
Rt 76 **GN** 3 **Sup** 73
Tenant Type % **Family** 2% **Single** 98%

Chester & District Housing Trust
✪ Not-for-Profit Company
TSA Reg ✓ 🖵 🛒 🄿 🔑 👤 🐾 ◊
Centurion House, 77 Northgate
Street, Chester, Cheshire, CH1 2HQ
T 01244 305503
E ServiceFirst@cdht.org
W www.cdht.org
CE Mr John Denny
Sec Mrs Su Bramley
Ch Mr Robert Thompson
Total Staff 348
Region North West
Owned or managed 6556
Rt 6196 **GN** 4506 **OP** 1690 **SO** 360
Tot lets 582 **GN bs** 4482
Tenant Type % **Family** 37%
Older 40% **Single** 23%
Development Total 190
NBA 99 **NBC** 91
Parent Association Cosmopolitan
Housing Group Ltd

Chesterfield Churches HA
○ Charitable HA
TSA Reg ✓ 🐾
Harehill Court, Harehill Road,
Chesterfield, Derbyshire, S40 2NZ
T 01246 230172
E ccha1@btconnect.com
Sec Mrs Katy Martin
Ch Mrs Jeanette Clayton
Total Staff 10
Region East Midlands
Owned or managed 31
Rt 31 **OP** 31
Tenant Type % **Older** 100%

Chevin HA Ltd
○ Charitable HA
TSA Reg ✓ 🖵 🛒 🄿 🔑 ◊
Harrison Street, Wakefield,
West Yorkshire, WF1 1PS
T 0845 270 1088
E enquiries@chevinha.co.uk
W www.togetherhousing.co.uk
CE Mr Steve Close
Sec Mr Steve Close
Ch Mr David Green
Total Staff 219
Regions Yorkshire & Humberside +
East Midlands
Owned or managed 8284
Rt 7671 **GN** 6503 **Sup** 585 **OP** 583
SO 594 **NSO** 19 **Tot lets** 1768
GN bs 6231
Tenant Type % **Family** 40%
Older 10% **Single** 50%
Development Total 644
NBA 452 **NBC** 192
Parent Association
Together Housing Group Ltd

Cheviot HA Ltd
○ Charitable HA
TSA Reg ✓ 🄿 🔑 🐾 ◊
Beaminster Way East, Kingston Park,
Newcastle Upon Tyne,
Tyne And Wear, NE3 2ER
T 0191 238 3800
E enquiries@bernicia.com
W www.bernicia.com
CE Mr Bill Heads
Sec Mr Bill Heads
Ch Mr William Gilbert
Total Staff 145
Region North East
Owned or managed 2998
Rt 2859 **GN** 1779 **Sup** 96 **OP** 984
SO 139 **Tot lets** 397 **GN bs** 1772
Tenant Type % **Family** 43%
Older 36% **Single** 21%
Development Total 64
NBA 38 **NBC** 26
Parent Association
Bernicia Group Ltd

Chichester Greyfriars HA Ltd
○ Charitable HA
TSA Reg ✓
The Forum, Stirling Road, Chichester,
West Sussex, PO19 7DN
T 01243 531482
E chigreyfriars@btconnect.com
W www.chichestergreyfriars.org.uk
CE Mrs Shelagh Morgan
Sec Mrs Shelagh Morgan
Ch Mr David Siggs
Total Staff 3
Region South East
Owned or managed 83

Rt 83 **OP** 83
Tenant Type % **Older** 100%

Chisel Ltd
○ Charitable HA
TSA Reg ✓
188a Brockley Road, London,
Greater London, SE4 2RL
T 020 8692 5258
E director@chisel.org.uk
W www.chisel.org.uk
CE Ms Karen Cooper
Sec Ms Karen Cooper
Ch Ms Wendy Newell
Total Staff 6
Regions London + South East,
East of England
Owned or managed 241
Rt 241 **GN** 241
Tenant Type % **Family** 77%
Older 6% **Single** 17%

Chislehurst & Sidcup HA
○ Charitable HA
TSA Reg ✓ 🐾
23 Bushell Way, Chislehurst,
Kent, BR7 6SF
T 020 8467 9146
E csinfo@@csha.org.uk
W www.csha.org.uk
CE Ms Angela Williams-Brown
Sec Ms Angela Williams-Brown
Ch Mrs Barbara Stockbridge
Total Staff 11
Region London
Owned or managed 150
Rt 150 **GN** 4 **OP** 146
Tenant Type % **Family** 3%
Older 97%

CHOICES HA Ltd
○ Charitable HA
TSA Reg ✓ 👤 🐾 ◊
1a King Street, Newcastle-Under-
Lyme, Staffordshire, ST5 1EN
T 01782 254000
E info@choiceshousing.co.uk
W www.choiceshousing.co.uk
CE Mr John Broadhead
Sec Mr Chris Horton
Ch Mr Mike Lawton
Total Staff 268
Region West Midlands
Owned or managed 55
Rt 55 **Sup** 55
Tenant Type % **Single** 100%
Parent Association The Wrekin
Housing Group Ltd

Chorley Community Housing Ltd
○ Charitable HA
TSA Reg ✓ 🖵 📠 🔑 🕶 ◊
Ann James House, St. Thomas Road, Chorley, PR7 1HR
T 01257 244800
E enquiries@chorleych.co.uk
W www.chorleych.co.uk
CE Mr Richard Houghton
Sec Mr Brian Moran
Ch Paul Joyce
Total Staff 66
Region North West
Owned or managed 5396
Rt 5284 GN 4688 Sup 12 OP 584
SO 112 Tot lets 296 GN bs 2511
Tenant Type % Family 24%
Older 60% Single 16%
Parent Association
Adactus Housing Group

CHP
✪ Not-for-Profit Company
TSA Reg ✓ 🖵 📠 🄳 🔑 ♦
Myriad House, 23 Springfield Lyons Approach, Chelmsford, Essex, CM2 5LB
T 01245 613000
E enquiries@chp.org.uk
W www.chp.org.uk
CE Mr Stuart Stackhouse
Sec Mr Stuart Stackhouse
Ch Mr Martin Dean
Total Staff 267
Region East of England
Owned or managed 9441
Rt 7617 GN 5432 Sup 947 OP 1238
SO 877 NSO 947 Tot lets 908
GN bs 5319
Tenant Type % Family 35%
Older 49% Single 16%
Development Total 485
Rt 373 GN 373 NBC 485

Christ Church (St Leonards on Sea) House Improvement Soc Ltd
■ Non-Charitable HA
TSA Reg ✗
7 Wellington Square, Hastings, TN34 1PD
T 01424 721700
E info.hastings@manningtons.net
Sec Mr Patrick Langdon
Total Staff 0
Region South East
Tenant Type % Older 100%

Christian Action (Enfield) HA Ltd
○ Charitable HA
TSA Reg ✓ 🔑 🕶 ◊
Benedict House, 61 Island Centre Way, Enfield, Middlesex, EN3 6GS
T 01992 765900
E info@christianaction.org.uk
W www.christianaction.org.uk
CE Mr Mark Hayes
Sec Mr John Lower
Ch Ms Ziggy Crawford
Total Staff 121
Region London
Owned or managed 1559
Rt 1514 GN 1034 Sup 249 OP 231
SO 2 NSO 43 Tot lets 319
GN bs 770
Tenant Type % Family 40%
Older 30% Single 30%
Subsidiary Association(s) Christian Action Housing Special Projects Ltd

Christian Action Housing Special Projects Ltd
✪ Not-for-Profit Company
TSA Reg ✗ ◊
Benedict House, 61 Island Centre Way, Enfield, Middlesex, EN3 6GS
T 01992 765900
E info@christianaction.org.uk
W www.christianaction.org.uk
CE Mr Mark Hayes
Sec Mr John Lower
Ch Ms Ann Reynard
Total Staff 0
Region London
Parent Association Christian Action (Enfield) HA Ltd

CHS Group
○ Charitable HA
TSA Reg ✓ 🄳 🔑 ♦ 🕶
Endurance House, Chivers Way, Histon, Cambridge, Cambridgeshire, CB24 9ZR
T 01223 713555
E info@chsgroup.org.uk
W www.chsgroup.org.uk
CE Mr Nigel Howlett
Sec Mr Nigel Howlett
Ch Mrs Sheila Forrest
Total Staff 359
Region East of England
Owned or managed 2475
Rt 2166 GN 1747 Sup 204 OP 215
SO 298 NSO 11 Tot lets 401
GN bs 1745
Tenant Type % Family 51%
Older 24% Single 25%
Development Total 266
Rt 84 GN 84 LCHO 55 NBA 158
NBC 108

Church of England Pension Board
❏ Charitable Trust
TSA Reg ✗
29 Great Smith Street, Westminster, London, Greater London, SW1P 3PS
T 020 7898 1819
E firstname.secondname@c-of-e.org.uk
Total Staff 0
Region London

Church of England Soldiers' Sailors' & Airmen's HA
○ Charitable HA
TSA Reg ✓ 🕶
1 Shakespeare Terrace, 126 High Street, Portsmouth, Hampshire, PO1 2RH
T 023 9282 9319
W www.cessaha.co.uk
CE Mr Patrick Keefe
Sec Mr Patrick Keefe
Ch Rear Admiral Simon R J Goodall CBE
Total Staff 13
Region South East
Owned or managed 199
Rt 199 OP 199
Tenant Type % Older 100%

Churches HA of Dudley & District (CHADD)
○ Charitable HA
TSA Reg ✓ 🕶
98-99 Dixons Green Road, Dudley, West Midlands, DY2 7DJ
T 01384 456465
E admin@chaddltd.co.uk
W www.chadd.org.uk
CE Mrs Jane Clarke
Sec Mrs Jane Clarke
Ch Rt Rev David Walker
Total Staff 50
Region West Midlands
Owned or managed 213
Rt 158 Sup 113 OP 45 NSO 55
Tenant Type % Family 13%
Older 23% Single 64%

Circle
■ Non-Charitable HA
TSA Reg ✓ ♦ ◊
Circle Anglia House, 1-3 Highbury Station Road, Islington, London, Greater London, N1 1SE
T 020 7288 4000
E info@circleanglia.org
W www.circle.org.uk
CE Mr Mark Rogers
Sec Ms Deborah Upton
Ch Sir Robin Young, KCB
Total Staff 1274
Region London

Subsidiary Association(s) Circle
Thirty Three Housing Trust Ltd;
Mercian HA Ltd; Merton Priory
Homes; Mole Valley HA Ltd; Old
Ford HA; Roddons HA; Russet
Homes; South Anglia Housing Ltd;
Wherry HA Ltd

Circle Thirty Three Housing Trust Ltd
○ Charitable HA
TSA Reg ✓ 🖼 🖵 🗗 🔑 ♦
Circle Anglia, 1-3 Highbury Station
Road, London, Greater London,
N1 1SE
T 020 7288 4000
E info@circle.org.uk
W www.circleanglia.org
CE Mr Jeff Baker
Ch Baroness Maggie Jones
Total Staff 147
Regions London + South East,
East of England
Owned or managed 17516
Rt 14186 GN 12131 Sup 1012
OP 1043 SO 2370 NSO 960
Tot lets 1491 GN bs 10557
Tenant Type % Family 60%
Older 20% Single 20%
Development Total 498
NBA 307 NBC 191
Parent Association Circle

Cirencester Housing Society Ltd
○ Charitable HA
TSA Reg ✓ 🗗
Phoenix House, Phoenix Way,
Cirencester, GL7 1QG
T 01285 658377
E enquiries@cirencesterhs.org.uk
W www.cirencesterhs.org.uk
CE Mrs Lynne Barber
Sec Mrs Lynne Barber
Ch Mr Chris Winter
Total Staff 6
Region South West
Owned or managed 144
Rt 144 GN 144
Tenant Type % Family 37%
Older 35% Single 28%
Development Total 1
Rt 11 GN 11 NBA 1

City of Exeter YMCA HA
☆ Charitable Company
TSA Reg ✓ 🐝
39/41 St David's Hill, Exeter,
Devon, EX4 4DA
T 01392 410530
E office@exeterymca.org.uk
W www.exeterymca.org.uk
CE Mr Peter Stephenson
Sec Mr Peter Stephenson

Ch Mr Ian Awcock
Total Staff 9
Region South West
Owned or managed 43
Rt 43 Sup 43
Tenant Type % Single 100%

City of Liverpool YMCA
☆ Charitable Company
TSA Reg ✓ 🗗 🐝
15 Leeds Street, Liverpool,
Merseyside, L3 6HU
T 0151 600 3530
E info@liverpoolymca.org.uk
W www.liverpoolymca.org.uk
CE Mr Darren Lyons
Sec Mr Darren Lyons
Ch Mr Phil P Shackell
Total Staff 30
Region North West
Owned or managed 83
Rt 83 GN 13 Sup 70
Tenant Type % Single 100%
Development Total 3
Rt 20 Sup 20 NBA 3

City South Manchester Housing Trust
☆ Charitable Company
TSA Reg ✓ 🚚 🗗 🐝
Turing House, Archway 5, Hulme,
Manchester, Lancashire, M15 5RL
T 0161 227 1234
E info@citysouthmanchester.co.uk
W www.citysouthmanchester.co.uk
CE Mr David Power
Sec Mr John McGrail
Ch Mr Phil Summers
Total Staff 166
Region North West
Owned or managed 4707
Rt 4400 GN 4372 OP 28 NSO 307
Tenant Type % Family 40%
Older 35% Single 25%
Development Total 10
NBA 10

City West Housing Trust
○ Charitable HA
TSA Reg ✓ 🖼 🖵 🚚 🗗 🔑 ⚡
4th Floor, Centenary House, 1
Centenary Way, Eccles, Manchester,
Lancashire, M50 1RF
T 0161 605 7296
E enquiries@citywest.org.uk
W www.citywesthousingtrust.org.uk
CE Mr Tim Doyle
Sec Mr Paul Whitehead
Ch Mr Gerry Corless
Total Staff 406
Region North West
Owned or managed 15052
Rt 14620 GN 13713 Sup 31 OP 876
SO 432 Tot lets 1461 GN bs 13703

Tenant Type % Family 28%
Older 37% Single 35%
Development Total 7
NBA 7

City YMCA, London
☆ Charitable Company
TSA Reg ✓ 🐝
80-83 Long Lane, London, EC1A 9ET
T 020 7367 5500
W www.cityymca.org
CE Ms Gillian Bowen
Sec Mr Thomas Brettle
Ch Mr Robert Thompson
Total Staff 73
Region London
Owned or managed 367
Rt 367 GN 239 Sup 128
Tenant Type % Single 100%

Clanmil HA Ltd
○ Charitable HA
TSA Reg ✗ 🗗 🔑 🐝
Northern Whig House,
3 Waring Street, Belfast, County
Antrim, BT1 2DX
T 028 9087 6000
E housing@clanmil.org.uk
W www.clanmil.org
CE Ms Clare McCarty
Sec Ms Clare McCarty
Ch Joan Baird
Total Staff 213
Region No Region
Owned or managed 242
Rt 228 GN 39 Sup 88 OP 101 SO 14
Tot lets 412 GN bs 2985
Tenant Type % Family 52%
Older 42% Single 6%
Development Total 125
Rt 581 GN 553 Sup 8 OP 20
LCHO 3 NBC 125

Clapham Park Homes
☆ Charitable Company
TSA Reg ✓ 🗗 🔑 🔥 ♦
1 Headlam Road, Clapham Park,
London, Greater London, SW4 8HP
T 020 8623 8900
E cphenquiries@cph-online.co.uk
W www.cph-online.co.uk
CE Mr Owen Thompson
Ch Mr Joe Moll
Total Staff 58
Region London
Owned or managed 2103
Rt 1369 GN 1275 OP 94 SO 509
NSO 225 Tot lets 172 GN bs 1260
Tenant Type % Family 85%
Older 3% Single 12%
Development Total 233
NBA 133 NBC 100
Parent Association Metropolitan

See page 62 for key to symbols and abbreviations

Clapton Park Management Organisation
○ Charitable HA
TSA Reg ✗
Clapton Park Neighbourhood Office, 4A Gilpin Road, London, Greater London, E5 0HL
T 020 8356 6330
W www.cpmo.org
CE Mr Daren Willoughby
Sec Ms Karita Salomon
Ch Mrs Maureen Doe
Total Staff 30
Region London
Owned or managed 794
Rt 794 GN 645 OP 149
Tenant Type % Family 50%
Older 30% Single 20%

Clissold Housing Co-operative Ltd
★ Co-operative Society
TSA Reg ✓
7 Clissold Road, London, Greater London, N16 9EX
E tenfour@blueyonder.co.uk
Sec Robert Clarke
Ch Bocia Gamba
Total Staff 0
Region London
Owned or managed 24
Rt 24 GN 24
Tenant Type % Family 45%
Single 55%

Co-op Homes (South) Ltd
○ Charitable HA
TSA Reg ✓ ◊
8 Waldegrave Road, Teddington, Middlesex, TW11 8GT
T 0845 250 7276
E homes@coophomes.coop
W www.coophomes.coop
CE Ms Sue Philpott
Sec Ms Sue Philpott
Ch Mr Brian Rose
Total Staff 14
Regions London + South East, East of England
Owned or managed 702
Rt 702 GN 702
Tenant Type % Family 55%
Older 5% Single 40%
Parent Association Richmond Housing Partnership

Coast & Country Housing Ltd
✪ Not-for-Profit Company
TSA Reg ✓
■ ▢ 🖩 ◊ ✎ ♦ 🥾
14 Ennis Square, Dormanstown, Redcar, Cleveland, TS10 5JR
T 01642 771300

E enquiries@cchousing.org.uk
W www.cch-online.org.uk
CE Mr Iain Sim
Sec Mr Iain Sim
Ch Ms Paula Breen
Total Staff 526
Regions North East + Yorkshire & Humberside
Owned or managed 10270
Rt 10145 GN 10133 Sup 12 SO 112 NSO 13 Tot lets 1263 GN bs 10060
Tenant Type % Family 63%
Older 31% Single 6%
Development Total 126
NBA 91 NBC 35

Coastline Housing Ltd
☆ Charitable Company
TSA Reg ✓ 🖩 ◊ ✎ 🥾
Coastline House, 4 Barncoose Gateway Park, Barncoose, Redruth, Cornwall, TR15 3RQ
T 01209 200200
E customer.service@coastlinehousing.co.uk
W www.coastlinehousing.co.uk
CE Mr Robert Nettleton
Sec Mr David Wingham
Ch Mr Derek Law MBE
Total Staff 217
Region South West
Owned or managed 3874
Rt 3688 GN 2978 Sup 61 OP 649 SO 180 NSO 6 Tot lets 235 GN bs 2957
Tenant Type % Family 45%
Older 35% Single 20%
Development Total 113
Rt 77 GN 77 LCHO 15 NBA 66 NBC 47

Cobalt Housing Ltd
○ Charitable HA
TSA Reg ✓ ▢ ◊ ✎ 🥾 ◊
199 Lower House Lane, Liverpool, Merseyside, L11 2SF
T 0151 633 8000
E info@cobalthousing.org.uk
W www.cobalthousing.org.uk
CE Mr Alan Rogers
Sec Mr Alan Rogers
Ch Julie Roberts
Total Staff 130
Region North West
Owned or managed 5793
Rt 5782 GN 5777 Sup 5 SO 3 NSO 8 Tot lets 509 GN bs 5777
Tenant Type % Family 64%
Older 9% Single 27%
Development Total 188
NBA 96 NBC 92
Parent Association Symphony Housing Group

Coin Street Secondary Housing Co-operative Ltd
★ Co-operative Society
TSA Reg ✓
108 Stamford Street, South Bank, London, Greater London, SE1 9NH
T 020 7021 1600
E c.czechowski@coinstreet.org
W www.coinstreet.org
CE Ms Christine Czechowski
Sec Mr Iain Tuckett
Ch Neil Cole
Total Staff 0
Region London
Owned or managed 164
Rt 164 GN 164

Colebrook Housing Society Ltd
○ Charitable HA
TSA Reg ✗ 🥾
3 Woodland Terrace, Greenbank Road, Plymouth, PL4 8NL
T 01752 205210
E enquiries@colebrookhousing.co.uk
W www.colebrookhousing.co.uk
CE Ms Vicky Shipway
Sec Mr John Miskelly
Ch Mr Trevor Paul
Total Staff 63
Region South West
Owned or managed 3
NSO 3
Tenant Type % Single 100%

Colne Housing Society Ltd
○ Charitable HA
TSA Reg ✓ ◊ ✎ 🥾
Digby House, Riverside Office Centre, Causton Road, Colchester, Essex, CO1 1RJ
T 01206 244700
E info@colnehousing.co.uk
W www.colnehousing.co.uk
CE Mr Mark Powell Davies
Sec Mrs Lynne Shea
Ch Mr Tim Young
Total Staff 68
Region East of England
Owned or managed 2745
Rt 2541 GN 2031 Sup 162 OP 348 SO 129 NSO 75 Tot lets 464 GN bs 1780
Tenant Type % Family 50%
Older 25% Single 25%
Development Total 449
Rt 167 GN 161 Sup 6 NBA 261 NBC 188

Community Gateway Association Ltd
○ Charitable HA
TSA Reg ✓ ▢ 🔲 ▢
Deltic House, West Strand, Preston,
Lancashire, PR1 8UY
T 0800 953 0213
E customerservices@
communitygateway.co.uk
W www.communitygateway.co.uk
CE Ms Diane Bellinger
Sec Mr Paul Atkinson
Ch Ms Rose Kinsella
Total Staff 165
Region North West
Owned or managed 6084
Rt 6084 GN 5625 Sup 8 OP 451
Tenant Type % Family 48%
Older 24% Single 28%
Development Total 50
NBA 25 NBC 25

Community Meeting Point
☆ Charitable Company
TSA Reg ✗ ⏾
Hightown House, Maylands Avenue,
Hemel Hempstead Industrial Estate,
Hemel Hempstead, HP2 4XH
T 01582 831485
W www.cmph.org.uk
Sec Mr David Skinner
Ch Monica Cashman
Total Staff 1
Region East of England
Parent Association Hightown
Praetorian and Churches HA Ltd

Community Options Ltd
☆ Charitable Company
TSA Reg ✗ 🔱
2a Fielding Lane, Bromley,
Kent, BR2 9FL
T 020 8313 9725
E enquiry@community-options.org.uk
W www.community-options.org.uk
CE Ms Chris Mansi
Sec Ms Chris Mansi
Ch Mr John Wates
Total Staff 88
Region London
Owned or managed 12
Rt 12 GN 6 Sup 6
Tenant Type % Older 28%
Single 72%

Community Trust Housing
○ Charitable HA
TSA Reg ✓ ▢ 🔑 ⏾
143 Stockwell Road, London,
Greater London, SW9 9TP
T 020 7326 3700
E info@cth.org.uk
CE Mr Delroy Rankin
Sec Mr Richard Reger

Ch Mr Alan Head
Total Staff 22
Region London
Owned or managed 1395
Rt 944 GN 892 OP 52 SO 350
NSO 101 Tot lets 32 GN bs 830
Development Total 130
NBA 65 NBC 65
Parent Association
Network Housing Group Ltd

Connect HA Ltd
○ Charitable HA
TSA Reg ✓ ▢ 🔑 🔱
205 Roundhay Road, Leeds,
West Yorkshire, LS8 4HS
T 0300 500 0600
E corporate.services@
connecthousing.org.uk
W www.connecthousing.org.uk
CE Ms Jenny Brierley
Sec Ms Jenny Brierley
Ch Mr Vin McCabe
Total Staff 141
Region Yorkshire & Humberside
Owned or managed 3170
Rt 2793 GN 1772 Sup 272 OP 749
SO 195 NSO 182 Tot lets 674
GN bs 1722
Tenant Type % Family 44%
Older 28% Single 28%
Development Total 26
NBA 13 NBC 13

Contour Homes
○ Charitable HA
TSA Reg ✓
▢ ▢ 🔲 ▢ 🔑 🔱 ⏾
Quay Plaza 2, 1st Floor, Lowry Mall,
Salford Quays, Salford, Lancashire,
M50 3AH
T 0345 602 1120
E mail@contourhomes.co.uk
W www.contourhousing.co.uk
CE Mrs Judith Winterbourne
Ch Mr Tony Dobson
Total Staff 0
Regions North West +
East Midlands
Owned or managed 12404
Rt 11161 GN 9026 Sup 629 OP 1506
SO 1167 NSO 76 Tot lets 1317
GN bs 8965
Tenant Type % Family 42%
Older 19% Single 39%
Development Total 197
NBA 128 NBC 69
Parent Association
Symphony Housing Group

Contour Property Services Ltd
■ Non-Charitable HA
TSA Reg ✓ ⏾
Quay Plaza 2, 1st Floor - Lowry
Outlet Mall, Salford Quays, Salford,
Lancashire, M50 3AH
T 0345 602 1120
W www.symphonyhousing.org.uk
CE Mr Philip Gandy
Sec Mrs Audrey Davidson
Total Staff 25
Region North West
Parent Association
Symphony Housing Group

Cornerstone Housing Ltd
○ Charitable HA
TSA Reg ✓ ▢ 🔑
Cornerstone House, Western Way,
Exeter, Devon, EX1 1AL
T 01392 273462
E mail@cornerstonehousing.net
W www.cornerstonehousing.net
CE Cllr Rick Williams
Sec Cllr Rick Williams
Ch Mr Roger Norman
Total Staff 63
Region South West
Owned or managed 1215
Rt 1200 GN 1200 SO 15 Tot lets 79
GN bs 1200
Tenant Type % Family 50%
Older 35% Single 15%
Development Total 73
Rt 19 GN 19 LCHO 3 NBA 44
NBC 29

Cornwall CLT Ltd
○ Charitable HA
TSA Reg ✗ 🔑
1 Dreason Barns, Bodmin Road,
Bodmin, Cornwall, PL30 4BG
T 01208 892005
W www.crha.org.uk
Sec Mr Alan Fox
Ch Roger Jones
Total Staff 1
Region South West
Owned or managed 1
Rt 1 GN 1

Cornwall Rural HA Ltd
○ Charitable HA
TSA Reg ✓ 🔱
1 Dreason Barns, Bodmin Road,
Bodmin, Cornwall, PL30 4BG
T 01208 264530
E info@crha.org.uk
W www.crha.org.uk
CE Mr Peter Moore
Sec Mr Peter Moore
Ch Graham Facks-Martin, MBE
Total Staff 22

Region South West
Owned or managed 294
Rt 294 GN 294
Tenant Type % Older 100%

(The Lord Mayor of Portsmouth's) Coronation Homes
☆ Charitable Company
TSA Reg ✓
Administrative Office, 61 Coronation Cottages, Northern Parade, Portsmouth, Hampshire, PO2 9LZ
T 023 9265 4889
E info@coronationhomes.co.uk
W www.coronationhomes.co.uk
CE Mr David Smith
Sec Mr David Smith
Ch Mrs Audrey O'Hara
Total Staff 4
Region South East
Owned or managed 74
Rt 74 OP 74
Tenant Type % Family 27%
Single 73%

Corton House Ltd
○ Charitable IIA
TSA Reg ✓
Corton House, City Road, Norwich, Norfolk, NR1 3AP
T 01603 620119
W www.cortonhouse.co.uk
CE Mr Graham Moore
Sec Mr Roger Harrison
Ch Mr Robert Wells
Total Staff 53
Region East of England
Owned or managed 39
Rt 39 OP 39
Tenant Type % Older 100%

Cosmopolitan HA Ltd
○ Charitable HA
TSA Reg ✓ 🖎 🔑 ◊
Cosmopolitan House, 2 Marybone, Liverpool, Merseyside, L3 2BY
T 0151 227 3716
E webmaster@cosmopolitanhousing.co.uk
W www.cosmopolitanhousing.co.uk
CE Mr Geoff Redhead
Ch Ms Maria O'Brien
Total Staff 0
Regions North West + South East, North East
Owned or managed 3476
Rt 2713 GN 2199 Sup 285 OP 229
SO 204 NSO 559 Tot lets 661
GN bs 2176
Tenant Type % Family 52%
Older 26% Single 42%
Development Total 239
NBA 125 NBC 114

Parent Association
Cosmopolitan Housing Group Ltd

Cosmopolitan Housing Group Ltd
✪ Not-for-Profit Company
TSA Reg ✓ ◊
Cosmopolitan House, 2 Marybone, Liverpool, Merseyside, L3 2BY
T 0151 227 3716
E webmaster@cosmopolitanhousing.co.uk
W www.cosmopolitanhousing.co.uk
CE Mr Geoff Redhead
Ch Mr Bill Snell
Total Staff 111
Region North West
Subsidiary Association(s) Chester & District Housing Trust; Cosmopolitan HA Ltd

Cossington Housing Co-operative Ltd
★ Co-operative Society
TSA Reg ✓ 🖎
131 Loughborough Road, Leicester, Leicestershire, LE4 5LQ
T 0116 257 6800
E cossingtoncoophousing@asra.org.uk
W www.cossingtoncoop.org.uk
CE Mr Sanjay Manon
Sec Mrs J M Waite
Ch Mr Donald Greening
Total Staff 0
Region East Midlands
Owned or managed 139
Rt 139 GN 125 OP 14
Tenant Type % Family 80%
Older 10% Single 10%

Cotman HA Ltd
○ Charitable HA
TSA Reg ✓ 🔑 🖎 ◊
305 Gray's Inn Road, London, WC1X 8QR
T 01603 731699
E office@cotman-housing.org.uk
W www.cotman-housing.org.uk
CE Mrs Vivien Farrow
Sec Mrs Vivien Farrow
Ch Mrs Sarah Dixon
Total Staff 0
Regions East of England + South East
Owned or managed 2977
Rt 2881 GN 2656 Sup 84 OP 141
SO 96 Tot lets 257 GN bs 1114
Tenant Type % Family 30%
Older 20% Single 50%
Development Total 12
NBA 6 NBC 6
Parent Association
Places for People Group

Cottsway HA Ltd
○ Charitable HA
TSA Reg ✓ 🖎 🔑
Cottsway House, Heynes Place, Avenue Two, Witney, Oxfordshire, OX28 4YG
T 01993 890000
E contact@cottsway.co.uk
W www.cottsway.co.uk
CE Mr David Waters
Sec Mr David Waters
Ch Kate Wareing
Total Staff 142
Regions South East + South West, West Midlands
Owned or managed 4253
Rt 3985 GN 3985 SO 268
Tot lets 231 GN bs 3935
Tenant Type % Family 43%
Older 42% Single 14%
Development Total 379
Rt 653 GN 528 OP 125 LCHO 255
NBA 187 NBC 192

Coventry & Warwickshire YMCA
☆ Charitable Company
TSA Reg ✓ 🖎
Endeavour Court, 20 Chelmarsh, Daimler Green, Coventry, West Midlands, CV6 3LB
T 024 7659 7009
E admin@coventry-ymca.org.uk
CE Mr Andy Winter
Sec Mr Andy Winter
Ch Mr Oliver Charles
Total Staff 35
Region West Midlands
Tenant Type % Family 10%
Single 90%

Creative Support Ltd
○ Charitable HA
TSA Reg ✓ 🔑 ❋ 🖎
5th Floor, Dale House, 35 Dale Street, Manchester, Lancashire, M1 2HF
T 0161 236 0829
E enquiries@creativesupport.co.uk
W www.creativesupport.co.uk
CE Ms Anna Lunts
Sec Ms Anna Lunts
Ch Mr Martin Igoe
Total Staff 3740
Regions North West + East Midlands, West Midlands, Yorkshire & Humberside, North East
Owned or managed 939
Rt 939 Sup 939
Tenant Type % Family 2% Single 98%
Development Total 49
Rt 40 Sup 40 NBA 42 NBC 7

Crewe YMCA Foyer
☆ Charitable Company
TSA Reg ✓ 🕶
189 Gresty Road, Crewe,
Cheshire, CW2 6EL
T 01270 257673
E admin@creweymca.com
W www.creweymca.com
CE Mr Mike Fleming
Sec Mrs Sue Bishop
Ch Mr Robert Reed
Total Staff 34
Region North West
Owned or managed 59
Rt 59 Sup 59
Tenant Type % Single 100%

Crosby HA
○ Charitable HA
TSA Reg ✓
10 Church Road, Waterloo,
Liverpool, Merseyside, L22 5NB
T 0151 920 7300
E info@crosby-ha.org.uk
W www.crosby-ha.org.uk
CE Ms Mandy Elliott
Sec Ms Mandy Elliott
Ch Mr Nick Thompson
Total Staff 19
Region North West
Owned or managed 410
Rt 410 GN 349 Sup 61
Tenant Type % Family 35%
Older 28% Single 37%

Cross Keys Homes Ltd
☆ Charitable Company
TSA Reg ✓ 📺 ⬜ 🕶 🏠 🔑 ♦
Shrewsbury Avenue, Woodston,
Peterborough, Cambridgeshire,
PE2 7BZ
T 01733 385000
E info@crosskeyshomes.co.uk
W www.crosskeyshomes.co.uk
CE Mr Mick Leggett
Sec Mr Mick Leggett
Ch Dr Angus Kennedy OBE
Total Staff 257
Regions East of England +
East Midlands
Owned or managed 10929
Rt 9660 GN 8424 Sup 75 OP 1161
SO 226 NSO 1043 Tot lets 649
GN bs 8424
Tenant Type % Family 40%
Older 42% Single 18%
Development Total 101
Rt 331 GN 239 Sup 79 OP 13
LCHO 102 NBA 10 NBC 91

Crown HA Ltd
○ Charitable HA
TSA Reg ✓ 🕶
7 Cheam Court, Station Way,
Cheam, Sutton, Surrey, SM3 8SP
T 020 8642 2212
E enquiries@crownha.org.uk
W www.crownha.org.uk
CE Mr Nick Wood
Sec Mr Nick Wood
Ch Mrs Christine Beaumont
Total Staff 9
Region London
Owned or managed 339
Rt 339 GN 306 OP 33
Tenant Type % Family 73%
Older 9% Single 18%

Croydon Churches HA Ltd
○ Charitable HA
TSA Reg ✓ 🏠 🕶
6th Floor, Norfolk House, Wellesley
Road, Croydon, Surrey, CR0 1LH
T 020 8680 7532
E customers@ccha.biz
W www.ccha.biz
CE Tracy Cullen
Sec Ms Angela Simpson
Ch Mr Brian Dillon
Total Staff 41
Region London
Owned or managed 1331
Rt 1331 GN 792 Sup 234 OP 305
Tenant Type % Family 40%
Older 35% Single 25%
Development Total 1
Rt 47 GN 47 NBA 1

Croydon Unitarian HA Ltd
○ Charitable HA
TSA Reg ✓
C/O Eldon HA Ltd, 7 Banstead Road,
Purley, Surrey,
CR8 3EB
T 020 8668 9861
E info@eldonhousing.co.uk
Sec Elizabeth F Range
Ch Rev J McClelland
Total Staff 3
Region London
Owned or managed 14
Rt 14 OP 14
Tenant Type % Older 100%

Crystal Palace HA Ltd
■ Non-Charitable HA
TSA Reg ✓ 🔑 ♨
Grosvenor House, 125 High Street,
Croydon, Surrey, CR0 9XP
T 020 8726 8600
W www.amicushorizon.org.uk
Sec Mrs Alison Wignall
Ch Mr Chu Ofili
Total Staff 0

Region London
Owned or managed 307
SO 307 Tot lets 0 GN bs 0
Tenant Type % Family 80%
Single 20%
Parent Association
AmicusHorizon Ltd

Curo
✪ Not-for-Profit Company
TSA Reg ✓
The Maltings, Riverplace,
Lower Bristol Road, Bath, BA2 1EP
T 01225 366000
W www.curo-group.co.uk
CE Mr Victor da Cunha
Sec Miss Philippa Armstrong
Ch Mr Roger Thomas
Total Staff 72
Region South West

CWL Housing
○ Charitable HA
TSA Reg ✓
594 Rayleigh Road, Leigh-On-Sea,
Essex, SS9 5HU
T 01702 510523
E administrator@brentwoodcwl.co.uk
W www.cwlhousing.co.uk
CE Mrs Pamela Potter
Sec Mrs Pamela Potter
Ch Mr Anthony Doherty
Total Staff 5
Region East of England
Owned or managed 44
Rt 44 OP 44
Tenant Type % Older 100%

Cyron Housing Co-operative Ltd
★ Co-operative Society
TSA Reg ✓
6 Bridge House, Chamberlayne Road,
London, Greater London,
NW10 3NR
T 020 8964 5700
E info@cyron.eclipse.co.uk
CE Ms Tricia Johnstone
Sec Mr Jeremy Pike
Ch Mrs Angela Majothi
Total Staff 2
Region London
Owned or managed 53
Rt 53 GN 53
Tenant Type % Family 30%
Older 20% Single 50%

Dd

Dales Housing Ltd
✪ Not-for-Profit Company
TSA Reg ✓ 🔲 ⌖ ◊
Dimple Mill, Dimple Road, Matlock, Derbyshire, DE4 3JX
T 01629 593200
E DHL@Daleshousing.co.uk
W www.daleshousing.co.uk
CE Mr Gerald Taylor
Sec Mr Mike Finister-Smith
Ch Mr Barry Fletcher
Total Staff 106
Region East Midlands
Owned or managed 3251
Rt 3209 GN 1939 Sup 7 OP 1263
SO 42 Tot lets 308 GN bs 1937
Tenant Type % Family 60%
Older 34% Single 6%
Parent Association
Acclaim Housing Group Ltd

Darlington HA Ltd
○ Charitable HA
TSA Reg ✓ 🐚
72a St Pauls Place, North Road, Darlington, County Durham, DL1 2JG
T 01325 461352
W www.darlingtonha.co.uk
Sec Mr George McKellar
Ch Mr Ian Senior
Total Staff 6
Region North East
Owned or managed 258
Rt 258 GN 209 Sup 18 OP 31
Tenant Type % Family 14%
Older 38% Single 48%

Daventry & District Housing Ltd
☆ Charitable Company
TSA Reg ✓ 🐚 ◊
Nene House, Drayton Fields Industrial Estate, Daventry, Northamptonshire, NN11 8PB
T 01327 707500
E enquiries@ddh.org.uk
W www.ddh.org.uk
CE Ms Hayley Davies
Sec Mr Ian Skipp
Ch Ms Elaine Bradbury
Total Staff 72
Region East Midlands
Owned or managed 3076
Rt 3076 GN 2186 OP 890
Tenant Type % Family 40%
Older 40% Single 20%
Parent Association
Futures Housing Group

de Montfort Housing Society Ltd
○ Charitable HA
TSA Reg ✓ 🔲 ⌖ ◙ ⌖ 🐚 ◊
33 Millstone Lane', Leicester, Leicestershire, LE1 5JN
T 0116 223 3700
E admin@demontforthousing.co.uk
CE Mr David Pickering
Sec Mr Brian Desmond
Ch Mr Jeffrey Sharnock
Total Staff 0
Region East Midlands
Owned or managed 5467
Rt 3367 GN 3069 Sup 59 OP 239
SO 1577 NSO 523 Tot lets 491
GN bs 3069
Tenant Type % Family 50%
Older 30% Single 20%
Development Total 351
NBA 195 NBC 156
Parent Association
Waterloo Housing Group Ltd

Deddington HA Ltd
○ Charitable HA
TSA Reg ✗
3 Mill Close, Deddington, Banbury, Oxfordshire, OX15 0UN
T 01869 338367
Sec Mr Iain Gillespie
Ch Mr Iain Gillespie
Total Staff 0
Region South East
Tenant Type % Older 100%

Deepdale & Brancaster HS Ltd
○ Charitable HA
TSA Reg ✗
22-26 King Street, King's Lynn, PE30 1HJ
T 01485 518029
Sec Mrs Diana Bamber
Ch Mr Jim Herculson
Total Staff 0
Region East of England
Tenant Type % Family 23%
Older 54% Single 23%

Denbigh Methodist HA Ltd
○ Charitable HA
TSA Reg ✗
Lancaster Rd Methodist Church, 240 Lancaster Road, London, Greater London, W11 4AH
T 020 7229 3028
E exm@nottinghillmethodistchurch.org
CE Mr Matthew Stevenson, MCMI
Sec Mr Matthew Stevenson, MCMI
Ch Rev Kenneth Bartlett, OBE
Total Staff 0
Region London

Deptford Housing Co-operative Ltd
★ Co-operative Society
TSA Reg ✓ ⌖
16 Rochdale Way, Deptford, London, SE8 4EY
T 020 8692 4141
E deptfordhousing@tiscali.co.uk
Ch Anton Marku
Total Staff 0
Region London
Owned or managed 138
Rt 131 GN 131 SO 7 Tot lets 16
GN bs 131
Tenant Type % Family 9% Single 91%

Derwent & Solway HA
○ Charitable HA
TSA Reg ✓ 🐚 ◙ ⌖ 🐚 ◊
Your Housing Group, Thomson House, Faraday Street, Birchwood Park, Warrington, WA3 6GA
T 01925 236400
W www.yourhousinggroup.co.uk
CE Mr Brian Cronin
Sec Mrs Bronwen Rapley
Ch Mr Patrick Sharman
Total Staff 0
Region North West
Owned or managed 3209
Rt 3104 GN 3000 Sup 4 OP 100
SO 105 Tot lets 379 GN bs 2990
Tenant Type % Family 52%
Older 12% Single 36%
Development Total 92
Rt 84 OP 84 NBA 46 NBC 46
Parent Association
Your Housing Group

Derwent Living
■ Non-Charitable HA
TSA Reg ✓ 🔲 🐚 ◙ ⌖ 🐚
No.1. Centro Place, Pride Park, Derby, Derbyshire, DE24 8RF
T 01332 346477
E info@derwentliving.com
W www.derwentliving.com
CE Mr Peter McCormack
Sec Mr Peter McCormack
Ch Mrs Suzy Brain England
Total Staff 182
Regions East Midlands + South East, West Midlands, Yorkshire & Humberside
Owned or managed 9179
Rt 5974 GN 5339 Sup 86 OP 549
SO 1410 NSO 1795 Tot lets 1050
GN bs 4504
Tenant Type % Family 46%
Older 12% Single 42%
Development Total 1237
Rt 729 GN 687 OP 42 LCHO 82
NBA 1063 NBC 174

Derwentside Homes Ltd
☆ Charitable Company
TSA Reg ✓ ▢ ▦ 🅓
Greengates House, Amos Drive,
Greencroft Industrial Park, Stanley,
County Durham, DH9 7YE
T 0800 783 9295
E customer.services@
derwentsidehomes.co.uk
W www.derwentsidehomes.co.uk
CE Ms Geraldine Wilcox
Sec Keith Tallintire
Ch Phil Toal
Total Staff 225
Region North East
Owned or managed 6814
Rt 6645 **GN** 6412 **Sup** 8 **OP** 225
NSO 169
Tenant Type % Family 35%
Older 55% **Single** 10%
Development Total 8
Rt 102 **GN** 36 **OP** 66 **NBA** 4 **NBC** 4

Devon & Cornwall Housing Ltd
○ Charitable HA
TSA Reg ✓ ▢ ▣ 🄯 ▦ 🅓 🔑 ♦ ◊
The Mount, Paris Street, Exeter,
Devon, EX1 2JZ
T 01392 252566
E info@dchgroup.com
W www.dchgroup.com
CE Mr Paul Crawford
Sec Mrs Jill Farrar
Ch Ms Angela Dupont
Total Staff 717
Region South West
Owned or managed 18396
Rt 16330 **GN** 13612 **Sup** 562
OP 2156 **SO** 1886 **NSO** 180
Tot lets 2309 **GN bs** 13574
Tenant Type % Family 24%
Older 22% **Single** 54%
Development Total 560
Rt 1656 **GN** 1656 **LCHO** 684
NBA 1 **NBC** 559
Subsidiary Association(s)
Devon & Cornwall Leasehold
Solutions Ltd; Penwith HA Ltd; Tor
Homes

Devon & Cornwall Leasehold Solutions Ltd
■ Non-Charitable HA
TSA Reg ✗ ◊
The Mount, Paris Street, Exeter,
Devon, EX1 2JZ
T 01392 252566
E info@dchgroup.com
W www.dcha.co.uk
Sec Helen Anthony
Ch Mr John Saunders
Total Staff 0
Region South West

Tenant Type % Older 100%
Parent Association Devon &
Cornwall Housing Ltd

Dimensions UK Ltd
○ Charitable HA
TSA Reg ✓ 🅓 ▰
9-10 Commerce Park, Brunel Road,
Theale, RG7 4AB
T 0845 160 2292
E payments@dimensions-uk.org
W www.dimensions-uk.org
CE Mr Steve Scown
Sec Ms Jackie Fletcher
Ch Mr Geoff Rose
Total Staff 0
Regions South East + London,
South West, East Midlands,
West Midlands, East of England,
Yorkshire & Humberside,
North East, North West
Owned or managed 474
Rt 474 **Sup** 474
Development Total 2
NBA 2

Dolphin Square Charitable Foundation
❏ Charitable Trust
TSA Reg ✗ 🅓
1st Floor, 11 Belgrave Road, London,
Greater London, SW1V 1RB
T 020 7931 6460
E info@dolphinsquarefoundation.com
W www.dolphinsquarefoundation.
com
CE Mr Brian Ham
Sec Mr Brian Ham
Ch Mr Ian J Henderson
Total Staff 10
Region London
Owned or managed 16
Rt 16 **GN** 2 **Sup** 14
Tenant Type % Family 37%
Single 63%
Development Total 12
Rt 429 **GN** 405 **Sup** 24 **NBA** 2
NBC 10

Dorcas Housing + Community Support Association Ltd
○ Charitable HA
TSA Reg ✗ ▰ ▥
393A High Street, West Bromwich,
West Midlands, B70 9QW
T 0121 553 7737
E info@dorcashousing.co.uk
W www.dorcashousing.co.uk
CE Mr Gary Clarke
Sec Mr Hilary Mitchell
Ch Dalbir Masih
Total Staff 0
Region West Midlands

Dorking Charities
❏ Charitable Trust
TSA Reg ✓
Homefield, Fortyfoot Road,
Leatherhead, Surrey, KT22 8RP
T 01372 370073
E luchar@btinternet.com
CE Mr David Matanle
Sec Mr David Matanle
Ch Mr Michael Knott
Total Staff 1
Region South East
Owned or managed 20
Rt 20 **OP** 20
Tenant Type % Older 100%

Dorking Residential Care Homes Ltd
○ Charitable HA
TSA Reg ✗ ▰
Nower Care, Nower House,
Coldharbour Lane, Dorking,
Surrey, RH4 3BL
T 01306 740076
CE Mr C Horwood
Sec Mr David Montgomery
Ch Mr P Evans
Total Staff 0
Region South East
Tenant Type % Older 100%

Drum HA Ltd
○ Charitable HA
TSA Reg ✓ ▢ ▦ 🅓 🔑 ◊
Drum Court, The Spain, Petersfield,
Hampshire, GU32 3NG
T 0300 123 1567
E radiandirect@radian.co.uk
W www.radian.co.uk
CE Mr Lindsay Todd
Sec Mr Terry Walker
Ch Mrs Margaret Scott
Total Staff 24
Region South East
Owned or managed 5412
Rt 4978 **GN** 4271 **Sup** 88 **OP** 619
SO 432 **NSO** 2 **Tot lets** 497
GN bs 4026
Tenant Type % Family 67%
Older 14% **Single** 19%
Development Total 138
NBA 78 **NBC** 60
Parent Association
Radian Group Ltd

Ducane HA Ltd
○ Charitable HA
TSA Reg ✓
11 Du Cane House,
101 Du Cane Road, London,
Greater London, W12 0UR
T 020 8735 4990
E enquiries@ducaneha.org.uk
W www.ducaneha.org.uk

CE Mr Mike Wilkins
Sec Mr Kanti Gohil
Ch Mr Peter Redman
Total Staff 10
Region London
Owned or managed 192
Rt 47 GN 47 NSO 145
Tenant Type % Family 52%
Single 48%

Durham Aged Mineworkers' Homes Association
❏ Charitable Trust
TSA Reg ✓ ◙ 🔑 🖤
P O Box 31, The Grove, 168 Front Street, Chester Le Street, Durham, County Durham, DH3 3YH
T 0191 388 1111
E info@damha.org.uk
W www.damha.org.uk
Ch Mr Gordon Parkin
Total Staff 69
Region North East
Owned or managed 1736
Rt 1717 GN 1644 OP 73 SO 19
Tot lets 173 GN bs 1591
Tenant Type % Family 1%
Older 99%
Development Total 100
NBA 50 NBC 50

Dyers Company HA Ltd
◼ Non-Charitable HA
TSA Reg ✓
Finance Division, The University of Leeds, Leeds, West Yorkshire, LS2 9JT
T 0113 343 6060
E p.m.macdonald@leeds.ac.uk
Sec Mr Philip M MacDonald
Ch David Blackburn
Total Staff 0
Region Yorkshire & Humberside
Owned or managed 18
Rt 18 OP 18
Tenant Type % Older 100%

Ee

East Boro Housing Trust
◯ Charitable HA
TSA Reg ✓ ◙ 🖤
31 West Street, Wimborne, Dorset, BH21 1JS
T 01202 883503
E info@ebht.org.uk
W www.ebht.org.uk
CE Mr Kevin Hodder
Sec Mr Kevin Hodder
Ch Mr David Cawdery

Total Staff 126
Region South West
Owned or managed 340
Rt 339 GN 9 Sup 168 OP 162
NSO 1
Tenant Type % Family 2%
Older 48% Single 50%
Development Total 32
Rt 4 Sup 4 NBA 17 NBC 15

East Homes Ltd
◯ Charitable HA
TSA Reg ✓ ◼ ▯ ◙ 🔑 ◊
29-35 West Ham Lane, Stratford, London, Greater London, E15 4PH
T 020 8522 2000
E info@east-thames.co.uk
W www.east-homes.co.uk
CE Ms Pamela Gardner
Sec Mr Henry Potter
Ch Ms Johanna Holmes OBE
Total Staff 152
Regions London + South East, East of England
Owned or managed 13182
Rt 9700 GN 8067 Sup 1316 OP 317
SO 3043 NSO 439 Tot lets 338
GN bs 9499
Tenant Type % Family 75%
Older 15% Single 10%
Development Total 160
Rt 916 GN 769 Sup 69 OP 78
LCHO 493 NBC 160
Parent Association
East Thames Group Ltd

East Living Ltd
◯ Charitable HA
TSA Reg ✗ ♦ 🖤 ◊
29-35 West Ham Lane, Stratford, London, Greater London, E15 4PH
T 020 8522 2000
E info@east-living.co.uk
W www.east-living.co.uk
CE Mr Christian Woodhead
Sec Mr Henry Potter
Ch Ms Debbie Sorkin
Total Staff 369
Region London
Owned or managed 1834
Rt 1834 Sup 1517 OP 317
Tenant Type % Older 17%
Single 83%
Parent Association
East Thames Group Ltd

East Midlands HA Ltd
◯ Charitable HA
TSA Reg ✓ ▯ ◙ 🔑 🖤 ◊
Jubilee House, Whitwick Business Park, Stenson Road, Coalville, Leicestershire, LE67 4NA
T 01530 276000
E enquiries@emha.org

W www.emha.org
CE Mrs Christine Ashton
Sec Mrs Joanne Tilley
Ch Mrs Maggie Bodell-Stagg
Total Staff 136
Regions East Midlands + West Midlands
Owned or managed 8237
Rt 6426 GN 5333 Sup 421 OP 672
SO 1597 NSO 214 Tot lets 615
GN bs 5290
Tenant Type % Family 55%
Older 20% Single 25%
Development Total 349
NBA 240 NBC 109
Parent Association
East Midlands Housing Group

East Midlands Housing Group
◼ Non-Charitable HA
TSA Reg ✓ ◊
Memorial House, Whitwick Business Park, Stenson Road, Coalville, Leicestershire, LE67 4JP
T 01530 276000
E enquiries@emha.org
W www.emhgroup.org
CE Mr Chan Kataria
Sec Mrs Joanne Tilley
Ch Mr Michael Pearson
Total Staff 89
Region East Midlands
Subsidiary Association(s) East Midlands HA Ltd; Foundation HA Ltd; Midlands Rural Housing & Village Development Assn Ltd; Three Oaks Homes Ltd; Three Valleys Housing Ltd

East Potential
☆ Charitable Company
TSA Reg ✗ ◊
29-35 West Ham Lane, Stratford, London, Greater London, E15 4SF
T 020 8522 2000
E allusers@east-potential.org.uk
W www.east-potential.org.uk
CE Ms Pamela Gardner
Sec Mr Henry Potter
Ch Mr Malcolm Basing
Total Staff 34
Region London
Parent Association
East Thames Group Ltd

East Thames Group Ltd
☆ Charitable Company
TSA Reg ✓ ◊
29-35 West Ham Lane, Stratford, London, Greater London, E15 4PH
T 020 8522 2000
E info@east-thames.co.uk
W www.east-thames.co.uk

CE Ms June Barnes
Sec Mr Henry Potter
Ch Tina Tietjen
Total Staff 174
Region London
Subsidiary Association(s)
East Homes Ltd; East Living Ltd;
East Potential

East Yorkshire HA Ltd
○ Charitable HA
TSA Reg ✗ 🐦
Grove Centre, 78 Bessingby Road,
Bridlington, North Humberside,
YO16 4SH
T 01262 400789
E eyha.ltd@btinternet.com
Sec Marion Myerscough
Ch Joan Harding
Total Staff 0
Region Yorkshire & Humberside
Owned or managed 13
Rt 13 GN 13
Tenant Type % Family 1% Single 99%

EastendHomes Ltd
☆ Charitable Company
TSA Reg ✓ 🏠 🔑 🖍
1st Floor, Tayside House,
31 Pepper Street, London,
Greater London, E14 9RP
T 020 7517 4700
E enquiries@eastendhomes.net
W www.eastendhomes.net
CE Mr Paul Bloss
Sec Mr Peter Gibbs
Ch Mr Martin Young
Total Staff 96
Region London
Owned or managed 3623
Rt 2204 GN 2204 SO 1419
Tot lets 202 GN bs 2204
Development Total 156
NBA 78 NBC 78

Eastlands Homes Partnership Ltd
☆ Charitable Company
TSA Reg ✓ 🖥 🖍 🏠 🔑 ♦
Eastlands House, Victoria Street,
Openshaw, Manchester, Lancashire,
M11 2NX
T 0161 274 2390
E eastline@eastlandshomes.co.uk
W www.eastlandshomes.co.uk
CE Ms Sheila Doran
Sec Ms Sheila Doran
Ch Mrs Linda Wagner
Total Staff 312
Region North West
Owned or managed 8101
Rt 7965 GN 7677 Sup 36 OP 252
SO 136 Tot lets 555 GN bs 7677
Tenant Type % Family 72%

Older 3% Single 25%
Development Total 6
NBA 4 NBC 2

Ecco (Charitable) HA Ltd
○ Charitable HA
TSA Reg ✓
19 Thornwell Court, Bishops Road,
London, Greater London, W7 2PR
T 020 8617 0206
CE Mr Jack Hunt
Sec Mr Jack Hunt
Ch Mrs M Lane
Total Staff 0
Region London
Tenant Type % Family 30%
Older 18% Single 52%

Eddystone HA Ltd
○ Charitable HA
TSA Reg ✗
8 Quinnetts, Churt Road, Farnham,
Surrey, GU10 2NU
T 01428 712301
Sec Ms Alison Beattie
Ch Mr Peter Dacombe
Total Staff 0
Region South East
Owned or managed 20
Rt 20 OP 20
Tenant Type % Older 100%

Eden HA Ltd
■ Non-Charitable HA
TSA Reg ✓ 🖥 🏠 🔑 🐦
Blain House, Bridge Lane, Penrith,
Cumbria, CA11 8QU
T 01768 861400
E enquiry@edenha.org.uk
W www.edenha.org.uk
CE Mr John Clasper
Sec Mr Sean Relph
Ch Mr Henry Barker
Total Staff 70
Region North West
Owned or managed 1919
Rt 1840 GN 1690 Sup 106 OP 44
SO 70 NSO 9 Tot lets 181
GN bs 1452
Tenant Type % Family 35%
Older 50% Single 15%
Development Total 104
NBA 68 NBC 36

Edward Henry House Co-operative Ltd
★ Co-operative Society
TSA Reg ✓
23 Edward Henry House, Cornwall
Road, London, Greater London,
SE1 8YE
W www.cds.coop
Sec Ms Eileen Bowley
Ch Mr Gerald Hart

Total Staff 0
Region London
Owned or managed 69
Rt 69 GN 69
Tenant Type % Family 100%

Ekarro Housing Co-operative Ltd
★ Co-operative Society
TSA Reg ✓ 🔑
Ekarro House, 49a Guildford Road,
London, Greater London, SW8 2DT
T 020 7498 2496
E ekarro@globalnet.co.uk
W www.ekarro.org.uk
CE Tim Cummins
Sec Chris Goetze
Total Staff 3
Region London
Owned or managed 59
Rt 56 GN 56 SO 3 Tot lets 0
GN bs 0
Tenant Type % Family 40%
Single 60%

Ekaya HA Ltd
○ Charitable HA
TSA Reg ✓ 🐦 🏚
First Floor, Lincoln House,
1-3 Brixton Road, London,
Greater London, SW9 6DE
T 020 7091 1800
E info@ekaya.co.uk
W www.ekaya.co.uk
CE Ms Jackie Adusei
Sec Ms Jackie Adusei
Ch Minal Goswami
Total Staff 41
Region London
Owned or managed 426
Rt 426 GN 357 Sup 69
Tenant Type % Family 70%
Single 30%

Eldon HA Ltd
○ Charitable HA
TSA Reg ✓ 🐦
7 Banstead Road, Purley, Surrey,
CR8 3EB
T 020 8668 9861
E info@eldonhousing.co.uk
W www.eldonhousing.co.uk
CE Elizabeth F Range
Sec Miss Anne Dickson
Ch Mr David Scott
Total Staff 126
Regions London + South East
Owned or managed 194
Rt 194 GN 13 Sup 181
Tenant Type % Family 3%
Older 93% Single 4%

Eldonian Community Based HA Ltd
■ Non-Charitable HA
TSA Reg ✓ 🔒 🔑
The Tony McGann Centre, Eldonian Village, Burlington Street, Liverpool, Merseyside, L3 6LG
T 0151 207 3406
E mdragonette@eldonians.org.uk
W www.eldonians.org.uk
CE Mr George Evans
Sec Mr John Livingstone
Ch Mr Anthony McGann OBE
Total Staff 15
Region North West
Owned or managed 458
Rt 446 **GN** 382 **Sup** 36 **OP** 28 **SO** 12
Tot lets 36 **GN bs** 282
Tenant Type % Family 65%
Older 32% **Single** 3%
Development Total 36
NBC 36

Elim HA
○ Charitable HA
TSA Reg ✓ 🔒 🔑 👓
Unit 3 & 4 Pinkers Court, Briarlands Office Park, Gloucester Road, Rudgeway, Bristol, Avon, BS35 3QH
T 01454 411172
E info@elimhousing.co.uk
W www.elimhousing.co.uk
CE Mr Alistair Allender
Sec Mr Alistair Allender
Ch Mr Graham Russell
Total Staff 52
Regions South West + East Midlands, West Midlands
Owned or managed 727
Rt 706 **GN** 473 **Sup** 222 **OP** 11
SO 21 **Tot lets** 387 **GN bs** 393
Tenant Type % Family 50%
Single 50%
Development Total 81
Rt 21 **GN** 21 **LCHO** 2 **NBC** 81

Elmbridge Housing Trust Ltd
○ Charitable HA
TSA Reg ✓ 📇 🔒 🔑 👓 💧
Case House, 85-89 High Street, Walton On Thames, Surrey, KT12 1DZ
T 01932 235700
E info@elmbridgehousing.org.uk
W www.paragonchg.co.uk
CE Ms Jane Bolton
Sec Mark Rothwell
Ch Mr Paul Richmond
Total Staff 43
Region South East
Owned or managed 4875
Rt 4279 **GN** 3519 **OP** 760 **SO** 535
NSO 61 **Tot lets** 314 **GN bs** 3415
Tenant Type % Family 58%

Older 31% **Single** 11%
Development Total 38
NBA 19 **NBC** 19
Parent Association Paragon Community Housing Group

Empowering People Inspiring Communities Ltd
○ Charitable HA
TSA Reg ✓ 🔒
131-141 Ubberley Road, Bentilee, Stoke-On-Trent, Staffordshire, ST2 0EF
T 01782 252575
E mailbox@epichousing.co.uk
W www.epichousing.co.uk
CE Mr Len Gibbs
Sec Mr Len Gibbs
Ch Jakki Seaman
Total Staff 31
Region West Midlands
Owned or managed 952
Rt 952 **GN** 952
Tenant Type % Family 60%
Older 2% **Single** 38%
Development Total 12
NBA 12

Empty Homes Agency
○ Charitable HA
TSA Reg ✗
75 Westminster Bridge Road, London, Greater London, SE1 7HS
T 020 7921 4450
E info@emptyhomes.com
W www.emptyhomes.com
CE Mr David Ireland
Ch Mr Nick Aldridge
Total Staff 4
Region London

Enable HA Ltd
○ Charitable HA
TSA Reg ✗ 👓
Ellen House, Heath Road, Holmewood, Chesterfield, Derbyshire, S42 5RB
T 01246 599999
E info@enable-group.org.uk
W www.enable-group.org.uk
CE Ms Jackie King-Owen
Sec Miss Fay Keely
Total Staff 0
Region East Midlands
Tenant Type % Family 3%
Older 10% **Single** 87%

Endeavour HA
○ Charitable HA
TSA Reg ✓ 🔒 🔑 👓 💧
Endeavour House, St Mark's Court, Thornaby, Stockton-On-Tees, Cleveland, TS17 6QN

T 01642 796200
E info@endeavourha.co.uk
W www.endeavourha.co.uk
CE Mrs Angela Lockwood
Sec Mr Peter Lenehan
Ch Mr Jed Lester
Total Staff 60
Regions North East + Yorkshire & Humberside
Owned or managed 2257
Rt 2224 **GN** 1731 **Sup** 403 **OP** 90
SO 33 **Tot lets** 338 **GN bs** 1651
Tenant Type % Family 42%
Older 13% **Single** 45%
Development Total 82
Rt 80 **GN** 80 **NBA** 52 **NBC** 30
Parent Association North Star Housing Group Ltd

English Rural HA Ltd
○ Charitable HA
TSA Reg ✓ 🔒 🔑
First Floor, Hall House, 9 Graphite Square, Vauxhall Walk, London, Greater London, SE11 5EE
T 020 7820 7930
E info@englishrural.org.uk
W www.englishrural.org.uk
CE Mr Adrian Maunders
Sec Ms Karen Eagles
Ch Mr Adrian Parker
Total Staff 21
Regions South East + South West, East Midlands, East of England, North West
Owned or managed 990
Rt 628 **GN** 628 **SO** 362 **Tot lets** 31
GN bs 628
Tenant Type % Family 60%
Older 20% **Single** 20%
Development Total 20
Rt 58 **GN** 58 **LCHO** 2 **NBC** 20

Enham
☆ Charitable Company
TSA Reg ✓ 👓
Enham Place, Enham Alamein, Andover, Hampshire, SP11 6JS
T 01264 345800
E info@enham.org.uk
W www.enham.org.uk
CE Mrs Peta Wilkinson
Sec Richard Ashdown
Ch Roderick A Chamberlain
Total Staff 0
Region South East
Owned or managed 264
Rt 244 **GN** 186 **Sup** 58 **NSO** 20
Tenant Type % Family 41%
Older 25% **Single** 34%

Epsom & Ewell HA Ltd
○ Charitable HA
TSA Reg ✓ 🕶
The Epsom & Ewell HA Ltd,
Couthurst, 13 St. Martins Avenue,
Epsom, KT18 5HZ
T 01372 748558
E eeha@onetel.com
CE Mr Richard Long
Sec Mr Trevor Smith
Ch Mr Richard Harris
Total Staff 7
Region South East
Owned or managed 94
Rt 94 **GN** 3 **OP** 91
Tenant Type % Family 3%
Older 97%

Equity HA Ltd
■ Non-Charitable HA
TSA Reg ✓ 🔑 ♦
Armitt House, Monmouth Road,
Cheadle Hulme, Cheadle,
Cheshire, SK8 7EF
T 0161 486 9911
E info@equityhousing.co.uk
W www.equityhousing.co.uk
CE Mr David Fisher
Sec Mr David Fisher
Ch Mr Brian Ashfield
Total Staff 2
Regions North West +
East Midlands, West Midlands,
Yorkshire & Humberside
Owned or managed 1040
Rt 67 **GN** 45 **OP** 22 **SO** 966 **NSO** 7
Tot lets 4 **GN bs** 45
Tenant Type % Family 27%
Older 10% **Single** 63%
Parent Association Equity Housing
Group Ltd

Equity Housing Group Ltd
○ Charitable HA
TSA Reg ✓ 🏠 🔑 🕶 ♦
Armitt House, Monmouth Road,
Cheadle Hulme, Cheadle, Cheshire,
SK8 7EF
T 0161 486 9911
E info@equityhousing.co.uk
W www.equityhousing.co.uk
CE Mr David Fisher
Sec Mr David Fisher
Ch Mr Brian Ashfield
Total Staff 136
Regions North West +
East Midlands, West Midlands,
Yorkshire & Humberside
Owned or managed 3417
Rt 2858 **GN** 2070 **Sup** 117 **OP** 671
SO 463 **NSO** 96 **Tot lets** 406
GN bs 2027
Tenant Type % Family 24%
Older 22% **Single** 54%
Development Total 10
NBA 10
Subsidiary Association(s)
Equity HA Ltd; Provincial HA Ltd

Erimus Housing
☆ Charitable Company
TSA Reg ✓ 🖥 🖳 🚗 🏠 🔑 ♦ ♦
2 Hudson Quay, Windward Way,
Middlesborough, Cleveland,
TS2 1QG
T 01642 773600
E info@erimushousing.co.uk
W www.erimushousing.co.uk
CE Mrs Christine Smith
Sec Mrs Heather Ashton
Ch Mr Michael Carr
Total Staff 351
Region North East
Owned or managed 11247
Rt 11003 **GN** 9600 **OP** 1403 **SO** 241
NSO 3 **Tot lets** 991 **GN bs** 8605
Tenant Type % Family 43%
Older 33% **Single** 24%
Development Total 7
NBA 7
Parent Association
Fabrick Housing Group Ltd

Essex General HA Ltd
■ Non-Charitable HA
TSA Reg ✗
16 Buxton Avenue, Leigh-On-Sea,
SS9 3UB
T 01702 551003
CE Mr Mark Hidveghy
Sec Mr Mark Hidveghy
Ch Mr Ian Douglas
Total Staff 0
Region East of England
Tenant Type % Family 30%
Older 44% **Single** 26%

Estonian House Ltd
○ Charitable HA
TSA Reg ✗
18 Chepstow Villas, London,
Greater London, W11 2RB
T 020 7229 6700
Ch Mrs K Legrain
Total Staff 0
Region London
Tenant Type % Family 50%
Older 50%

Estuary HA Ltd
○ Charitable HA
TSA Reg ✓ 🏠 🔑 ♦ 🕶
8th & 9th Floors, Maitland House,
Warrior Square, Southend On Sea,
Essex, SS1 2JY
T 01702 462246
E info@estuary.co.uk
W www.estuary.co.uk
CE Mr Paul Durkin
Sec Ms Amanda Ashley-Smith MSc,
BSc, CIHM
Ch Mr Ken Johnson
Total Staff 311
Regions East of England + London
Owned or managed 3637
Rt 3013 **GN** 2851 **Sup** 84 **OP** 78
SO 309 **NSO** 315 **Tot lets** 284
GN bs 2820
Tenant Type % Family 79%
Older 4% **Single** 17%
Development Total 139
Rt 142 **GN** 142 **LCHO** 49 **NBA** 80
NBC 59

Evesham & Pershore HA Ltd
○ Charitable HA
TSA Reg ✓ 🖳 🏠 🔑 🕶 ♦
70 High Street, Evesham,
Worcestershire, WR11 4YD
T 01386 420800
E info@rooftopgroup.org
W www.rooftopgroup.org
CE Mr Ian Hughes
Sec Mrs Sheila Morris
Ch Mr John Stanley
Total Staff 0
Regions West Midlands +
South West
Owned or managed 5602
Rt 5308 **GN** 4573 **Sup** 309 **OP** 426
SO 294 **Tot lets** 710 **GN bs** 4534
Tenant Type % Family 50%
Older 15% **Single** 35%
Development Total 334
Rt 346 **GN** 304 **Sup** 42 **LCHO** 69
NBA 189 **NBC** 145
Parent Association
Rooftop Housing Group Ltd

Ff

Fabrick Housing Group Ltd
✪ Not-for-Profit Company
TSA Reg ✓ ♦
2 Hudson Quay, Windward Way,
Middlesbrough, Cleveland, TS2 1QG
T 01642 773600
E jeanette.bolton@fabrickgroup.co.uk
W www.fabrickgroup.co.uk
CE Ms Alison Thain, OBE
Sec Mrs Heather Ashton
Ch Mr Bob Brady
Total Staff 154
Region North East
Subsidiary Association(s) Erimus
Housing; Norcare Ltd; Tees Valley
Housing Ltd

Fairfield Moravian HA Ltd
○ Charitable HA
TSA Reg ✓
Arcon HA, 12 Lloyd Street,
Manchester, M2 5ND
T 0161 214 4120
E enquiries@arcon.org.uk
W www.arcon.org.uk
Ch Rev J Ingham
Total Staff 0
Region North West
Owned or managed 16
Rt 16 GN 16
Tenant Type % Family 100%

Fairhazel Co-operative Ltd
★ Co-operative Society
TSA Reg ✓
Basement Office, 23 Compayne
Gardens, London, Greater London,
NW6 3DE
T 020 7624 1098
E fairhazel@co-op.org
W www.fairhazel.org.uk
Sec Ms Anita Plattner
Ch Mrs Rose Foot
Total Staff 4
Region London
Owned or managed 152
Rt 152 GN 152
Tenant Type % Family 50%
Older 33% Single 17%

Fairoak HA
○ Charitable HA
TSA Reg ✓ 🔑
48 Stramongate, Kendal,
Cumbria, LA9 4BD
T 01539 720082
E enquiries@fairoakhousing.co.uk
W www.fairoakhousing.co.uk
CE Mrs Alexandra Wolfenden
Sec Mr Clive Wigley
Ch Mr John Handley
Total Staff 4
Regions North West + North East
Owned or managed 57
Rt 47 Sup 47 SO 10 Tot lets 0
GN bs 0
Tenant Type % Family 2% Older 16%
Single 82%

Falcon Rural Housing Ltd
○ Charitable HA
TSA Reg ✓ 🔑
Falcon House, 3a South Street,
Wellington, Somerset, TA21 8NR
T 01823 667343
W www.falconruralhousing.com
CE Mrs Samantha Southam
Sec Mrs Samantha Southam
Ch Mr Adrian Little
Total Staff 6
Region South West

Owned or managed 272
Rt 260 GN 260 SO 12 Tot lets 0
GN bs 0
Tenant Type % Family 75%
Older 15% Single 10%

Family First Ltd
○ Charitable HA
TSA Reg ✓ 🦅 ◊
174 Derby Road, Nottingham,
Nottinghamshire, NG7 1NF
T 0115 924 8001
E patrick.taylor@asra.org.uk
W www.familyfirst.org.uk
CE Mr Patrick Taylor
Ch Mr Mark Robinson
Total Staff 36
Region East Midlands
Owned or managed 391
Rt 386 GN 377 Sup 9 NSO 5
Tenant Type % Family 65%
Older 1% Single 34%
Parent Association
Asra Housing Group Ltd

Family HA (Birkenhead & Wirral) Ltd
○ Charitable HA
TSA Reg ✓
Marcus House, Marcus Street,
Birkenhead, Merseyside, CH41 3NY
T 0151 647 5000
E admin@familyha.org
W www.familyha.org
CE Mr Keith Molony
Sec Mr Keith Molony
Ch Mr Richard Hamilton
Total Staff 6
Region North West
Owned or managed 368
Rt 368 GN 309 OP 59
Tenant Type % Family 52%
Older 21% Single 27%

Family HA (Birmingham) Ltd
○ Charitable HA
TSA Reg ✓ ◊ 🔑 🦅
Bordesley House, 44-46 Coventry
Road, Small Heath, Birmingham,
West Midlands, B10 0RX
T 0121 766 1100
E post@family-housing.co.uk
W www.family-housing.co.uk
CE Mr Tim Sewell
Sec Mr Rob Ellis
Ch Angela Parks
Total Staff 95
Region West Midlands
Owned or managed 2348
Rt 2154 GN 1843 Sup 166 OP 145
SO 194 Tot lets 328 GN bs 1801
Tenant Type % Family 49%
Older 13% Single 38%
Development Total 225
NBA 201 NBC 24

Family HA (York) Ltd
○ Charitable HA
TSA Reg ✓
54 Blossom Street, York,
North Yorkshire, YO24 1AP
T 01904 628167
E fhayork@btconnect.com
CE Mr Martin Morgan
Sec Mr Martin Morgan
Ch Christine Little
Total Staff 4
Region Yorkshire & Humberside
Owned or managed 47
Rt 47 GN 47
Tenant Type % Family 90%
Single 10%

Family Mosaic Home Ownership Ltd
■ Non-Charitable HA
TSA Reg ✗ ◊
Albion House, 20 Queen Elizabeth
Street, London, Greater London,
SE1 2RJ
T 020 7089 1000
E enquiries@familymosaic.co.uk
W www.familymosaic.co.uk
CE Mr Brendan Sarsfield
Sec Mr John Gibbons
Total Staff 0
Region London
Tenant Type % Family 50%
Single 50%
Parent Association
Family Mosaic Housing

Family Mosaic Housing
○ Charitable HA
TSA Reg ✓
🟦 🖥 🔊 🏠 🔑 ♦ 🦅 ◊
Albion House, 20 Queen Elizabeth
Street, London, Greater London,
SE1 2RJ
T 020 7089 1000
E info@fha.org.uk
W www.familymosaic.co.uk
CE Mr Brendan Sarsfield
Sec Mr John Gibbons
Ch Mr Ian Peacock
Total Staff 1460
Regions London + East of England
Owned or managed 21401
Rt 18495 GN 15650 Sup 2403
OP 442 SO 2796 NSO 110 Tot lets
2233 GN bs 15351
Development Total 1253
NBA 792 NBC 461
Subsidiary Association(s) Charlton
Triangle Homes Ltd; Family Mosaic
Home Ownership Ltd; Old Oak HA
Ltd

Farnborough (War Memorial) HS Ltd
○ Charitable HA
TSA Reg ✗ 🦇
83 Canterbury Road, Farnborough, Hampshire, GU14 6QN
T 01252 542169
E knellwood@aol.com
W www.knellwood.co.uk
Sec Mr John S Campbell
Ch Mr R A Owen
Total Staff 0
Region South East
Tenant Type % Older 100%

Fellowship Houses Trust
❑ Charitable Trust
TSA Reg ✓ ♨
Rosemary House, Portsmouth Road, Esher, Surrey, KT10 9AA
T 01372 461440
E housing@rsmha.org.uk
W www.rsmha.org.uk
Ch Mr Alistair Court-Smith
Total Staff 7
Region South East
Owned or managed 57
Rt 57 GN 57
Tenant Type % Older 97% Single 3%
Parent Association Rosemary Simmons Memorial HA Ltd

Fern Housing
☆ Charitable Company
TSA Reg ✓ 🦇
82 Closton Street, Bristol, Avon, BS1 5BB
T 0300 111 1881
E info@fern-gateways.co.uk
W www.fernhousing.org
CE Mitchell St.Aimie
Total Staff 3
Region South West
Owned or managed 42
Rt 42 Sup 42
Tenant Type % Family 20% Single 80%

Festival Housing
■ Non-Charitable HA
TSA Reg ✓ 🖵 🅐 ⚲ ♦ 🦇
Festival House, Grovewood Road, Malvern Link, Worcestershire, WR14 1GD
T 01684 579579
E info@festivalhousing.org
W www.festivalhousing.org
CE Mr Guy Weston
Sec Mrs Janet Cole
Ch Mr Mike Moyles
Total Staff 429
Region West Midlands
Owned or managed 9307
Rt 8290 GN 6963 Sup 84 OP 1243

SO 794 NSO 223 Tot lets 1151
GN bs 6960
Tenant Type % Family 41%
Older 37% Single 22%
Development Total 167
Rt 349 GN 304 OP 45 LCHO 90
NBA 64 NBC 103

Field Lane Foundation
☆ Charitable Company
TSA Reg ✓ 🦇
Victoria Charity Centre, Second Floor, 11 Belgrave Road, London, SW1V 1RB
T 020 7748 0303
E info@fieldlane.org.uk
W www.fieldlane.org.uk
CE Mr Jeremy Lamb
Sec Mr Jeremy Lamb
Ch Mr John Furber
Total Staff 206
Regions London + South East, East of England
Owned or managed 56
Rt 56 Sup 40 OP 16
Tenant Type % Family 35%
Older 30% Single 35%

Firbank Housing Society Ltd
○ Charitable HA
TSA Reg ✓
7 High Grove, Welwyn Garden City, Hertfordshire, AL8 7DW
T 01707 326105
E pauline@treacher.net
CE Mrs Pauline Treacher
Sec Mrs Pauline Treacher
Ch Mr Stephen Wentworth
Total Staff 0
Region East of England
Owned or managed 16
Rt 16 OP 16
Tenant Type % Older 100%

First Choice Homes Oldham
○ Charitable HA
TSA Reg ✓ ■ 🖵 🅐 ⚲ ♦
1 Medtia Square, Phoenix Street, Oldham, Lancashire, OL1 1AN
T 0161 770 4552
E firstname.lastname@fcho.co.uk
W www.fcho.co.uk
CE Ms Cath Green
Sec Vinny Roche
Ch Mr Harry Burns
Total Staff 502
Region North West
Owned or managed 12724
Rt 11718 GN 11468 OP 250 SO 914
NSO 92 Tot lets 1328 GN bs 11468
Development Total 28
Rt 48 GN 48 NBA 16 NBC 12

First Wessex
○ Charitable HA
TSA Reg ✓
■ 🖵 🚌 🅐 ⚲ ♦ 🦇
Peninsular House, Wharf Road, Portsmouth, Hampshire, PO2 8HB
T 0845 055 3377
E info@firstwessex.org
W www.firstwessex.org
CE Mr Peter Walters
Sec Mrs Jane Long
Ch Mr Ben Stoneham
Total Staff 859
Region South East
Owned or managed 17116
Rt 14849 GN 12849 Sup 657
OP 1343 SO 1564 NSO 703
Tot lets 1179 GN bs 12394
Tenant Type % Family 21%
Older 10% Single 69%
Development Total 921
NBA 495 NBC 426

Five Villages Home Association Ltd
○ Charitable HA
TSA Reg ✓ 🦇
Five Villages House, Oast House Field, Icklesham, East Sussex, TN36 4BQ
T 01424 814608
CE Ms Jo Munyard
Sec Ms Jo Munyard
Ch Mrs C Merricks
Total Staff 10
Region South East
Owned or managed 50
Rt 50 OP 50
Tenant Type % Older 100%

Flagship Housing Group Ltd
○ Charitable HA
TSA Reg ✓ ■ 🖵 🚌 🅐 ⚲ ♦
🦇 🏠
Keswick Hall, Keswick, Norfolk, NR4 6TJ
T 01603 255400
E info@flagship-housing.co.uk
W www.flagship-housing.co.uk
CE Mr David McQuade
Sec Rod Ayden
Ch Mr Peter Lakey
Total Staff 541
Region East of England
Owned or managed 22349
Rt 19898 GN 18102 Sup 264
OP 1532 SO 1676 NSO 775
Tot lets 1614 GN bs 18009
Tenant Type % Family 58%
Older 22% Single 20%
Development Total 725
NBA 384 NBC 341

Forest HA Ltd
■ Non-Charitable HA
TSA Reg ✓ 🕶
20 Edgar House, 1 Blake Hall Road, Wanstead, London, Greater London, E11 2QH
T 020 8530 2113
E office@foresthousing.co.uk
Sec Mr Matthew Hutfield
Ch Mr Keith Salter
Total Staff 5
Region London
Owned or managed 124
Rt 120 GN 120 NSO 4
Tenant Type % Family 44%
Older 34% Single 22%

Forest YMCA
☆ Charitable Company
TSA Reg ✓ 🕶
642 Forest Road, Walthamstow, Greater London, E17 3EF
T 020 8509 4600
E cso@forestymca.org.uk
W www.forestymca.org.uk
CE Mr Timothy Pain
Ch Mark Hayes
Total Staff 59
Region London
Owned or managed 305
Rt 305 Sup 305
Tenant Type % Single 100%

Forum HA Ltd
◯ Charitable HA
TSA Reg ✓ 🕶
2nd Floor, 84 Market Street, Birkenhead, Merseyside, CH41 6HB
T 0151 649 9718
E info@forumhousing.co.uk
W www.forumhousing.co.uk
CE Mrs Chris Allen
Sec Mrs Chris Allen
Ch Mr Christopher Drake
Total Staff 125
Region North West
Owned or managed 324
Rt 324 GN 19 Sup 305
Tenant Type % Single 100%

Forward HA Ltd
✪ Not-for-Profit Company
TSA Reg ✗
20 Avoncroft Road, Bromsgrove, Worcestershire, B60 4NG
Sec Mr Paul Cole
Ch Mr Mike Merriman
Total Staff 0
Region West Midlands
Tenant Type % Family 30%
Older 25% Single 45%

Forward Housing SW
TSA Reg ✗ ◊
The West House, Alpha Court, Swingbridge Road, Grantham, Lincolnshire, NG31 7XT
Total Staff 0
Region East Midlands
Parent Association Thera Trust

Foundation
☆ Charitable Company
TSA Reg ✓ 🔎 ♦ 🕶
Tennant Hall, Blenheim Grove, Leeds, West Yorkshire, LS2 9ET
T 0113 303 0150
E central@foundationuk.org
W www.foundationuk.org
CE Mr Steve Woodford
Sec Mr Steve Woodford
Ch Mr Nigel Lockett
Total Staff 325
Region Yorkshire & Humberside
Owned or managed 836
Rt 827 Sup 827 SO 9 Tot lets 0
GN bs 0
Tenant Type % Family 20%
Single 80%

Foundation HA Ltd
◯ Charitable HA
TSA Reg ✓ 🔎 🕶 ◊ 🏠
8 Faraday Court, 40 Conduit Street, Leicester, Leicestershire, LE2 0JN
T 0116 254 4230
E enquiries@foundationhousing.co.uk
W www.foundationhousing.org
CE Ms Nikki Chawda
Sec Mrs Joanne Tilley
Ch Kathleen Alick
Total Staff 38
Region East Midlands
Owned or managed 810
Rt 801 GN 769 Sup 22 OP 10 SO 9
Tot lets 100 GN bs 407
Tenant Type % Family 60%
Older 10% Single 30%
Parent Association
East Midlands Housing Group

Foundation66
☆ Charitable Company
TSA Reg ✓ 🕶
2nd Floor, 7 Holyrood Street, London, Greater London, SE1 2EL
T 020 7234 9940
E info@foundation66.org.uk
W www.foundation66.org.uk
CE Ms Sally Scriminger
Sec Ms Sally Scriminger
Ch Mr Ian Jones
Total Staff 147
Region London
Owned or managed 135
Rt 135 Sup 135
Tenant Type % Single 100%

Four Housing Group
■ Non-Charitable HA
TSA Reg ✓ 🕶 ◊
Three Rivers House, Abbeywoods Business Park, Pity Me, Durham, County Durham, DH1 5TG
T 0191 384 1122
E contact@4hg.co.uk
W www.4hg.co.uk
CE Mr Paul Tanney
Sec Mr Mike Axe
Ch Mr Peter Gavin
Total Staff 36
Region North East
Subsidiary Association(s) Berwick Borough Housing; Three Rivers HA Ltd

Framework HA
☆ Charitable Company
TSA Reg ✓ 📷 ♦ 🕶
Val Roberts House, 25 Gregory Boulevard, Nottingham, NG7 6NX
T 0115 841 7711
E info@frameworkha.org
W www.frameworkha.org
CE Mr Andrew Redfern
Sec Mr John Millard
Ch Mr Bob McKittnick
Total Staff 582
Region East Midlands
Owned or managed 813
Rt 813 Sup 813
Tenant Type % Family 3% Older 4%
Single 93%
Development Total 25
NBA 1 NBC 24

Franklands Village HA Ltd
■ Non-Charitable HA
TSA Reg ✓
Estate Office, Franklands Village, Haywards Heath, West Sussex, RH16 3RS
T 01444 413771
E patricia.shadforth@fvha.org.uk
W www.fvha.org.uk
CE Ms Patricia Shadforth
Sec Ms Patricia Shadforth
Ch David Langridge
Total Staff 10
Region South East
Owned or managed 277
Rt 277 GN 277
Tenant Type % Family 50%
Older 33% Single 17%

Freebridge Community Housing
○ Charitable HA
TSA Reg ✓ ▭ ▣ ▣ ✎
Juniper House, Austin Street,
King's Lynn, Norfolk, PE30 1DZ
T 01553 667700
E enquiries@freebridge.org.uk
W www.freebridge.org.uk
CE Mr Tony Hall
Sec Mr Angus MacQueen
Ch Mr Ray Johnson
Total Staff 201
Region East of England
Owned or managed 6787
Rt 6772 GN 6156 Sup 616 SO 15
Tot lets 606 GN bs 6156
Tenant Type % Family 40%
Older 50% Single 10%
Development Total 34
NBA 21 NBC 13

Friendship Care and Housing
○ Charitable HA
TSA Reg ✓ ▣ ✎ ♦ ✎ ◊
50 Newhall Hill, Birmingham,
West Midlands, B1 3JN
T 0300 123 1745
W www.fch.org.uk
CE Mr Jonathan Driffill
Sec Mr Jonathan Driffill
Ch Ernie Hendricks
Total Staff 469
Regions West Midlands + East Midlands
Owned or managed 4594
Rt 4219 GN 4130 Sup 89 SO 352
NSO 23 Tot lets 329 GN bs 4071
Tenant Type % Family 53%
Older 20% Single 27%
Development Total 6
NBA 4 NBC 2
Parent Association
Longhurst Group Ltd

Frontis
■ Non-Charitable HA
TSA Reg ✓ ✎ ✎ ◊
Your Housing Group, Thomson House, Faraday Street, Birchwood Park, Warrington, WA3 6GA
T 01925 236400
W www.yourhousinggroup.co.uk
CE Mr Brian Cronin
Sec Mrs Bronwen Rapley
Ch Mrs Kathy Cowell
Total Staff 0
Regions North West + South East, Yorkshire & Humberside
Owned or managed 2606
Rt 1451 GN 1303 Sup 29 OP 119
SO 349 NSO 806 Tot lets 173
GN bs 1068

Tenant Type % Family 33%
Older 22% Single 45%
Parent Association
Your Housing Group

Fry Housing Trust
☆ Charitable Company
TSA Reg ✗ ✎ ◊
43 Rowley Village, Rowley Regis, West Midlands, B65 9AS
T 0121 559 6406
E admin@fryha.org.uk
W www.fryha.org.uk
CE Mr Robert Donath
Sec Miss Frances Broomhall
Ch Mr Andrew Wall
Total Staff 75
Region West Midlands
Owned or managed 197
Rt 197 Sup 197
Tenant Type % Single 100%
Parent Association Accord HA Ltd

Futures Homescape Ltd
☆ Charitable Company
TSA Reg ✓ ▭ ✎ ▣ ✎ ◊
PO Box 6458, Asher Lane Business Park, Ripley, Derbyshire, DE5 3BF
T 01773 573100
E enquiries@futureshomescape.co.uk
W www.futureshomescape.co.uk
CE Mr Paul Parkinson
Sec Mr Ian Skipp
Ch Ms Leann Hearne
Total Staff 149
Region East Midlands
Owned or managed 5726
Rt 5696 GN 3367 Sup 34 OP 2295
SO 30 Tot lets 605 GN bs 3282
Tenant Type % Family 39% Older 53% Single 8%
Development Total 166
Rt 79 GN 79 LCHO 7 NBA 87
NBC 79
Parent Association
Futures Housing Group

Futures Housing Group
✪ Not-for-Profit Company
TSA Reg ✓ ◊
Asher House, Asher Lane Business Park, Ripley, Derbyshire, DE5 3SW
T 0845 094 8300
E enquiries@futureshg.co.uk
W www.futureshg.co.uk
CE Ms Lindsey Williams
Sec Mr Ian Skipp
Ch Dr Mark Flynn
Total Staff 57
Region East Midlands
Subsidiary Association(s) Daventry & District Housing Ltd; Futures Homescape Ltd

G3 Inspiring Individuals
○ Charitable HA
TSA Reg ✗ ✎ ◊
70 High Street, Evesham, Worcestershire, WR11 4YD
T 01386 420800
E info@rooftopgroup.org
W www.rooftopgroup.org
CE Mr Ian Hughes
Sec Mrs Sheila Morris
Ch Mr John Stanley
Total Staff 0
Region West Midlands
Owned or managed 101
Rt 101 Sup 101
Tenant Type % Single 100%
Parent Association
Rooftop Housing Group Ltd

Gallions HA Ltd
○ Charitable HA
TSA Reg ✓ ▭ ▣ ✎
Heather Court, 6 Maidstone Road, Sidcup, Kent, DA14 5HH
T 020 8308 4080
E info@gallionsha.co.uk
W www.gallionsha.co.uk
CE Mr Tony Cotter
Sec Mrs Jane Rothery
Ch Mr John Sands
Total Staff 192
Region London
Owned or managed 5636
Rt 5388 GN 5330 OP 58 SO 241
NSO 7 Tot lets 569 GN bs 5270
Development Total 185
Rt 311 GN 311 LCHO 211 NBA 185

Gatesbield Quaker HA Ltd
○ Charitable HA
TSA Reg ✗ ✎
Gatesbield House, New Road, Windermere, Cumbria, LA23 2LA
T 0153 94 45578
E info@gatesbield.org.uk
W www.gatesbield.org.uk
CE Andree Cook
Sec Mr Martin Rouen
Ch Mrs Hilary Southall
Total Staff 0
Region North West
Tenant Type % Older 100%

Gateway HA Ltd
○ Charitable HA
TSA Reg ✓ 🏠 🔑 🤝
409 - 413 Mile End Road, London,
Greater London, E3 4PB
T 020 8709 4300
E enquiries@gatewayhousing.org.uk
W www.gatewayhousing.org.uk
CE Ms Sheron Carter
Sec Ms Sheron Carter
Ch Mr Jonathan Rosser
Total Staff 121
Region London
Owned or managed 2694
Rt 2355 **GN** 1813 **Sup** 107 **OP** 435
SO 339 **Tot lets** 166 **GN bs** 1813
Tenant Type % Family 52%
Older 28% **Single** 20%
Development Total 160
NBA 80 **NBC** 80

Gedling Homes
☆ Charitable Company
TSA Reg ✓ 🚐 🤝 🔥
Gedling House, Wood Lane, Gedling,
Nottingham, Nottinghamshire,
NG4 4AD
T 0115 905 1515
E enquiries@gedlinghomes.co.uk
W www.gedlinghomes.co.uk
CE Ms Lynn Clayton
Sec Mr Danny McLoughlin
Ch Mr Adam Jacobs
Total Staff 88
Region East Midlands
Owned or managed 3350
Rt 3350 **GN** 2447 **OP** 903
Tenant Type % Family 45%
Older 44% **Single** 11%
Parent Association
New Charter Housing Trust Ltd

Genesis HA
○ Charitable HA
TSA Reg ✓
🔲 🔳 🚐 🏠 🔑 👤 🤝 🔥
Capital House, 25 Chapel Street,
London, Greater London, NW1 5DT
T 020 7563 0120
E info@ghg.org.uk
W www.ghg.org.uk
CE Mr Neil Hadden
Sec Mrs Jackie Bligh
Ch Mr Charles Gurassa
Total Staff 1400
Region London
Owned or managed 30992
Rt 25592 **GN** 22370 **Sup** 1869
OP 1353 **SO** 5377 **NSO** 23
Tot lets 2336 **GN bs** 14744
Tenant Type % Family 56%
Older 5% **Single** 39%
Development Total 1886
NBA 1144 **NBC** 742

Subsidiary Association(s)
Springboard Two HA Ltd

Gentoo Group Ltd
✪ Not-for-Profit Company
TSA Reg ✓ 🚐 🏠 👤 🤝 🔥
Emperor House, 2 Emperor Way,
Doxford International Business Park,
Sunderland, Tyne And Wear,
SR3 3XR
T 0191 525 5000
E info@gentoogroup.com
W www.gentoogroup.com
CE Mr Peter Walls
Sec Joanne Williams
Ch Mr John R Walker
Total Staff 739
Region North East
Owned or managed 241
Rt 204 **GN** 189 **Sup** 15 **NSO** 37
Tenant Type % Family 59%
Older 10% **Single** 31%
Development Total 40
NBA 24 **NBC** 16
Subsidiary Association(s)
Gentoo Sunderland Ltd

Gentoo Sunderland Ltd
✪ Not-for-Profit Company
TSA Reg ✓
🔲 🔳 🚐 🚐 🏠 🔑 👤 🤝 🔥
Emperor House, 2 Emperor Way,
Doxford International Business Park,
Sunderland, Tyne And Wear,
SR3 3XR
T 0191 525 5000
E info@gentoogroup.com
W www.gentoogroup.com
CE Mr Peter Walls
Sec Joanne Williams
Ch Mr Frederick McQueen
Total Staff 880
Region North East
Owned or managed 30009
Rt 29420 **GN** 29003 **Sup** 176 **OP** 241
SO 540 **NSO** 49 **Tot lets** 2379
GN bs 28734
Tenant Type % Family 46%
Older 37% **Single** 17%
Development Total 628
NBA 314 **NBC** 314
Parent Association
Gentoo Group Ltd

German Lutheran HA Ltd
○ Charitable HA
TSA Reg ✓ 🤝 🏠
Luckington House, 8 Marlborough
Lane, Bath, Avon, BA1 2NQ
T 01225 312092
Sec Dr Bruno Bubna-Kasteliz
Ch Dr Bruno Bubna-Kasteliz
Total Staff 0
Region South West
Tenant Type % Older 100%

GFS Platform
☆ Charitable Company
TSA Reg ✗ 🤝
Unit 2, Angel Gate, 326 City Road,
London, Greater London, EC1V 2PT
T 020 7837 9669
E joy.lauezzari@gfsplatform.org.uk
W www.gfsplatform.org.uk
CE Ms Joy Lauezzari
Sec Ms Joy Lauezzari
Total Staff 0
Region East of England
Tenant Type % Older 40%
Single 60%

Gipton Supported Independent Living Ltd
○ Charitable HA
TSA Reg ✗ 🤝
27-33 Brander Street, Leeds,
West Yorkshire, LS 9 6QH
T 0113 248 1301
E info@gipsil.org.uk
W www.gipsil.org.uk
CE Ms Julia Preston
Sec Ms Julia Preston
Ch Rev Roger Harington
Total Staff 24
Region Yorkshire & Humberside
Owned or managed 40
Rt 40 **OP** 40
Tenant Type % Family 50%
Single 50%

Glebe HA Ltd
○ Charitable HA
TSA Reg ✓ 🔑 🤝
Glebe House, Bencurtis Park,
Corkscrew Hill, West Wickham,
Kent, BR4 9QD
T 020 8777 1122
E g.h.a@talk21.com
W www.glebehousingassociation.
co.uk
CE Mr Graham Lilly
Sec Mrs Jayne Hollands
Ch Mr Rodney Beale
Total Staff 104
Region London
Owned or managed 204
Rt 137 **OP** 137 **SO** 65 **NSO** 2
Tot lets 0 **GN bs** 0
Tenant Type % Older 100%

Gloucestershire Housing Society Ltd
○ Charitable HA
TSA Reg ✗
2 St Michael's Court, Brunswick
Road, Gloucester, Gloucestershire,
GL1 1JB
T 01452 529255
E surnameinitial@glosha.co.uk
W www.glosha.co.uk

Ch Sid Pritchard
Total Staff 0
Region South West

Gloucestershire Rural HA Ltd
○ Charitable HA
TSA Reg ✓ ⚲
c/o Severn Vale Housing Society Ltd, Shannon Way, Tewkesbury, Gloucestershire, GL20 8ND
T 01452 529255
Sec Alan Keddie
Ch Mr Neil Pascoe
Total Staff 0
Region South West
Owned or managed 115
Rt 109 GN 109 SO 6 Tot lets 3
GN bs 0
Tenant Type % Family 68%
Older 14% Single 18%

God's Port Housing Society Ltd
○ Charitable HA
TSA Reg ✓
White House, Northcott Close, Bury Hall Lane, Alverstoke, Gosport, Hampshire, PO12 2PP
T 023 9251 0016
E northcott01@btconnect.com
W www.northcotthousing.org.uk
CE Shaun Cully
Sec Shaun Cully
Ch Dennis Wright
Total Staff 74
Region South East
Owned or managed 33
Rt 33 GN 33
Tenant Type % Older 100%

Golden Gates Housing Trust Ltd
❑ Charitable Trust
TSA Reg ✓ ⬛ ◎ ⚲ ♦ 🤝
Bank House, 88 Sankey Street, Warrington, Cheshire, WA1 1RH
T 0800 252627
E info@gght.org.uk
W www.gght.org.uk
CE Mr Peter Mercer
Sec Mr Peter Mercer
Ch Mr Roy Smith
Total Staff 314
Region North West
Owned or managed 8950
Rt 8645 GN 7218 Sup 143 OP 1284
SO 305 Tot lets 1045 GN bs 7215
Development Total 32
NBA 32

Golding Homes
☆ Charitable Company
TSA Reg ✓ ⬛ 🚚 ◎ ⚲
Whatman House, St Leonard's Road, Allington, Maidstone, Kent, ME16 0LS
T 01622 212600
E enquiries@goldinghomes.org.uk
W www.goldinghomes.org.uk
CE Mr Peter Stringer
Sec Mr Michael Chandler
Ch Mr Roger Ford
Total Staff 120
Region South East
Owned or managed 6713
Rt 6230 GN 5190 Sup 6 OP 1034
SO 440 NSO 43 Tot lets 486
GN bs 5190
Tenant Type % Family 34%
Older 52% Single 14%
Development Total 39
Rt 370 GN 370 LCHO 16 NBC 39

Grand Union Housing Group Ltd
■ Non-Charitable HA
TSA Reg ✓ ◊
Martell House, University Way, Cranfield, Bedford, Bedfordshire, MK43 0TR
T 01525 844590
E enquiry@grandunionhousing.co.uk
W www.grandunionhousing.co.uk
CE Mr Alan Humphreys
Sec Mr Alan Humphreys
Ch James Sparrow
Total Staff 53
Region East of England
Subsidiary Association(s)
Aragon HA Ltd;
MacIntyre HA Ltd; South Northants Homes

Grange Management (Southern) Ltd
■ Non-Charitable HA
TSA Reg ✗ 🤝 ◊
6 Godalming Business Centre, Woolsack Way, Godalming, Surrey, GU7 1XW
T 0845 330 3444
E info@grangemanagement.com
W www.grangemanagement.com
Ch Mr Peter Reynolds
Total Staff 0
Region South East
Tenant Type % Family 8%
Older 85% Single 7%
Parent Association Affinity Sutton

Granta Housing Society Ltd
○ Charitable HA
TSA Reg ✓ ⚲ ♦ 🤝 ◊
1 Horizon Park, Barton Road, Comberton, Cambridge, Cambridgeshire, CB23 7AF
T 020 3535 2345
E info@grantahousing.org.uk
W www.grantahousing.org.uk
CE Jon Maxwell
Ch Mr Steve Lamb
Total Staff 438
Region East of England
Owned or managed 2879
Rt 2511 GN 2001 Sup 406 OP 104
SO 344 NSO 24 Tot lets 0
GN bs 1602
Tenant Type % Family 56%
Older 5% Single 39%
Parent Association Metropolitan

Gravesend Churches HA Ltd
○ Charitable HA
TSA Reg ✓
Ingram House, 17 London Road, Northfleet, Kent, DA11 9JQ
T 01474 369830
E general@gcha.org.uk
W www.gcha.org.uk
CE Ms Veronica Mabey
Sec Ms Veronica Mabey
Ch Mr Tom Maddison
Total Staff 13
Region South East
Owned or managed 516
Rt 516 GN 488 Sup 28
Tenant Type % Family 64%
Older 20% Single 16%

Grayshott & District HA Ltd
○ Charitable HA
TSA Reg ✗
Burley & Geach, International House, Headley Road, Grayshott, Surrey, GU26 6NG
T 01428 714329
W www.grayshott.com/gdpage176.html
CE Dr Clive Purkiss
Sec Miss Joanna Clay
Ch Dr Clive Purkiss
Total Staff 1
Region South East
Owned or managed 30
Rt 30 GN 27 OP 3
Tenant Type % Family 50%
Older 33% Single 17%

Great Places HA

○ Charitable HA
TSA Reg ✓ ■ □ 500 ◎ ⚷ ♦ ♦
729 Princess Road, West Didsbury,
Manchester, Lancashire, M20 2LT
T 0161 447 5000
E info@greatplaces.org.uk
W www.greatplaces.org.uk
CE Mr Stephen Porter
Sec Mr Philip Elvy
Ch Mr Lars Hansen
Total Staff 420
Regions North West +
East Midlands, West Midlands,
Yorkshire & Humberside
Owned or managed 14962
Rt 13438 **GN** 11826 **Sup** 1247
OP 365 **SO** 969 **NSO** 555 **Tot lets**
2227 **GN bs** 10991
Tenant Type % Family 61% **Older** 9%
Single 30%
Development Total 1765
NBA 1164 **NBC** 601
Parent Association
Great Places Housing Group

Great Places Housing Group

■ Non-Charitable HA
TSA Reg ✓ ♦
Southern Gate, 729 Princess
Road, West Didsbury, Manchester,
Lancashire, M20 2LT
T 0161 447 5000
W www.greatplaces.org.uk
CE Mr Stephen Porter
Sec Mr Philip Elvy
Ch Mr Edward Stott
Total Staff 195
Region North West
Subsidiary Association(s) Great
Places HA; Plumlife Homes Ltd;
Terra Nova Developments Ltd

Green Vale Homes Ltd

○ Charitable HA
TSA Reg ✓ TVHG ⚷ ♦
Green Vale Court, New Hall Hey
Road, Rawtenstall, Rossendale,
Lancashire, BB4 6HR
T 01706 836333
E enquiries@greenvalehomes.co.uk
W www.greenvalehomes.co.uk
CE Mr Tom Miskell
Sec Mr George Paterson
Ch Mr Stephen Griffiths
Total Staff 137
Region North West
Owned or managed 3667
Rt 3665 **GN** 3017 **OP** 648 **SO** 2
Tot lets 410 **GN bs** 3017
Parent Association Together
Housing Group Ltd

Greenoak HA Ltd

○ Charitable HA
TSA Reg ✓ 👓
155 Goldsworth Road, Woking,
Surrey, GU21 6LS
T 01483 747900
E info@greenoakha.org
W www.greenoakha.org
CE Mrs Diana Kingdon
Sec Mrs Diana Kingdon
Ch Mr Bryn Edwards
Total Staff 14
Region South East
Owned or managed 391
Rt 377 **GN** 141 **Sup** 102 **OP** 134
NSO 14
Tenant Type % Family 26%
Older 62% **Single** 12%

GreenSquare Group Ltd

○ Charitable HA
TSA Reg ✓ 👓 ♦
Barbury House, Stonehill Green,
Westlea, Swindon, Wiltshire,
SN5 7HB
T 01793 602820
E enquiries@greensquaregroup.com
W www.greensquaregroup.com
CE Mr David Ashmore
Sec Mrs Catherine Dixon
Ch Ms Hilary Gardner
Total Staff 120
Region South West
Subsidiary Association(s)
Oxford Citizens HA Ltd; Westlea
HA

Greenwich Housing Society

○ Charitable HA
TSA Reg ✓
12 Glenluce Road, Blackheath,
London, Greater London, SE3 7SB
Sec Miss Alison Leggatt
Ch Ms Dorothy Martin
Total Staff 0
Region London
Owned or managed 17
Rt 17 **OP** 17
Tenant Type % Older 1%

Grenfell HA

○ Charitable HA
TSA Reg ✗ 👓
16-20 Kingston Road, London,
Greater London, SW19 1JZ
T 020 8545 2588
E info@grenfell-housing.co.uk
W www.grenfell-housing.co.uk
CE Ms Lola Barrett
Sec Ms Lola Barrett
Ch Mr Russell Humphreys
Total Staff 24
Region London
Owned or managed 240

Rt 240 **GN** 120 **Sup** 120
Tenant Type % Single 100%

Gretton Court Ltd

○ Charitable HA
TSA Reg ✗
Gretton Court , High Street, Girton,
Cambridge, Cambridgeshire,
CB3 0QN
T 01223 277527
E gretton.court@btinternet.com
CE Mr Peter Stevenson
Ch Mr Richard Morris
Total Staff 13
Region East of England
Tenant Type % Older 100%

Grimsby, Cleethorpes & Humber Region YMCA

☆ Charitable Company
TSA Reg ✓ 👓
St. Aidans Church, Grimsby Road,
Cleethorpes, N E Lincolnshire,
DN35 7RQ
T 01472 693388
E info@gcymca.org.uk
W www.gcymca.com
CE Mr Malcolm Smith
Sec Mr Malcolm Smith
Ch Rev David Swannack
Total Staff 73
Region Yorkshire & Humberside
Owned or managed 98
Rt 98 **Sup** 98
Tenant Type % Single 100%

Guildford Sunset Homes

○ Charitable HA
TSA Reg ✓ 👓
The Estate Office, Thrupp House,
Merrow Street, Guildford, Surrey,
GU4 7DE
T 01483 563204
E customerservices@rlha.org.uk
W www.rlha.org.uk
CE Mrs Lorraine Collis
Sec Mrs Lorraine Collis
Ch Mr Richard King
Total Staff 2
Region South East
Owned or managed 88
Rt 87 **OP** 87 **NSO** 1
Tenant Type % Older 100%

Guinness Care & Support Ltd

○ Charitable HA
TSA Reg ✓ ♦ 👓 ♦
Hillfields House, Matford Court,
Sigford Road, Exeter, Devon,
EX2 8NL
T 01392 686686
E info.careandsupport@guinness.
org.uk

W www.guinnesspartnership.com
CE Mr Paul Watson
Sec Mr David Watson
Ch Mr Peter Cotton
Total Staff 914
Region South West
Owned or managed 812
Rt 812 GN 88 Sup 151 OP 573
Tenant Type % Family 4%
Older 75% Single 21%
Parent Association
The Guinness Partnership

Guinness HA Ltd

■ Non-Charitable HA
TSA Reg ✓ 🔑 ♨
Building C, Estune Business Park,
Wild Country Lane, Long Ashton,
Bristol, BS41 9AF
T 01275 395300
E westregion@guinness.org.uk
W www.guinnesstrust.org.uk
Sec Mr David Watson
Total Staff 0
Region South West
Owned or managed 601
Rt 576 GN 232 Sup 6 OP 338
SO 25 Tot lets 61 GN bs 0
Tenant Type % Family 20%
Older 60% Single 20%
Parent Association
The Guinness Partnership

Habinteg HA

○ Charitable HA
TSA Reg ✓ 🔑
Holyer House, 20-21 Red Lion
Court, London, Greater London,
EC4A 3EB
T 020 7822 8700
E info@habinteg.org.uk
W www.habinteg.org.uk
CE Mr Paul Gamble
Sec Mr Barry Chalkley
Ch Mrs Judith Newton
Total Staff 119
Regions London + South East,
South West, East Midlands,
West Midlands, East of England,
Yorkshire & Humberside,
North East, North West
Owned or managed 3200
Rt 3174 GN 2376 Sup 693 OP 105
SO 3 NSO 23 Tot lets 234
GN bs 2376
Tenant Type % Family 82%
Older 10% Single 8%

Haig Homes

❏ Charitable Trust
TSA Reg ✗ 🏠
Alban Dobson House, Green Lane,
Morden, Surrey, SM4 5NS
T 020 8685 5777
E haig@haighomes.org.uk
W www.haighomes.org.uk
CE Mr Peter Besgrove
Sec Mrs Lynda Stevens
Ch Mr David Stewart
Total Staff 37
Regions London + South East,
South West, East Midlands,
West Midlands, East of England,
Yorkshire & Humberside,
North East, North West
Owned or managed 1163
Rt 1123 GN 1123 NSO 40
Tenant Type % Family 43%
Older 48% Single 9%
Development Total 1
NBA 1

Haig Housing Trust

☆ Charitable Company
TSA Reg ✗
Alban Dobson House, Green Lane,
Morden, Surrey, SM4 5NS
T 020 8685 5777
W www.haighousingtrust.org.uk
Sec Mr Peter Besgrove
Ch Mr D Stewart
Total Staff 0
Regions London + South West,
East of England
Tenant Type % Family 38%
Older 53% Single 9%

Halton Housing Trust

☆ Charitable Company
TSA Reg ✓ 🏠 🏢 🏠
Daresbury Point, Green Wood
Drive, Manor Park, Runcorn,
Cheshire, WA7 1UG
T 0800 195 3172
E info@haltonhousing.org
W www.haltonhousing.org
CE Mr Nick Atkin
Sec Neil McGrath
Ch Mrs Ingrid Fife
Total Staff 0
Region North West
Owned or managed 6284
Rt 6174 GN 6077 Sup 97 NSO 110
Tenant Type % Family 62%
Older 15% Single 23%
Development Total 73
Rt 49 GN 20 OP 29 NBA 39
NBC 34

Halton YMCA Ltd

☆ Charitable Company
TSA Reg ✗
Halton Lodge Avenue, Halton Lodge,
Runcorn, Cheshire, WA7 5YQ
T 01928 591680
E john.mackie@haltonymca.org.uk
CE Mr John Mackie
Sec Mr John Mackie
Ch Mr Dave Griffiths
Total Staff 45
Region North West
Owned or managed 66
Rt 66 Sup 66
Tenant Type % Single 100%

Hanover HA

○ Charitable HA
TSA Reg ✓ ■ 🏠 🏠 🔑 ♦
Hanover House, 1 Bridge Close,
Staines, Middlesex, TW18 4TB
T 01784 446000
E reception@hanover.org.uk
W www.hanover.org.uk
CE Mr Bruce Moore
Sec Mr Michael Fuller
Ch Lord Best, OBE
Total Staff 911
Regions South East + London,
South West, East Midlands,
West Midlands, East of England,
Yorkshire & Humberside,
North East, North West
Owned or managed 18171
Rt 13423 GN 158 OP 13265 SO 336
NSO 4412 Tot lets 1805 GN bs 143
Tenant Type % Family 1%
Older 98% Single 1%
Development Total 102
NBA 51 NBC 51

Harborne Parish Lands Charity

❏ Charitable Trust
TSA Reg ✓ 🤝
109 Court Oak Road, Harborne,
Birmingham, West Midlands,
B17 9AA
T 0121 426 1600
E theclerk@hplc.org.uk
W www.hplc.org.uk
CE Lynda Bending
Sec Lynda Bending
Ch Mr Michael Lloyd
Total Staff 14
Region West Midlands
Owned or managed 97
Rt 97 OP 97
Tenant Type % Family 5%
Older 85% Single 10%

Harewood Housing Society Ltd
■ Non-Charitable HA
TSA Reg ✓ ◊
Royd House, Low Mills, Guiseley, Leeds, West Yorkshire, LS20 9LU
T 0113 202 1260
W www.togetherhousing.co.uk
CE Mr Steve Close
Sec Mr Steve Close
Ch Mr Alan K Stoneley
Total Staff 8
Region Yorkshire & Humberside
Owned or managed 315
NSO 315
Parent Association
Together Housing Group Ltd

Haringey Association for Independent Living
○ Charitable HA
TSA Reg ✗ 🐦
Tottenham Town Hall, Town Hall Approach Road, Tottenham, London, N15 4RY
T 020 8275 6550
E admin@hailltd.org
W www.hailltd.org
CE Mr Kevin Dowd
Sec Mr Kevin Dowd
Ch Mr J Foyle
Total Staff 0
Region London
Tenant Type % Family 5% Single 95%

Harlington Rectory HA Ltd
○ Charitable HA
TSA Reg ✓
1 Woodforde Court, St. Peters Way, Harlington, Middlesex, UB3 5AB
T 020 8759 0326
E hrha@btconnect.com
Sec Miss Pamela K Lucas
Ch Miss J L Halfacree
Total Staff 0
Region London
Tenant Type % Family 53%
Older 45% Single 2%

Harrison Housing
☆ Charitable Company
TSA Reg ✓ 🐦
42-46 St James's Gardens, London, Greater London, W11 4RQ
T 020 7603 4332
E info@harrisonhousing.org.uk
W www.harrisonhousing.org.uk
CE Mr Raymond Bernstein
Sec Mr Raymond Bernstein
Ch Mr Colin Senior
Total Staff 13
Region London
Owned or managed 148
Rt 148 GN 26 OP 122
Tenant Type % Older 100%

Harrogate Families HA Ltd
○ Charitable HA
TSA Reg ✓ 🔑
10 The High Street, Starbeck, Harrogate, North Yorkshire, HG2 7HY
T 01423 884018
E customerservice@harrogate.gov.uk
W www.harrogate.gov.uk
CE Mr Malcolm Bowker
Sec Mr D Burns
Ch Mr C R R Smailes
Total Staff 8
Region Yorkshire & Humberside
Owned or managed 209
Rt 207 GN 156 OP 51 SO 2
Tot lets 0 GN bs 1
Tenant Type % Family 70%
Older 23% Single 7%

Harrogate Flower Fund Homes Ltd
○ Charitable HA
TSA Reg ✓
c/o Harrogate Families HA Ltd, 10 High Street, Harrogate, North Yorkshire, HG2 7HY
T 01423 531235
E brian.rushton@tiscali.co.uk
Sec Mr Brian Rushton
Ch Mr Brian Rushton
Total Staff 0
Region Yorkshire & Humberside
Owned or managed 27
Rt 27 GN 27
Tenant Type % Older 100%

Harrogate Neighbours HA Ltd
○ Charitable HA
TSA Reg ✓ 🐦
6 Pannal Ash Road, Harrogate, North Yorkshire, HG2 9AB
T 01423 709409
E info@harrogateneighbours.co.uk
W www.harrogateneighbours.co.uk
CE Mrs Susan Ullmann
Ch Dr John Givans
Total Staff 19
Region Yorkshire & Humberside
Owned or managed 98
Rt 49 OP 49 NSO 49
Tenant Type % Older 100%

Harrow Churches HA
○ Charitable HA
TSA Reg ✓ 📷 🐦
Penn House, 16 Peterborough Road, Harrow, Middlesex, HA1 2BQ
T 020 8426 4995
W www.hcha.org.uk
CE Mr Christopher Holley
Sec Mr Christopher Holley

Ch John Newby
Total Staff 34
Region London
Owned or managed 348
Rt 348 GN 44 Sup 65 OP 239
Tenant Type % Family 10%
Older 71% Single 19%
Development Total 40
NBA 40

Hassocks Housing Society Ltd
○ Charitable HA
TSA Reg ✓ 🐦
24 Chancellors Park, Hassocks, West Sussex, BN6 8EZ
T 01273 845988
E daisue@btinternet.com
CE Mrs Susan Miles
Sec Mrs Susan Miles
Total Staff 1
Region South East
Owned or managed 14
Rt 14 OP 14
Tenant Type % Older 100%

Hastoe HA Ltd
■ Non-Charitable HA
TSA Reg ✓ 🔲500 📷 🔑 ◊
Marina House, 17 Marina Place, Hampton Wick, Kingston Upon Thames, Surrey, KT1 4BH
T 0300 123 2250
E info@hastoe.com
W www.hastoe.com
CE Mrs Sue Chalkley
Sec Melanie O'Doherty
Ch Ms Margaret Clark OBE
Total Staff 99
Regions London + South East, South West, East Midlands, East of England
Owned or managed 4315
Rt 3278 GN 3209 OP 69 SO 1025
NSO 12 Tot lets 456 GN bs 3020
Tenant Type % Family 73%
Older 4% Single 23%
Development Total 591
NBA 333 NBC 258
Subsidiary Association(s) Hastoe Wyvern HA Ltd

Hastoe Wyvern HA Ltd
○ Charitable HA
TSA Reg ✓ 🔑 ◊
Hastoe HA, Marina House, 17 Marina Place, Hampton Wick, Kingston Upon Thames, Surrey, KT1 4BH
T 020 8943 4433
E info@hastoe.com
W www.hastoe.com
CE Mrs Sue Chalkley
Sec Ms Melanie Doherty
Ch Mr Nick Lear

Total Staff 0
Regions South West +
East of England
Owned or managed 460
Rt 179 **GN** 179 **SO** 281 **Tot lets** 0
GN bs 0
Tenant Type % Family 90%
Older 5% **Single** 5%
Parent Association Hastoe HA Ltd

Hatton Housing Trust Ltd
○ Charitable HA
TSA Reg ✓
Bank House, Bank Street,
Tonbridge, Kent, TN9 1BL
T 01732 770660
Sec Warners Solicitors
Ch Mr Colin Barber
Total Staff 0
Region South East
Owned or managed 100
Rt 100 **GN** 100
Tenant Type % Older 100%

Havant HA Ltd
○ Charitable HA
TSA Reg ✓ 🏠 🤝
25 East Street, Havant,
Hampshire, PO9 1AA
T 023 9264 3743
W www.havantha.co.uk
CE Mr Raife West
Sec Mr Raife West
Ch Mrs Julia Potter
Total Staff 7
Region South East
Owned or managed 112
Rt 112 **Sup** 112
Tenant Type % Single 100%
Development Total 4
Rt 14 **Sup** 14 **NBC** 4

Haven Green HA Ltd
○ Charitable HA
TSA Reg ✓ 🤝
18 Montpelier Road, Ealing, London,
Greater London, W5 2QP
T 020 8810 9362
E greenhavenhome@btconnect.com
Sec Ms Alison Haigh
Ch Sir Alastair Norris
Total Staff 20
Region London
Tenant Type % Older 100%

Hawkridge HA Ltd
○ Charitable HA
TSA Reg ✓
Hawkridge, Cox Green, Rudgwick,
Horsham, West Sussex, RH12 3DE
T 01403 822038
CE Mrs Marion Williams
Sec Mr Rob Wild

Ch Mr David Norman
Total Staff 1
Region South East
Owned or managed 21
Rt 21 **OP** 21
Tenant Type % Older 100%

Headrow Ltd
○ Charitable HA
TSA Reg ✓ 🔑 🤝 🔥
Ingots Building, Cemetery Road,
Yeadon, Leeds, West Yorkshire,
LS19 7UP
T 0113 250 4337
E admin@headrow.org.uk
W www.headrow.org.uk
CE Mr Paul Common
Sec Mr Campbell McLay
Ch David Exall
Total Staff 0
Region Yorkshire & Humberside
Owned or managed 1413
Rt 969 **GN** 570 **Sup** 12 **OP** 387
SO 171 **NSO** 273 **Tot lets** 0 **GN bs** 0
Tenant Type % Family 41%
Older 58% **Single** 1%
Parent Association
Arena Housing Group Ltd

Heantun Care HA Ltd
○ Charitable HA
TSA Reg ✗ 🤝 🔥
3 Wellington Road, Bilston,
West Midlands, WV14 6AA
T 01902 571100
E care@heantun.co.uk
W www.heantun.org
CE Mr Nicolas Crombie
Sec Diana Jackson
Ch Mr Michael Ager
Total Staff 196
Region West Midlands
Tenant Type % Older 100%
Parent Association
Heantun HA Ltd

Heantun HA Ltd
○ Charitable HA
TSA Reg ✓ 🏠 🔑 ♦ 🤝 🔥
3 Wellington Road, Bilston,
West Midlands, WV14 6AA
T 01902 571100
E housing@heantun.co.uk
W www.heantun.org
CE Mr Nicolas Crombie
Sec Diana Jackson
Ch Mr Henry Foster
Total Staff 468
Region West Midlands
Owned or managed 1206
Rt 1170 **GN** 634 **Sup** 207 **OP** 329
SO 36 **Tot lets** 205 **GN bs** 596
Tenant Type % Family 29%
Older 29% **Single** 42%

Development Total 61
NBA 38 **NBC** 23
Subsidiary Association(s) Heantun
Care HA Ltd

Heart of Medway HA Ltd
○ Charitable HA
TSA Reg ✓ 🏠 🔑 ♦
Broadside, Leviathan Way,
Chatham, ME4 4LL
CE Mr Ashley Hook
Sec Mr Carl Dewey
Ch Mr Ken Wheeler
Total Staff 0
Region South East
Owned or managed 148
Rt 137 **GN** 137 **SO** 11 **Tot lets** 40
GN bs 0
Development Total 31
Rt 93 **GN** 93 **LCHO** 26 **NBC** 31
Parent Association
MHS Homes Ltd

Heathview Tenants' Co-operative Ltd
★ Co-operative Society
TSA Reg ✓
8 Heathview, Gordon House Road,
London, Greater London, NW5 1LR
T 020 7267 4451
E enquiries@8heathview.net
CE Jenny Crook
Sec Mr Kuba Pickard
Ch Mr Michael Westmoreland
Total Staff 3
Region London
Owned or managed 58
Rt 58 **GN** 58
Tenant Type % Family 38%
Older 19% **Single** 43%

Helena Partnerships Ltd
☆ Charitable Company
TSA Reg ✓
📕 📗 📻 🏠 🔑 ♦ 🤝
4 Corporation Street, Prescot Road,
St Helens, Merseyside, WA9 1LD
T 01744 637383
E onecall@helenapartnerships.co.uk
W www.helenapartnerships.co.uk
CE Mr Rob Young
Sec Mrs Catherine Phillips
Ch Mr Peter Styche OBE
Total Staff 667
Region North West
Owned or managed 13331
Rt 12725 **GN** 11581 **Sup** 16 **OP** 1128
SO 493 **NSO** 113 **Tot lets** 1297
GN bs 11575
Tenant Type % Family 42%
Older 25% **Single** 34%
Development Total 90
Rt 106 **GN** 101 **OP** 5 **LCHO** 188
NBA 8 **NBC** 82

Helix HA Ltd
○ Charitable HA
TSA Reg ✗ ⌂
54 Parish Lane, Penge, London,
Greater London, SE20 7LJ
T 020 8778 9841
E houses01@btconnect.com
Sec M Wise
Ch K D Lucas
Total Staff 3
Region London
Owned or managed 370
Rt 370 OP 370
Tenant Type % Family 20%
Older 60% Single 20%
Development Total 1
NBA 1

Hendon Christian HA Ltd
○ Charitable HA
TSA Reg ✓
115 Premier House,
112 Station Road, Edgware, London,
Middlesex, HA8 7BJ
T 020 8731 5880
E denise@m-r-j.co.uk
W www.hcha.info
Sec Mr T Williams
Ch Mr Akin Durowuju
Total Staff 2
Region London
Owned or managed 138
Rt 138 GN 121 OP 17
Tenant Type % Family 20%
Older 35% Single 45%

Henley & District Housing Trust Ltd
○ Charitable HA
TSA Reg ✓
58 Market Place, Henley-On-Thames,
Oxfordshire, RG9 2AQ
T 01491 579803
E enquiries@henleyhousingtrust.
fsnet.co.uk
CE Mrs Desme Smith
Sec Mr John Morrow
Ch Mrs Oriel Emmett
Total Staff 3
Region South East
Owned or managed 67
Rt 67 GN 67
Tenant Type % Family 58%
Older 40% Single 2%

Herefordshire Housing Ltd
☆ Charitable Company
TSA Reg ✓ ▯ 🚐 ▯ 🚐
Legion Way, Hereford,
Herefordshire, HR1 1LN
T 01432 384000
E info@hhl.org.uk
W www.hhl.org.uk
CE Mr Peter Brown

Sec Mr Richard Woolley
Ch Mr Andy Ballard
Total Staff 236
Region West Midlands
Owned or managed 5418
Rt 5418 GN 4470 Sup 948
Tenant Type % Family 40%
Older 40% Single 20%
Development Total 1
NBA 1

Herefordshire Old Peoples HS Ltd
○ Charitable HA
TSA Reg ✗ 🚐
Hampton House, Hampton Bishop,
Hereford, Herefordshire, HR1 4JZ
T 01432 870287
CE Mrs Carol Thompson
Sec Mrs Carol Thompson
Ch Ms Judith Hereford
Total Staff 38
Region West Midlands
Tenant Type % Older 100%

Hestia Housing and Support
☆ Charitable Company
TSA Reg ✗ ♦ 🚐
3rd Floor, Sovereign Court, 15-21
Staines Road, Hounslow, Middlesex,
TW3 3HR
T 020 8538 2940
E info@hestia.org
W www.hestia.org
CE Mr Patrick Ryan
Sec Mr Patrick Ryan
Ch Mr Jon Wilkinson
Total Staff 272
Region London
Tenant Type % Family 5% Single 95%

Hexagon HA Ltd
○ Charitable HA
TSA Reg ✓ ▯ 🔑 🚐 🔥
130-136 Sydenham Road, London,
Greater London, SE26 5JY
T 020 8778 6699
E customer_desk@hexagon.org.uk
W www.hexagon.org.uk
CE Mr Tom McCormack
Sec Mr Tom McCormack
Ch Mr Roy Coulter
Total Staff 153
Regions London + South East
Owned or managed 3636
Rt 3457 GN 3167 Sup 278 OP 12
SO 172 NSO 7 Tot lets 258
GN bs 3130
Tenant Type % Family 55%
Older 10% Single 35%
Development Total 290
Rt 325 GN 325 LCHO 81 NBA 162
NBC 128
Subsidiary Association(s)
Horniman HA Ltd

Hibiscus HA
○ Charitable HA
TSA Reg ✓ 🚐 ⌂
Hibiscus House, Yew Street,
Wolverhampton, West Midlands,
WV3 0DA
T 01902 716780
E kfinch@hibiscus-housing.co.uk
Sec Ms Elaine Bayley
Ch Eseata Steele
Total Staff 5
Region West Midlands
Owned or managed 29
Rt 29 GN 19 OP 10
Tenant Type % Older 100%

Hightown Praetorian and Churches HA Ltd
○ Charitable HA
TSA Reg ✓ ▯ 🔑 ♦ 🚐 🔥
Hightown House, Maylands Avenue,
Hemel Hempstead, Hertfordshire,
HP2 4XH
T 01442 292300
E general.enquiries@hpcha.org.uk
W www.hpcha.org.uk
CE Mr David Bogle
Sec Mr David Skinner
Ch Mr Michael Bailey
Total Staff 411
Regions East of England + South East
Owned or managed 3841
Rt 2777 GN 2137 Sup 559 OP 81
SO 429 NSO 635 Tot lets 734
GN bs 1967
Tenant Type % Family 65%
Older 3% Single 32%
Development Total 493
NBA 258 NBC 235
Subsidiary Association(s)
Community Meeting Point

Hill Homes
○ Charitable HA
TSA Reg ✓
Unit A, 2-4 Broadlands Road,
Highgate, London, N6 4AN
T 020 8347 3680
E info@hillhomes.co.uk
W www.hillhomes.co.uk
CE Mr Joe Scullion
Sec Mr Joe Scullion
Ch Mrs Charlotte Elworthy
Total Staff 12
Region London
Owned or managed 67
Rt 66 GN 1 OP 65 NSO 1
Tenant Type % Older 100%

Hillside Housing Trust
○ Charitable HA
TSA Reg ✓ 🔑 ♦ 🏠
30 Park Street, London,
Greater London, SE1 9EQ
T 020 8961 0278
E hillsidecso@hillsidehousing.co.uk
W www.hyde-housing.co.uk
CE Mr Shaun Holdcroft
Sec Mr John Edwards
Ch Ms Estella Magloire
Total Staff 47
Region London
Owned or managed 1134
Rt 1075 GN 1075 SO 1 NSO 58
Tot lets 40 GN bs 0
Tenant Type % Family 72%
Older 14% Single 14%
Parent Association
Hyde HA Ltd

Holt & Neighbourhood HS Ltd
○ Charitable HA
TSA Reg ✗
17 Thompson Avenue, Holt, Norfolk,
NR25 6EN
T 01263 712509
Sec Mrs Julie High
Ch Mr Robin Combe
Total Staff 0
Region East of England
Tenant Type % Family 50%
Older 25% Single 25%

Holtspur HA Ltd
■ Non-Charitable HA
TSA Reg ✓
Jaggard Baker, 45 Wycombe End,
Beaconsfield, Buckinghamshire,
HP9 1LZ
T 01494 677755
E gra@jagbak.co.uk
W www.jaggardbaker.co.uk
CE Mr Graham Atkinson
Sec Alec Quinton
Ch Andrea Essery
Total Staff 0
Region South East
Owned or managed 29
Rt 29 GN 29
Tenant Type % Family 67%
Older 33%

Holy Trinity (Guildford) HA Ltd
○ Charitable HA
TSA Reg ✓
18 Addison Court, Addison Road,
Guildford, GU1 3QD
T 01483 569533
W www.addisoncourt.org.uk
CE Mrs Caroline Herington
Sec Mrs Marilyn Higgs Goodwin

Ch Mr Michael Bishop
Total Staff 3
Region South East
Owned or managed 30
Rt 30 GN 30
Tenant Type % Older 100%

Home From Home HA Ltd
○ Charitable HA
TSA Reg ✓ 🤝 🏠
230 Portway, London, E15 3QY
T 020 8472 7711
E homefromhomeha@gmail.com
W www.hfhhousing.org
CE Ms Maggie Severin
Sec Mrs Theresa Mitchell
Ch Mrs Barbara Maxwell
Total Staff 5
Region London
Owned or managed 51
Rt 51 GN 36 Sup 15
Tenant Type % Family 70%
Older 20% Single 10%

Home Group Ltd
○ Charitable HA
TSA Reg ✓
■ ▢ ▣ 500 🅳 🔑 ♦ 🤝
2 Gosforth Park Way, Gosforth
Business Park, Newcastle Upon Tyne,
Tyne And Wear, NE12 8ET
T 0845 155 1234
E homegroup@homegroup.org.uk
W www.homegroup.org.uk
CE Mr Mark Henderson
Sec Steve Thompson
Ch Mr Bob Davies
Total Staff 3679
Regions North East + London,
South East, South West,
East Midlands, West Midlands,
East of England, Yorkshire &
Humberside, North West
Owned or managed 48660
Rt 42641 GN 34049 Sup 6963
OP 1629 SO 3951 NSO 2068
Tot lets 12412 GN bs 33849
Tenant Type % Family 65%
Older 10% Single 25%
Development Total 1040
NBA 555 NBC 485

Homesdale (Woodford Baptist Homes) Ltd
○ Charitable HA
TSA Reg ✓ 🤝
5/7 New Wanstead, Wanstead,
London, Greater London, E11 2SH
T 020 8989 0847
E ptownrow@aol.com
W www.homesdale.co.uk
CE Mr Peter Townrow
Sec Mr Kenneth Webb
Ch Mr Keith Hawkins

Total Staff 34
Region London
Owned or managed 71
Rt 70 OP 70 NSO 1
Tenant Type % Older 100%

Horniman HA Ltd
■ Non-Charitable HA
TSA Reg ✓ 🔑 ♦
130-136 Sydenham Road, Sydenham,
London, Greater London, SE26 5JY
T 020 8778 6699
CE Mr Tom McCormack
Sec Ms Phil Newsam
Ch Ms Jacqueline Esimaje-Heath
Total Staff 0
Region London
Owned or managed 39
SO 33 NSO 6 Tot lets 0 GN bs 0
Tenant Type % Family 20%
Single 80%
Parent Association
Hexagon HA Ltd

Hornsey (North London) YMCA HS Ltd
○ Charitable HA
TSA Reg ✓ 🤝 🏠
184 Tottenham Lane, Hornsey,
London, Greater London, N8 8SG
T 020 8340 2345
E lal@ymcahornsey.org.uk
W www.ymcahornsey.org
CE Mr Tim Fallon
Ch Mr Michael Baker
Total Staff 38
Region London
Owned or managed 159
Rt 159 Sup 159
Tenant Type % Single 100%

Hornsey Housing Trust Ltd
○ Charitable HA
TSA Reg ✓
62 Mayfield Road, London,
Greater London, N8 9LP
T 020 8340 6374
E admin@hornseyht.co.uk
W www.hornseyht.co.uk
CE Mr Howard Cresswell
Sec Mr Tom Davidson
Ch Greg Gordon
Total Staff 12
Region London
Owned or managed 385
Rt 385 GN 229 Sup 48 OP 108
Tenant Type % Family 1%
Older 90% Single 9%

Horton HA
○ Charitable HA
TSA Reg ✗ 🕸 ◊
Chartford House, 54 Little Horton Lane, Bradford, West Yorkshire, BD5 0BS
T 01274 370689
E headoffice@hortonhousing.co.uk
W www.hortonhousing.co.uk
CE Ms Sheila Bamford
Sec Mr Ernie Gray
Ch Mr Huw Jones
Total Staff 202
Region Yorkshire & Humberside
Owned or managed 164
Rt 164 Sup 164
Tenant Type % Family 5% Single 95%
Subsidiary Association(s) Horton Housing Support Ltd

Horton Housing Support Ltd
✪ Not-for-Profit Company
TSA Reg ✗ 🕸 ◊
Chartford House,
54 Little Horton Lane, Bradford, West Yorkshire, BD5 0BS
T 01274 370689
E headoffice@hortonhousing.co.uk
W www.hortonhousing.co.uk
CE Ms Sheila Bamford
Sec Mr David Collier
Ch Mr Huw Jones
Total Staff 0
Region Yorkshire & Humberside
Tenant Type % Family 5% Single 95%
Parent Association
Horton HA

Housing & Community Association
○ Charitable HA
TSA Reg ✗ 🕸
Enterprise House, Kings Head Hill, Chingford, Greater London, E4 7NB
T 020 8524 0318
E housingcommunity@btconnect.com
CE Mr Antonio Masella
Sec Mr Michael Osborne
Ch Mr Antonio Masella
Total Staff 17
Region London
Owned or managed 188
Rt 185 OP 185 NSO 3
Tenant Type % Older 100%

Housing 21
○ Charitable HA
TSA Reg ✓
🖥 ▢ 📟 💾 🏠 🔧 ♦ 🕸
The Triangle, Baring Road, Beaconsfield, Buckinghamshire, HP9 2NA
T 0370 192 4000
E enquiries@housing21.co.uk
W www.housing21.co.uk
CE Ms Pushpa Raguvaran
Sec Ms Claire Luxton
Ch Lord Ben Stoneham
Total Staff 6342
Regions South East + London, South West, East Midlands, West Midlands, East of England, Yorkshire & Humberside, North East, North West
Owned or managed 18117
Rt 16704 GN 781 Sup 79 OP 15844
SO 1405 NSO 8 Tot lets 2874
GN bs 624
Tenant Type % Family 2%
Older 97% Single 1%
Development Total 1227
NBA 655 NBC 572

Housing for Women
☆ Charitable Company
TSA Reg ✓ 🕸
Sixth Floor, Blue Star House, 234-244 Stockwell Road, London, Greater London, SW9 9SP
T 020 7501 6120
E info@h4w.co.uk
W www.h4w.org.uk
CE Ms Elizabeth Clarson
Sec Ms Elizabeth Clarson
Ch Ms Barbara Riddell
Total Staff 54
Region London
Owned or managed 871
Rt 870 GN 838 Sup 32 NSO 1
Tenant Type % Family 41%
Older 30% Single 29%

Housing Hartlepool Ltd
☆ Charitable Company
TSA Reg ✓ ▢ 🖥 🏠 🔑 ♦ 🕸 ◊
Greenbank, Stranton, Hartlepool, Cleveland, TS24 7QS
T 01429 525252
E enquiries@housinghartlepool.co.uk
W www.housinghartlepool.org.uk
CE Mrs Cath Purdy
Sec Ms Linda Minns
Ch Peter Olsen
Total Staff 327
Region North East
Owned or managed 7222
Rt 7051 GN 5662 Sup 14 OP 1375
SO 159 NSO 12 Tot lets 867
GN bs 5525

Development Total 279
NBA 169 NBC 110
Parent Association Vela Group

Housing Partnership (London) Ltd
○ Charitable HA
TSA Reg ✓
The Office, Bridgacre, Manhattan Drive, Cambridge, Cambridgeshire, CB4 1JU
T 01223 324016
E ronccousins@yahoo.co.uk
CE Mr Ron Cousins
Sec Mr Ron Cousins
Ch Mr Patrick Elwood
Total Staff 4
Regions East of England + London, South East
Owned or managed 170
Rt 170 GN 170
Tenant Type % Family 50%
Older 10% Single 40%

Housing Pendle
○ Charitable HA
TSA Reg ✓ 🖥 🏠 🔑 🕸 ◊
Shackleton Hall, 32 Church St, Colne, Lancashire, BB8 0LG
T 01282 873700
E ian.clark@togetherhousing.co.uk
W www.housingpendle.co.uk
CE Mr Ian Clark
Sec Mr Ian Clark
Ch Mr David Clegg
Total Staff 150
Region North West
Owned or managed 3344
Rt 3261 GN 1990 OP 1271 SO 83
Tot lets 319 GN bs 1987
Tenant Type % Family 39%
Older 41% Single 20%
Development Total 5
NBA 5
Parent Association
Together Housing Group Ltd

Housing Solutions Ltd
■ Non-Charitable HA
TSA Reg ✓ 🏠 🔑
Crown House, Crown Square, Waldeck Road, Maidenhead, Berkshire, SL6 8BY
T 01628 543100
E contact@mdha.co.uk
W www.mdha.co.uk
CE Mr John Petitt
Sec Mr John Petitt
Ch Mr Roger Mabey
Total Staff 162
Regions South East + East of England
Owned or managed 4732
Rt 3870 GN 3332 Sup 180 OP 358
SO 427 NSO 435 Tot lets 315

GN bs 3221
Tenant Type % Family 43%
Older 39% **Single** 18%
Development Total 318
NBA 160 **NBC** 158

Howard Cottage HA
○ Charitable HA
TSA Reg ✓ 📷 🔑 🦐
Pioneer House, Norton Way
South, Letchworth Garden City,
Hertfordshire, SG6 1NY
T 01462 683307
E enquiries@howard-cottage.co.uk
W www.howard-cottage.co.uk
CE Mr John Welch
Sec Mrs Michelle Cross
Ch Mr Gary Grindal
Total Staff 40
Region East of England
Owned or managed 1514
Rt 1480 **GN** 1298 **Sup** 7 **OP** 175
SO 34 **Tot lets** 121 **GN bs** 1274
Tenant Type % Family 52%
Older 32% **Single** 16%
Development Total 87
NBA 49 **NBC** 38

Hull Churches HA Ltd
○ Charitable HA
TSA Reg ✓
31 Beverley Road, Hull, North
Humberside, HU3 1XH
T 01482 210842
E info@hullchurcheshousing.org.uk
CE Mrs Kate Atkinson
Sec Mrs Kate Atkinson
Ch Mr Robbie Walker-Brown
Total Staff 48
Region Yorkshire & Humberside
Owned or managed 355
Rt 355 **GN** 106 **Sup** 44 **OP** 205
Tenant Type % Family 20%
Older 60% **Single** 20%

Hull House Improvement Society Ltd
○ Charitable HA
TSA Reg ✓
1 Parliament Street, Hull, North
Humberside, HU1 2AS
T 01482 224763
Sec Mr Michael Craughan
Ch Mr John Broughton
Total Staff 0
Region Yorkshire & Humberside
Owned or managed 34
Rt 34 **GN** 34
Tenant Type % Family 60%
Older 20% **Single** 20%

Hull Resettlement Project
☆ Charitable Company
TSA Reg ✓ 🦐
20 Bourne Street, Hull, North
Humberside, HU2 8AE
T 01482 585323
E enquiries@hrpltd.org.uk
CE Mr John Black
Sec Mr John Black
Ch Mr Robert Batty
Total Staff 20
Region Yorkshire & Humberside
Owned or managed 45
Rt 45 **Sup** 45
Tenant Type % Single 100%

Hundred Houses Society Ltd
○ Charitable HA
TSA Reg ✓ 📷 🔑
51 Scotland Road, Cambridge,
Cambridgeshire, CB4 1QW
T 01223 315036
E info@hhs.org.uk
W www.hhs.org.uk
CE Mr Chris Jackson
Sec Ms Jane Cantor
Ch Ian Kidman
Total Staff 20
Region East of England
Owned or managed 1203
Rt 1119 **GN** 1075 **OP** 44 **SO** 84
Tot lets 55 **GN bs** 963
Tenant Type % Family 26%
Older 69% **Single** 5%
Development Total 108
NBA 70 **NBC** 38

Hyde HA Ltd
○ Charitable HA
TSA Reg ✓ 📺 🖥 📦 📷 🔑 ♦ ◊
30 Park Street, London, SE1 9EQ
T 020 3207 2600
E info@hyde-housing.co.uk
W www.hyde-housing.co.uk
CE Mr Steve White
Sec Mr John Edwards
Ch Dr Julie Hollyman
Total Staff 1238
Regions London + South East,
East Midlands, East of England
Owned or managed 33616
Rt 27067 **GN** 23613 **Sup** 2241
OP 1213 **SO** 3662 **NSO** 2887
Tot lets 2422 **GN bs** 16873
Tenant Type % Family 80%
Older 8% **Single** 12%
Development Total 1170
Rt 1950 **GN** 1950 **LCHO** 672
NBA 655 **NBC** 515
Subsidiary Association(s)
Hillside Housing Trust; Hyde
Southbank Homes Ltd; Martlet
Homes Ltd; Minster General
HA Ltd

Hyde Southbank Homes Ltd
○ Charitable HA
TSA Reg ✓ 📦 🔑 ◊
30 Park Street, London, SE1 9EQ
T 020 7346 6500
E info@hyde-housing.co.uk
W www.hyde-housing.co.uk
CE Mr Shaun Holdcroft
Sec Mr John Edwards
Ch Mr Mike Jones
Total Staff 55
Region London
Owned or managed 3205
Rt 2296 **GN** 2254 **OP** 42 **SO** 30
NSO 879 **Tot lets** 79 **GN bs** 2244
Tenant Type % Family 65%
Older 17% **Single** 34%
Parent Association
Hyde HA Ltd

Hyelm Group
☆ Charitable Company
TSA Reg ✓ 🦐
Arthur West House, 79 Fitzjohns
Avenue, Hampstead, London,
Greater London, NW3 6PA
T 020 7435 8793
E hampstead@hyelm.com
W www.hyelm.com
CE Mr Keith Douglas
Sec Mr Keith Douglas
Ch Ms Arvinda Gohil
Total Staff 18
Region London
Owned or managed 358
Rt 307 **GN** 307 **NSO** 51
Tenant Type % Single 100%

Hyndburn Homes Ltd
○ Charitable HA
TSA Reg ✓ 📦 🔑 🦐 ◊
1a Enterprise Way, The Globe
Centre, Accrington, BB5 0FL
T 01254 300500
E housing@hyndburnhomes.co.uk
W www.symphonyhousing.co.uk
CE Mr Nigel Fenton
Sec Mrs Audrey Davidson
Ch Mr Kevin Ruth
Total Staff 119
Region North West
Owned or managed 3423
Rt 3271 **GN** 2089 **OP** 1182 **SO** 152
Tot lets 362 **GN bs** 1997
Tenant Type % Family 57%
Older 43%
Parent Association
Symphony Housing Group

Ii

Imani Housing Co-op Ltd
★ Co-operative Society
TSA Reg ✓ 🏠
2 The Hayloft, 17a Seely Road,
Tooting, London, SW17 9QP
T 020 8672 1800
E info@imani.org.uk
W www.imani.org.uk
CE Mr Khalid Mair
Sec Ms Maxine Stephens
Ch Mr Khalid Mair
Total Staff 2
Region London
Owned or managed 52
Rt 52 GN 52
Tenant Type % Family 40%
Single 60%

Impact HA Ltd
◯ Charitable HA
TSA Reg ✓ 🏠 🔑 🤝
Nook Street, Workington, Cumbria,
CA14 4EH
T 0344 873 6290
E enquiry@impacthousing.org.uk
W www.impacthousing.org.uk
CE Mike Muir
Sec Norman Parry
Ch Mr Adrian Waite
Total Staff 205
Region North West
Owned or managed 2750
Rt 2523 GN 2020 Sup 423 OP 80
SO 28 NSO 199 Tot lets 522
GN bs 2014
Tenant Type % Family 30%
Older 30% Single 40%
Development Total 7
Rt 141 GN 117 Sup 24 LCHO 7
NBA 7

Inclusion Housing CIC
✪ Not-for-Profit Company
TSA Reg ✗ 🏠 🤝
York CVS, Priory Street Centre,
15 Priory Street, York,
North Yorkshire, YO1 6ET
T 01904 675207
E info@inclusionhousingcic.org.uk
W www.inclusionhousingcic.org.uk
CE Mr David de Silva
Sec Mr John Chrystal
Ch Mr Pete Ottowell
Total Staff 0
Regions Yorkshire & Humberside +
South East, North West
Owned or managed 43
Rt 43 Sup 43
Tenant Type % Single 100%

Development Total 2
NBA 2

Incommunities Group Ltd
✪ Not-for-Profit Company
TSA Reg ✓ 🖼 ♦ 🤝 🔥
Trust House, 5 New Augustus Street,
Bradford, West Yorkshire, BD1 5LL
T 0845 120 8171
W www.incommunities.co.uk
CE Mrs Geraldine Howley
Sec Mr Peter Newbould
Ch Cllr Martin Smith
Total Staff 1067
Region Yorkshire & Humberside
Subsidiary Association(s)
Incommunities Ltd

Incommunities Ltd
■ Non-Charitable HA
TSA Reg ✓ 🖼 🖥 📷 🔑 ♦ 🤝 🔥
Trust House, 5 New Augustus Street,
Bradford, West Yorkshire, BD1 5LL
T 0845 120 8171
E enquiry@incommunities.co.uk
W www.incommunities.co.uk
CE Mrs Geraldine Howley
Sec Mr Peter Newbould
Ch Dave Procter
Total Staff 1040
Region Yorkshire & Humberside
Owned or managed 22493
Rt 21355 GN 18718 Sup 20 OP 2617
SO 1042 NSO 96 Tot lets 2835
GN bs 18688
Tenant Type % Family 47%
Older 34% Single 19%
Development Total 91
NBA 46 NBC 45
Parent Association
Incommunities Group Ltd

Inkerman HA
◯ Charitable HA
TSA Reg ✗
Inkerman House, 14-18 Nevern
Road, London, London, SW5 9PH
T 020 7370 6778
E iha@inkerman.org.uk
W www.inkerman.org.uk
CE Mr David Elavia
Sec Mrs Penni Cox
Ch Mr Stephen Tanner
Total Staff 4
Region London
Owned or managed 1
Rt 1 OP 1
Tenant Type % Older 100%

Innisfree HA
◯ Charitable HA
TSA Reg ✓ 🤝 🏠
190 Iverson Road, West Hampstead,
London, NW6 2HL
T 020 7625 1818
E info@innisfree.org.uk
W www.innisfree.org.uk
CE Mr John Delahunty
Sec Mr Liam O'Shaughnessy
Ch Ms Anne McLoughlin
Total Staff 22
Regions London + East of England
Owned or managed 550
Rt 550 GN 487 Sup 38 OP 25
Tenant Type % Family 56%
Older 12% Single 32%

Inquilab HA Ltd
◯ Charitable HA
TSA Reg ✓ 🏠 🔑 🏠
Grove House, 77 North Road,
Southall, Middlesex, UB1 2JL
T 020 8843 1263
W www.inquilabha.org
CE Miss Gina Amoh
Sec Miss Gina Amoh
Ch Mr Olu Olanrewaju
Total Staff 21
Regions London + South East
Owned or managed 1172
Rt 1109 GN 1103 Sup 6 SO 63
Tot lets 76 GN bs 1040
Tenant Type % Family 59%
Older 6% Single 35%
Development Total 174
Rt 100 GN 100 LCHO 20 NBA 137
NBC 37

Irish Centre Housing Ltd
◯ Charitable HA
TSA Reg ✓ 📷 🤝
1 Holmes Road, Kentish Town,
London, NW5 3AA
T 020 7485 8889
E info@irishcentrehousing.org
W www.irishcentrehousing.org
CE Ms Patricia Durkan
Sec Ms Patricia Durkan
Ch Ms Sally Buckley
Total Staff 47
Regions London + East of England
Owned or managed 644
Rt 340 GN 150 Sup 165 OP 25
NSO 304
Tenant Type % Family 2% Older 8%
Single 90%
Development Total 12
Rt 60 Sup 60 NBA 6 NBC 6

Irwell Valley HA Ltd
○ Charitable HA
TSA Reg ✓
5th Floor, Paragon House, 48 Seymour Grove, Manchester, Lancashire, M16 0LN
T 0161 610 1000
E info@irwellvalleyha.co.uk
W www.irwellvalleyha.co.uk
CE Dr Tom Manion
Sec Angela Garvin
Ch Ms Lynne Garsden
Total Staff 185
Region North West
Owned or managed 7449
Rt 6865 GN 6109 Sup 303 OP 453
SO 476 NSO 108 Tot lets 792
GN bs 6021
Tenant Type % Family 45%
Older 31% Single 24%
Development Total 25
NBA 25
Subsidiary Association(s)
Pendleton Improved HA Ltd

Island Cottages Ltd
○ Charitable HA
TSA Reg ✓
1 Taylor Court, The Green, Shorwell, Newport, Isle Of Wight, PO30 3LQ
T 01983 741001
E islandcottages@talktalkbusiness.net
CE Mrs Sarah Bennett
Sec Mr David Williamson
Ch Winifred Hollis
Total Staff 3
Region South East
Owned or managed 38
Rt 38 GN 38
Tenant Type % Family 50%
Older 25% Single 25%

Islington & Shoreditch HA Ltd
○ Charitable HA
TSA Reg ✓
102 Blackstock Road, London, Greater London, N4 2DR
T 020 7226 3753
E isha@isha.co.uk
W www.isha.co.uk
CE Ms Clare Thomson
Sec Ms Clare Thomson
Ch Mr James Cannon
Total Staff 55
Region London
Owned or managed 1767
Rt 1501 GN 1365 Sup 95 OP 41
SO 238 NSO 28 Tot lets 281
GN bs 1360
Tenant Type % Family 55%
Older 25% Single 20%
Development Total 262
NBA 145 NBC 117

Subsidiary Association(s)
Lien Viet HA Ltd

Islington Community Housing Co-op Ltd
★ Co-operative Society
TSA Reg ✓
Unit 33, Bickerton House, 25 Bickerton Road, London, Greater London, N19 5JT
T 020 7263 1176
E office@ichc.org.uk
W www.ichcoop.org
Sec Emma Cairns
Ch Ms Laura Schaaf
Total Staff 3
Region London
Owned or managed 135
Rt 135 GN 135
Tenant Type % Family 29%
Older 1% Single 70%

Isos Housing Ltd
○ Charitable HA
TSA Reg ✓
Number Five, Gosforth Park Avenue, Gosforth Business Park, Newcastle Upon Tyne, Tyne And Wear, NE12 8EG
T 0191 292 3000
E info@isoshousing.co.uk
W www.isoshousing.co.uk
CE Mr Keith Loraine
Sec Mr Mark Reid
Ch Ms Jackie Axelby
Total Staff 371
Regions North East + North West
Owned or managed 12048
Rt 11027 GN 10036 Sup 991
SO 1021 Tot lets 1106 GN bs 10008
Tenant Type % Family 29%
Older 37% Single 34%
Development Total 149
Rt 166 GN 130 OP 36 NBA 76
NBC 73

Janes Housing Society Ltd
○ Charitable HA
TSA Reg ✗
6 Houghton Hall Business Park, Porz Avenue, Houghton Regis, Bedfordshire, LU5 5UZ
T 01582 869100
CE Mr Steve Shelley Davis
Sec Mrs Sally Sumner
Ch Mr David Janes
Total Staff 0
Regions East of England + South East

Owned or managed 48
Rt 48 Sup 48
Tenant Type % Older 100%

Jephson HA Ltd
○ Charitable HA
TSA Reg ✓
Jephson House, Blackdown, Leamington Spa, Warwickshire, CV32 6RE
T 01926 339311
E info@jephson.org.uk
W www.jephson.org.uk
CE Mr Bob Strachan
Sec Mr David Jefferson
Ch Ms Rose Green
Total Staff 60
Regions West Midlands + South East, South West, East Midlands, East of England, Yorkshire & Humberside
Owned or managed 3273
Rt 3171 GN 2233 Sup 127 OP 811
SO 102 Tot lets 479 GN bs 2222
Tenant Type % Family 54%
Older 36% Single 10%
Development Total 289
Rt 96 GN 96 LCHO 46 NBA 225
NBC 64
Parent Association
Jephson Homes HA Ltd

Jephson Homes HA Ltd
■ Non-Charitable HA
TSA Reg ✓
Jephson House, Blackdown, Leamington Spa, Warwickshire, CV32 6RE
T 01926 339311
E info@jephson.org.uk
W www.jephson.org.uk
CE Mr Bob Strachan
Sec Mr Bob Strachan
Ch Dr M Collins
Total Staff 353
Regions West Midlands + South East, South West, East Midlands, East of England, Yorkshire & Humberside, North West
Owned or managed 10209
Rt 8063 GN 7566 Sup 181 OP 316
SO 1738 NSO 408 Tot lets 1069
GN bs 7461
Tenant Type % Family 20%
Older 14% Single 66%
Development Total 529
Rt 90 GN 90 LCHO 4 NBA 283
NBC 246
Subsidiary Association(s) Jephson HA Ltd; Marches HA Ltd

Jesus Fellowship HA Ltd
○ Charitable HA
TSA Reg ✗ 🄐
c/o TBS Ltd, Hackwood Road,
Daventry, Northamptonshire,
NN11 4ES
T 01327 708519
E tim.white@tbsmerchants.co.uk
CE Mr Tim White
Sec Mr Ian Mason
Ch Mr John Campbell
Total Staff 0
Regions East Midlands +
West Midlands, East of England
Owned or managed 12
Rt 12 GN 12
Tenant Type % Family 90%
Single 10%
Development Total 1
NBA 1

Jewish Community HA Ltd
○ Charitable HA
TSA Reg ✓ 🔑 🐾 🄐
Harmony Close, Princes Park
Avenue, London, Greater London,
NW11 0JJ
T 020 8381 4901
W www.jcha.org.uk
CE Mrs Sara Clarke
Sec Mrs Sara Clarke
Ch Eric Shapiro
Total Staff 39
Regions London + South East,
East of England
Owned or managed 481
Rt 448 GN 39 Sup 17 OP 392 SO 33
Tot lets 0 GN bs 39
Tenant Type % Older 85% ·
Single 15%

Johnnie Johnson HA Ltd
■ Non-Charitable HA
TSA Reg ✓ 🐾 ◊
Astra House, Spinners Lane,
Poynton, Cheshire, SK12 1GA
T 0845 604 1095
E general.enquiries@jjhousing.co.uk
W www.jjhousing.co.uk
CE Mr Jim Lunney
Sec Mr Jim Lunney
Ch Ms Kath Lavery
Total Staff 1
Region North West
Tenant Type % Family 8%
Older 92%
Parent Association
Johnnie Johnson Housing Trust Ltd

Johnnie Johnson Housing Trust Ltd
○ Charitable HA
TSA Reg ✓ 🄐 🔑 ♦ 🐾 ◊
Astra House, Spinners Lane,
Poynton, Cheshire, SK12 1GA
T 0845 604 1095
E general.enquiries@jjhousing.co.uk
W www.jjhousing.co.uk
CE Mr Jim Lunney
Sec Mr Jim Lunney
Ch Ms Kath Lavery
Total Staff 315
Regions North West + South East,
East Midlands, East of England,
Yorkshire & Humberside, North East
Owned or managed 4856
Rt 4272 GN 1537 Sup 98 OP 2637
SO 584 Tot lets 589 GN bs 1258
Tenant Type % Family 26%
Older 72% Single 2%
Development Total 192
NBA 121 NBC 71
Subsidiary Association(s)
Johnnie Johnson HA Ltd

Joseph Kaye's Almshouses
❑ Charitable Trust
TSA Reg ✗
94 Bates Street, Sheffield,
South Yorkshire, S10 1NQ
T 0114 268 2088
E francescacullen@aol.com
CE Ms Francesca Cullen
Sec Ms Judith Webster
Ch Mr Paul Voyse
Total Staff 1
Region Yorkshire & Humberside
Tenant Type % Older 100%

Joseph Rowntree Housing Trust
❑ Charitable Trust
TSA Reg ✓ 🄐 🔑 ♦ 🐾
The Garth, White Rose Avenue,
New Earswick, York, YO32 4TZ
T 01904 735000
E information@jrf.org.uk
W www.jrf.org.uk
CE Ms Julia Unwin, CBE
Sec Mr John Hocking
Ch Mr Tony Stoller CBE
Total Staff 693
Regions Yorkshire & Humberside +
North East
Owned or managed 2281
Rt 1457 GN 1148 Sup 47 OP 262
SO 629 NSO 195 Tot lets 179
GN bs 1148
Tenant Type % Family 47%
Older 40% Single 13%
Development Total 33
NBA 18 NBC 15

Julian House
○ Charitable HA
TSA Reg ✓ 🐾
55 New King Street, Bath,
Avon, BA1 2BN
T 01225 354650
E admin@julianhouse.org.uk
W www.julianhouse.org.uk
Ch Mr Bob Alderman
Total Staff 40
Region South West
Owned or managed 51
Rt 51 Sup 51
Tenant Type % Single 100%

Kk

Karin HA Ltd
○ Charitable HA
TSA Reg ✗ 🔑 🄐
Unit 124 Cavell Street, Whitechapel,
London, Greater London, E1 2JA
T 020 7392 9622
E info@karin-ha.org
W www.karin-ha-org
CE Ms Zahra Hassan
Sec Mr Abdi Hassan
Ch Ms Salma Rauf Shirin
Total Staff 5
Region London
Owned or managed 283
Rt 272 GN 272 SO 11 Tot lets 70
GN bs 0
Tenant Type % Family 89%
Older 4% Single 7%

Kemble Housing Ltd
○ Charitable HA
TSA Reg ✓ ◊
44 Berrington Street, Hereford,
Herefordshire, HR4 0BJ
T 01432 377900
W www.wmhousing.co.uk
CE Mrs Pat Brandum
Sec Miss Zoe Moncrieff
Ch Mr Andy Johnson
Total Staff 0
Region West Midlands
Owned or managed 1067
Rt 1067 GN 936 Sup 80 OP 51
Tenant Type % Family 70%
Older 6% Single 24%
Parent Association
WM Housing Group

Keniston HA Ltd
○ Charitable HA
TSA Reg ✓ 🐾
13 Artington Close, Farnborough,
Kent, BR6 7UL
T 01689 889700
E enquiries@kenistonha.co.uk
W www.kenistonha.co.uk
CE Mr Nevil Osborne
Sec Mrs Helene Harris

Ch Mr Bruce Shelmerdine
Total Staff 38
Regions London + South East
Owned or managed 752
Rt 712 **GN** 586 **OP** 126 **NSO** 40
Tenant Type % Family 65%
Older 24% **Single** 11%

Kensington & Chelsea TMO Ltd
✪ Not-for-Profit Company
TSA Reg ✗ 🦇
Unit A, 292 Kensal Road, London,
Greater London, W10 5BE
T 020 7605 6352
E ContactUs@kctmo.org.uk
W www.kctmo.org.uk
CE Mr Robert Black
Sec Angela Bosnjak-Szekeres
Ch Fay Edwards
Total Staff 204
Region London
Tenant Type % Family 50%
Older 35% **Single** 15%

Keystone Developments (LG) Ltd
✪ Not-for-Profit Company
TSA Reg ✗ ◊
Leverett House, Gilbert Drive,
Endeavour Park, Boston,
Lincolnshire, PE21 7TQ
T 0845 309 0700
E retirementliving@longhurst-group.
org.uk
W www.keystonedevelopments.co.uk
Sec Mr Bob Walder
Ch Mr David Armes
Total Staff 0
Region East Midlands
Parent Association
Longhurst Group Ltd

Kilmersdon Rural HA
☆ Charitable Company
TSA Reg ✓
c/o Flourish Homes Ltd,
Flourish House, 2 Cathedral Avenue,
Wells, BA5 1FD
T 01749 832009
CE Allison Clements
Ch Mr Michael Brotherton
Total Staff 0
Region South West
Owned or managed 96
Rt 96 **GN** 96
Tenant Type % Family 75%
Older 10% **Single** 15%

King Alfred HA Ltd
○ Charitable HA
TSA Reg ✓ 🦇
Spillers House, Old Boundary Road,
Shaftesbury, Dorset, SP7 8EP

T 01747 853128
E kingalfredha@aol.com
CE Mrs Gina Dent
Sec Mrs P Sykes
Ch Mrs J Wade
Total Staff 4
Region South West
Owned or managed 37
Rt 37 **OP** 37
Tenant Type % Older 95% **Single** 5%

King's Barton HA Ltd
○ Charitable HA
TSA Reg ✓
5 Moravian Road, Kingswood,
Avon, BS15 8LY
T 0117 961 1171
E info@kingsbarton.co.uk
CE Mrs Patricia O'Driscoll
Sec Ms Anna Page
Ch Mr Derek Brewer
Total Staff 1
Region South West
Owned or managed 131
Rt 131 **GN** 131
Tenant Type % Older 90%
Single 10%

Kingston Upon Thames Churches HA Ltd
○ Charitable HA
TSA Reg ✓ 🦇
Meadway House, 17-21 Brighton
Road, Surbiton, Surrey, KT6 5LR
T 020 8399 7221
E office@kcha.co.uk
W www.kcha.co.uk
CE Mr John Castelberg
Sec Mr John Castelberg
Ch Mr Declan Terry
Total Staff 8
Regions London + South East
Owned or managed 277
Rt 277 **GN** 181 **Sup** 7 **OP** 89
Tenant Type % Family 39%
Older 33% **Single** 28%

Kirby Muxloe Free Church HA Ltd
○ Charitable HA
TSA Reg ✗ 🦇
Carey House, Carey Gardens, 1
Main Street, Kirby Muxloe, Leicester,
Leicestershire, LE9 2AY
T 0116 238 7116
Sec Mr S Hargraves
Ch Mr Graham Couling
Total Staff 0
Region East Midlands
Owned or managed 7
Rt 7 **OP** 7
Tenant Type % Older 100%

Knightstone Charitable Housing Ltd
○ Charitable HA
TSA Reg ✗ ◊
c/o Arcadia Housing Ltd,
2 Station Road, Worle, Weston-
Super-Mare, Somerset, BS22 6AP
T 01934 524300
W www.knightstone.co.uk
CE Mr Nick Horne
Sec Miss Charlotte Ferris
Ch Mr Richard Taylor
Total Staff 0
Region South West
Parent Association Knightstone
HA Ltd

Knightstone HA Ltd
○ Charitable HA
TSA Reg ✓
🖥 🖳 🚐500 Ⓓ 🔑 🌳 🦇 ◊
c/o Arcadia Housing Ltd,
2 Station Road, Worle, Weston-
Super-Mare, Avon, BS22 6AP
T 01934 524300
E talktous@knightstone.co.uk
W www.knightstone.co.uk
CE Mr Nick Horne
Sec Miss Charlotte Ferris
Ch Mrs Delyth Lloyd-Evans
Total Staff 303
Regions South West + South East
Owned or managed 10335
Rt 9011 **GN** 7759 **Sup** 829 **OP** 423
SO 1272 **NSO** 52 **Tot lets** 1292
GN bs 7485
Tenant Type % Family 52%
Older 24% **Single** 24%
Development Total 945
Rt 1060 **GN** 920 **Sup** 20 **OP** 120
LCHO 110 **NBA** 708 **NBC** 237
Parent Association
Arcadia Housing Ltd
Subsidiary Association(s)
Knightstone Charitable Housing Ltd

Knowsley Housing Trust
☆ Charitable Company
TSA Reg ✓
🖥 🖳 🚐YTHO Ⓓ 🔑 🌳 🦇 ◊
Lakeview, Kings Business Park,
Prescot, Merseyside, L34 1PJ
T 0151 290 7000
E enquiries@k-h-t.org
W www.k-h-t.org
CE Mr Bob Taylor
Sec Mr Jason Ridley
Ch Helen White
Total Staff 455
Region North West
Owned or managed 13680
Rt 13393 **GN** 12594 **Sup** 112 **OP** 687
SO 287 **Tot lets** 1163 **GN bs** 12542
Tenant Type % Family 37%
Older 26% **Single** 37%

See page 62 for key to symbols and abbreviations

Development Total 127
Rt 229 GN 204 Sup 25 NBA 54
NBC 73
Parent Association First Ark Group

Kurdish HA Ltd
○ Charitable HA
TSA Reg ✓ 🕶 🏠
Selby Centre, Selby Road, London,
Greater London, N17 8JL
T 020 8808 9954
E info@kurdishhousing.org
W www.kurdishhousing.org
CE Dana Abbas
Sec Peter Hudd
Ch Mr Hishyar Abid
Total Staff 3
Region London
Owned or managed 114
Rt 114 GN 114
Tenant Type % Family 86%
Older 4% Single 10%

Lace Housing Ltd
○ Charitable HA
TSA Reg ✓ 🔑 🚶 🤝
Lace House, 2 Olsen Rise, Lincoln,
Lincolnshire, LN2 4UZ
T 01522 514444
E enquiries@lacehousing.org.uk
W www.lacehousing.org
CE Mr Nicholas Chambers
Sec Miss Catriona M A Wheeler
Ch Mr Philip Hutchings
Total Staff 275
Region East Midlands
Owned or managed 197
Rt 167 GN 25 OP 142 SO 27 NSO 3
Tot lets 37 GN bs 0
Tenant Type % Older 100%

Ladybur Housing Co-op Ltd
★ Co-operative Society
TSA Reg ✓
Ladybur House, Burbridge Way,
Tottenham, London,
Greater London, N17 9GY
T 020 8801 6700
E ladybur@aol.com
CE Mr David Meade
Sec Mr Paul Ambler
Ch Mr Clive Finnis
Total Staff 1
Region London
Owned or managed 158
Rt 158 GN 158
Tenant Type % Family 72%
Older 15% Single 13%

Lake District HA Ltd
○ Charitable HA
TSA Reg ✗
Calgarth Park, Troutbeck Bridge,
Windermere, Cumbria, LA23 1LF
T 0153 94 43016
E calgarth.park@btconnect.com
W www.calgarthpark.co.uk
Sec Mrs Heather Cook
Total Staff 4
Region North West
Owned or managed 24
Rt 24 OP 24
Tenant Type % Family 20%
Older 100% Single 80%

Lambeth & Southwark HA Ltd
○ Charitable HA
TSA Reg ✓ 🏠
7a St Agnes Place, London, SE11 4AU
T 020 7735 3935
E housing@lsha.org.uk
W www.lsha.org.uk
CE Mr Tony Withnell
Sec Mr Tony Withnell
Ch Mr Matthew Wicks
Total Staff 6
Region London
Owned or managed 315
Rt 315 GN 315
Tenant Type % Family 66%
Older 9% Single 25%
Development Total 10
NBA 10

Lambeth Self Help HA Ltd
★ Co-operative Society
TSA Reg ✓
Room 405, Bon Marche Centre,
241-251 Ferndale Road, London,
Greater London, SW9 8BJ
T 020 7274 8848
E admin@lshha.fsnet.co.uk
W www.lambethselfhelp.co.uk
CE Mr Abraham Krespin
Sec Mr Robert Speak
Ch Ms Janet Dymka
Total Staff 3
Region London
Owned or managed 53
Rt 53 GN 53
Tenant Type % Family 40%
Older 4% Single 56%

Langley House Trust
❑ Charitable Trust
TSA Reg ✓ 🕶
PO Box 181, Witney,
Oxfordshire, OX28 6WD
T 01993 774075
E info@langleyhousetrust.org
W www.langleyhousetrust.org
CE Miss Tracy Wild

Ch Mr Antony Howlett-Bolton
Total Staff 204
Regions South West + London,
South East, East Midlands, West
Midlands, East of England, Yorkshire
& Humberside, North West
Owned or managed 499
Rt 497 GN 62 Sup 435 NSO 2
Tenant Type % Single 100%

Larcombe HA Ltd
○ Charitable HA
TSA Reg ✓ 🕶
Wellesley Lodge, 41 Worcester
Road, Sutton, Surrey, SM2 6PY
T 020 8643 9086
E larcombeha@yahoo.co.uk
W www.larcombeha.netfirms.com
CE Mr A Wilson
Sec Mrs C Adams
Ch Mr A Wilson
Total Staff 29
Region London
Owned or managed 36
Rt 34 GN 8 Sup 5 OP 21 NSO 2
Tenant Type % Older 56%
Single 44%

Leasowe Community Homes
☆ Charitable Company
TSA Reg ✓ 🕶 🏠 🔑 ♨
Your Housing Group, Thomson
House, Faraday Street, Birchwood
Park, Warrington, WA3 6GA
T 01925 236400
W www.yourhousinggroup.co.uk
CE Mr Brian Cronin
Sec Mrs Bronwen Rapley
Ch Mr James D Murphy
Total Staff 0
Region North West
Owned or managed 1337
Rt 1331 GN 1331 SO 6 Tot lets 75
GN bs 976
Tenant Type % Family 70%
Older 10% Single 20%
Development Total 1
NBA 1
Parent Association
Arena Housing Group Ltd

Leatherhead United Charities
❑ Charitable Trust
TSA Reg ✓
Homefield, Forty Foot Road,
Leatherhead, Surrey, KT22 8RP
T 01372 370073
E luchar@btinternet.com
CE Mr David Matanle
Sec Mr David Matanle
Ch Mr John Henderson
Total Staff 2
Region South East

Owned or managed 30
Rt 30 OP 30
Tenant Type % Older 100%

Lee HA
○ Charitable HA
TSA Reg ✓ 🔑 ✒
227 High Street, Ponders End,
Enfield, Middlesex, EN3 4DX
T 020 8805 0548
E reception@leeha.co.uk
W www.leeha.co.uk
CE Mr Donald Douglas
Sec Brenda Barrett
Ch Mr Mark Sweeny
Total Staff 14
Region London
Owned or managed 357
Rt 341 GN 341 SO 8 NSO 8
Tot lets 0 GN bs 0
Tenant Type % Single 100%

Leeds & Yorkshire HA Ltd
○ Charitable HA
TSA Reg ✓ 🏠 ✒
2 Shire Oak Road, Leeds,
West Yorkshire, LS6 2TN
T 0113 278 3335
E info@lyha.co.uk
W www.lyha.co.uk
CE Miss Lisa Pickard
Ch Mr David Horner
Total Staff 36
Regions Yorkshire & Humberside +
North West
Owned or managed 1223
Rt 1211 GN 1081 OP 130 NSO 12
Tenant Type % Family 85%
Older 5% Single 10%
Development Total 29
NBA 29

Leeds Federated HA Ltd
○ Charitable HA
TSA Reg ✓ 🏠 🔑 ✒
Arthington House,
30 Westfield Road, Leeds,
West Yorkshire, LS3 1DE
T 0113 386 1000
E homes@lfha.co.uk
W www.lfha.co.uk
CE Mr Matthew Walker
Sec Mrs Ann Marie Matson
Ch Eric Bowen
Total Staff 117
Region Yorkshire & Humberside
Owned or managed 3635
Rt 3393 GN 2802 Sup 105 OP 486
SO 157 NSO 85 Tot lets 499
GN bs 2802
Tenant Type % Family 58%
Older 20% Single 42%
Development Total 20
Rt 26 GN 26 NBC 20

Leeds Housing Concern
☆ Charitable Company
TSA Reg ✗ ✒
4 Ashbrooke Business Park,
Parkside Lane, Leeds,
West Yorkshire, LS11 5SF
T 0113 276 0616
E info@leedshc.org.uk
W www.leedshc.org.uk
CE Ms Janet Spencer
Sec Mr Alan Marriott
Ch Mr Keith Hearn
Total Staff 97
Region Yorkshire & Humberside
Tenant Type % Family 1% Older 5%
Single 94%

Leeds Irish Health & Homes Ltd
○ Charitable HA
TSA Reg ✗ ✒ 🏠
Unit 5, Gemini Business Park,
Sheepscar Way, Leeds,
West Yorkshire, LS7 3JB
T 0113 262 5614
E info@lihh.org
W www.lihh.org
CE Mr Anthony Hanlon
Sec Mr Anthony Hanlon
Ch Mr Mel Nally
Total Staff 19
Region Yorkshire & Humberside
Owned or managed 72
Rt 72 Sup 72
Tenant Type % Older 17%
Single 83%

Leeds Jewish HA Ltd
○ Charitable HA
TSA Reg ✓ 🏠 🔑 ✒ 🏠
311 Stonegate Road, Moortown,
Leeds, West Yorkshire, LS17 6AZ
T 0113 203 4910
E info@ljha.co.uk
W www.ljha.co.uk
CE Mr Darren Cooper
Sec Mr Darren Cooper
Ch Dr Stephen Lewis
Total Staff 24
Region Yorkshire & Humberside
Owned or managed 482
Rt 444 GN 193 Sup 12 OP 239
SO 38 Tot lets 80 GN bs 444
Tenant Type % Family 25%
Older 50% Single 25%
Development Total 25
NBC 25

Leicester HA Ltd
■ Non-Charitable HA
TSA Reg ✓ 🖥 🏠 🔑 ✒ 🔥
3 Bede Island Road, Leicester,
Leicestershire, LE2 7EA
T 0116 257 6700

E itdept@asra.org.uk
W www.lha.org.uk
CE Mr Matt Cooney
Sec Mr Matt Cooney
Ch Sadru Visram, OBE
Total Staff 244
Regions East Midlands +
West Midlands
Owned or managed 8165
Rt 7554 GN 6472 Sup 438 OP 644
SO 311 NSO 300 Tot lets 1065
GN bs 5518
Tenant Type % Family 65%
Older 15% Single 20%
Development Total 227
NBA 121 NBC 106
Parent Association
Asra Housing Group Ltd

Leicester Quaker HA Ltd
○ Charitable HA
TSA Reg ✓ ✒
28 Queens Road, Leicester,
Leicestershire, LE2 1WP
T 0116 270 0748
W www.leicesterquakerhousing.co.uk
CE Mr Alastair Jackson
Sec Mr Alastair Jackson
Ch Marion Cullen
Total Staff 59
Region East Midlands
Owned or managed 112
Rt 69 Sup 49 OP 20 NSO 43
Tenant Type % Older 100%

Leicestershire Rural HA Ltd
○ Charitable HA
TSA Reg ✗ 🔑
Whitwick Business Centre, Whitwick
Business Park, Stenson Road,
Coalville, Leicestershire, LE67 4JP
T 01530 278080
E midlandsrural@midlandsrh.org.uk
W www.leicestershirerha.org.uk
Sec Mr Craig Felts
Ch Mr Richard Blunt
Total Staff 0
Region East Midlands
Owned or managed 134
Rt 110 GN 110 SO 24 Tot lets 9
GN bs 0
Tenant Type % Family 61%
Older 24% Single 15%

Lench's Trust
❏ Charitable Trust
TSA Reg ✓ 🔑
William Lench Court,
80 Ridgacre Road, Quinton,
Quinton, Birmingham, West
Midlands, B32 2AQ
T 0121 426 0455
E theclerk@lenchs-trust.co.uk
W www.lenchs-trust.co.uk

CE Mr Jean-Luc Priez
Sec Mr Jean-Luc Priez
Ch Ms Kate Cooper
Total Staff 13
Region West Midlands
Owned or managed 170
Rt 153 **OP** 153 **SO** 17 **Tot lets** 0
GN bs 0
Tenant Type % Older 100%

Leo Baeck HA Ltd
○ Charitable HA
TSA Reg ✓ 👓
Clara Nehab House, 13-19 Leeside
Crescent, London, Londonderry,
NW11 0DA
T 020 8455 2286
E david@lbha.co.uk
W www.lbha.co.uk
CE Mr David Lightburn
Sec Mr David Lightburn
Ch Mr Richard Fisher
Total Staff 29
Region London
Owned or managed 41
Rt 41 **Sup** 41
Tenant Type % Older 100%

Lewisham Family Self Help Association Ltd
○ Charitable HA
TSA Reg ✗
188 Brockley Road, London,
Greater London, SE4 2RN
T 020 8692 9294
CE Mr Barrie Stanbrook
Ch Mr Per von Scheibner
Total Staff 1
Region London
Owned or managed 96
Rt 96 **GN** 96
Tenant Type % Family 80%
Single 20%

Lewisham Park HA Ltd
○ Charitable HA
TSA Reg ✗ 👓 🏠
St Mauritius House,
65-67 Lewisham Park, Lewisham,
London, Greater London, SE13 6QX
T 020 8314 5391
W www.lewishampark.com
CE Mrs Helen Jackson
Sec Mrs Helen Jackson
Ch Mrs Joan Newman
Total Staff 0
Region London
Tenant Type % Older 100%

Ley Community Drug Services
❑ Charitable Trust
TSA Reg ✗
Sandy Croft, Sandy Lane, Yarnton,
Oxford, Oxfordshire, OX5 1PB
T 01865 371777
E enq@ley.co.uk
W www.ley.co.uk
CE Mrs Wendy Dawson
Sec Mr Chris Swann
Ch Mr Giles Charrington
Total Staff 0
Region South East
Tenant Type % Single 100%

Lien Viet HA Ltd
○ Charitable HA
TSA Reg ✓ 🔧 👓 ◊ 🏠
100 Morning Lane, Hackney, London,
Greater London, E9 6LH
T 020 8986 6123
E lienviet@lienviet.org.uk
W www.lienviet.org.uk
CE Mr Jonathan Card
Sec Mr Jonathan Card
Ch Mr Peter Ton-That
Total Staff 5
Region London
Owned or managed 143
Rt 140 **GN** 121 **Sup** 19 **SO** 3
Tot lets 0 **GN bs** 0
Tenant Type % Family 80%
Single 20%
Parent Association Islington &
Shoreditch HA Ltd

Limpsfield & Oxted Cottage Society Ltd
○ Charitable HA
TSA Reg ✗
C/o Payne & Co, Station Road West,
Oxted, Surrey, RH8 9EG
T 01883 712261
E mja@payneandco.com
Sec Mr Malcolm J Abbott
Ch M Rainbird
Total Staff 0
Region South East
Owned or managed 72
Rt 72 **GN** 72
Tenant Type % Family 40%
Older 30% **Single** 30%

Lincolnshire Rural HA Ltd
○ Charitable HA
TSA Reg ✓ 🔧
Markime House, Poole's Lane,
Spilsby, Lincolnshire, PE23 5EY
T 01790 754219
E customerservice@lrha.co.uk
W www.lrha.co.uk
CE Mr John D Howes, FRICS
Sec Mr John D Howes, FRICS

Ch Mr Robert Whetton
Total Staff 8
Regions East Midlands + East of
England, Yorkshire & Humberside
Owned or managed 387
Rt 363 **GN** 363 **SO** 24 **Tot lets** 21
GN bs 0
Tenant Type % Family 81%
Older 11% **Single** 8%

Little Black Bag HA Ltd
○ Charitable HA
TSA Reg ✓ 👓
c/o Eldon HA Ltd,
7 Banstead Road, Purley,
Surrey, CR8 3EB
T 020 8668 9861
E info@eldonhousing.co.uk
Sec Elizabeth F Range
Ch Mr David Lawrence
Total Staff 9
Region South East
Owned or managed 25
Rt 25 **OP** 25
Tenant Type % Older 100%

Liverpool Housing Trust
○ Charitable HA
TSA Reg ✓ 🖥 🖨 📷 🔧 ♦ 👓 ◊
12 Hanover Street, Liverpool,
Merseyside, L1 4AA
T 01928 796000
E info@lht.co.uk
W www.lht.co.uk
CE Ms Sue Westwater
Sec Mrs Audrey Davidson
Ch Ms Clare Nelson
Total Staff 302
Region North West
Owned or managed 10401
Rt 9939 **GN** 8240 **Sup** 1090 **OP** 609
SO 391 **NSO** 71 **Tot lets** 1214
GN bs 8233
Tenant Type % Family 55%
Older 11% **Single** 34%
Development Total 336
Rt 197 **GN** 174 **Sup** 23 **LCHO** 45
NBA 174 **NBC** 162
Parent Association
Symphony Housing Group

Liverpool Jewish HA Ltd
○ Charitable HA
TSA Reg ✓ 👓
61 Rex Cohen Court, Lathbury Lane,
Liverpool, Merseyside, L17 2BH
T 0151 280 0551
CE Mr Gareth Jones
Sec Mr Gareth Jones
Ch Alan Tinger
Total Staff 9
Region North West
Owned or managed 228
Rt 208 **GN** 40 **OP** 168 **NSO** 20

Tenant Type % Family 17%
Older 74% Single 9%

Liverpool Mutual Homes Ltd
○ Charitable HA
TSA Reg ✓ ▦ ▭ 🚚 ♦ 🤝
Commutation Plaza, 1 Commutation
Row, Liverpool, Merseyside, L3 8QF
T 0800 678 1894
E info@liverpoolmh.co.uk
W www.liverpoolmutualhomes.org
CE Mr Steve Coffey
Sec Mr Peter Fieldsend
Ch Mr William Lacey
Total Staff 319
Region North West
Owned or managed 15201
Rt 15201 GN 14478 OP 723
Tenant Type % Family 74%
Older 12% Single 15%

livin
○ Charitable HA
TSA Reg ✓ ▭ 🖾
Farrell House, Arlington Way,
DurhamGate, Spennymoor, Durham,
DL16 6NL
T 0845 505 5500
E finance@livin.co.uk
W www.livin.co.uk
CE Mr Colin Steel
Sec Mr Alan Smith
Ch Mr Ian Youll
Total Staff 0
Region North East
Owned or managed 8536
Rt 8536 GN 5437 OP 3099
Tenant Type % Family 64%
Older 36%
Development Total 10
NBA 10

Local Space Ltd
○ Charitable HA
TSA Reg ✓ 🖾
58 Romford Road, Stratford,
London, Greater London, E15 4BZ
T 020 8221 4034
E info@localspace.co.uk
W www.localspace.co.uk
CE Mr Bob Young
Sec Mr Bob Young
Ch Mr Tony Shoults
Total Staff 23
Region London
Owned or managed 1758
Rt 1758 GN 1758
Development Total 5
NBA 5

Locking Deanery HS Ltd
○ Charitable HA
TSA Reg ✓ 🤝
Clarence House, 17 Clarence Road
North, Weston Super Mare,
North Somerset, BS23 4AS
T 01934 644434
W www.clarencehouse.org
CE Mr Mike Harding
Sec Mr Mike Harding
Ch Mr David Martin
Total Staff 22
Region South West
Owned or managed 34
Rt 34 OP 34
Tenant Type % Older 100%

London & Quadrant Housing Trust
○ Charitable HA
TSA Reg ✓ ▦ ▭ 🚚 🖾 🔑 ♦
One Kings Hall Mews, Lewisham,
London, Greater London, SE13 5JQ
T 0844 406 9000
E lqdirect@lqgroup.org.uk
W www.lqgroup.org.uk
CE Mr David Montague
Sec Miss Mo Siakpere
Ch Mr Turlogh O'Brien
Total Staff 1143
Regions London + South East,
East of England
Owned or managed 62505
Rt 51525 GN 47325 Sup 2139
OP 2061 SO 9204 NSO 1776
Tot lets 4817 GN bs 47206
Tenant Type % Family 53%
Older 4% Single 36%
Development Total 1602
Rt 1488 GN 1488 LCHO 789
NBC 1602

London Cyrenians Housing Ltd
☆ Charitable Company
TSA Reg ✓ ♦ 🤝
1st Floor, 181 Kensington High
Street, London, Greater London,
W8 6SH
T 020 7938 2004
W www.londoncyrenians.org.uk
CE Ms Tracey Dann
Sec Mr James McNicholas
Ch Mr Stephen Bashorun
Total Staff 272
Regions London + South East
Owned or managed 273
Rt 273 Sup 273
Tenant Type % Single 100%

London Housing Trust
✪ Not-for-Profit Company
TSA Reg ✓ 🤝
4 Cliff Terrace, London, SE8 4DZ
T 07956 926666
E housing@londonhousingtrust.org
W www.londonhousingtrust.org
CE Dr Stephen Dellar
Ch Miss Nazmun Nahar
Total Staff 3
Region London
Owned or managed 116
Rt 116 Sup 116
Tenant Type % Older 10%
Single 100%

London Strategic Housing Ltd
○ Charitable HA
TSA Reg ✓ 🖾 🔑 🜄
5th Floor, Olympic Office Centre,
8 Fulton Road, Wembley, Middlesex,
HA9 0NU
T 020 8782 4850
E enquiries@londonstrategichousing.
com
W www.londonstrategichousing.com
CE Mr Jon Dawson
Sec Mr Richard Reger
Ch Ms Linda Walton
Total Staff 26
Regions London + East of England
Owned or managed 1616
Rt 1564 GN 1564 SO 14 NSO 38
Tot lets 779 GN bs 6
Tenant Type % Family 15%
Single 85%
Development Total 52
NBA 26 NBC 26
Parent Association
Network Housing Group Ltd

Longdendale Housing Society Ltd
■ Non-Charitable HA
TSA Reg ✓
Cheethams House, 96 Market Street,
Stalybridge, Cheshire, SK15 2AB
T 0161 304 8309
CE Mr G L Eckersall
Sec Mr G L Eckersall
Ch Mr C A Meredith
Total Staff 1
Region North West
Tenant Type % Family 34%
Older 49% Single 17%

Longhurst & Havelok Homes Ltd
○ Charitable HA
TSA Reg ✓
Leverett House, Gilbert Drive, Endeavour Park, Boston, Lincolnshire, PE21 7TQ
T 0800 111 4013
E service.centre@longhurst-group.org.uk
W www.landh.org.uk
CE Mr Mike Hardy
Sec Mr Mike Hardy
Ch Mr Sidney McFarlane MBE
Total Staff 355
Regions East Midlands + East of England, Yorkshire & Humberside
Owned or managed 7748
Rt 6168 GN 5690 Sup 86 OP 392 SO 787 NSO 793 Tot lets 1280 GN bs 5400
Tenant Type % Family 51%
Older 26% Single 23%
Development Total 510
Rt 362 GN 310 OP 52 LCHO 102 NBA 302 NBC 208
Parent Association Longhurst Group Ltd

Longhurst Group Ltd
✪ Not-for-Profit Company
TSA Reg ✓ ◊
Leverett House, Gilbert Drive, Endeavour Park, Boston, Lincolnshire, PE21 7TQ
T 0845 309 0700
E service.centre@longhurst-group.org.uk
W www.longhurst-group.org.uk
CE Mr Bob Walder
Sec Mr Bob Walder
Ch Mr David Armes
Total Staff 145
Region East Midlands
Subsidiary Association(s) Friendship Care and Housing; Keystone Developments (LG) Ltd; Longhurst & Havelok Homes Ltd; Spire Homes (LG) Ltd

Longlife Housing Co-operative Ltd
★ Co-operative Society
TSA Reg ✓
6b Tower Hamlets Road, Forest Gate, London, Greater London, E7 9BZ
T 020 8519 9708
E office@longlife.org.uk
Sec Mr Barry Rowan
Ch Mr Mickey Kannemeyer
Total Staff 0
Region London

Owned or managed 64
Rt 64 GN 64
Tenant Type % Family 49%
Older 5% Single 46%

Look Ahead Housing and Care Ltd
○ Charitable HA
TSA Reg ✓
1 Derry Street, Kensington, London, Greater London, W8 5HY
T 020 7937 1166
E info@lookahead.org.uk
W www.lookahead.org.uk
CE Victoria Stark
Sec Victoria Stark
Ch Mr Stephen Alexander
Total Staff 741
Regions London + South East
Owned or managed 1901
Rt 1888 GN 13 Sup 1875 NSO 13
Tenant Type % Family 10%
Single 90%

Lowther & District HA Ltd
■ Non-Charitable HA
TSA Reg ✓
c/o Eden HA, Blain House, Bridge Lane, Penrith, Cumbria, CA11 8QU
T 01768 861400
E enquiry@edenha.org.uk
CE Mr John Clasper
Sec Mr Sean Relph
Ch Mrs S E Duff
Total Staff 0
Region North West
Owned or managed 99
Rt 99 GN 99
Tenant Type % Family 51%
Older 37% Single 12%

Luminus Group
■ Non-Charitable HA
TSA Reg ✓ ◊
Brook House, Ouse Walk, Huntingdon, Cambs, Cambridgeshire, PE29 3QW
T 01480 428701
E info@luminus.org.uk
W www.luminus.org.uk
CE Dr Chan Abraham
Sec Dr Chan Abraham
Ch Mrs Roz Brench
Total Staff 91
Region East of England
Owned or managed 4
NSO 4
Tenant Type % Family 100%
Subsidiary Association(s) Luminus Homes; Oak Foundation

Luminus Homes
■ Non-Charitable HA
TSA Reg ✓
Brook House, Ouse Walk, Huntingdon, Cambridgeshire, PE29 3QW
T 01480 428701
E info@luminus.org.uk
W www.luminus.org.uk
CE Dr Chan Abraham
Sec Dr Chan Abraham
Ch Mr David Vessey
Total Staff 151
Regions East of England + South East
Owned or managed 6447
Rt 5719 GN 5700 Sup 19 SO 686 NSO 42 Tot lets 697 GN bs 5588
Tenant Type % Family 38%
Older 50% Single 12%
Development Total 78
Rt 143 GN 143 LCHO 50 NBA 39 NBC 39
Parent Association Luminus Group

Lune Valley Rural HA Ltd
☆ Charitable Company
TSA Reg ✓
Ann James House, 32-34 St Thomas's Road, Chorley, PR7 1HR
T 01257 244800
E info@adactushousing.co.uk
W www.chorleych.co.uk
CE Mr Richard Houghton
Sec Mr Simon Noble
Ch Mr Hugh Clay
Total Staff 0
Regions North West + Yorkshire & Humberside
Owned or managed 77
Rt 77 GN 77
Tenant Type % Family 77%
Older 19% Single 4%

Luton Community Housing Ltd
○ Charitable HA
TSA Reg ✓
108 Wellington Street, Luton, Bedfordshire, LU1 5AF
T 01582 391053
E office@lch-ltd.co.uk
W www.lutonhousing.org
CE Mrs Lynda Rees
Sec Mrs Lynda Rees
Ch Mr Bashir Ul Hafeez
Total Staff 59
Region East of England
Owned or managed 541
Rt 541 GN 379 Sup 135 OP 27
Tenant Type % Family 57% Older 7%
Single 36%

Lyng Community Association
☆ Charitable Company
TSA Reg ✓
3 Frank Fisher Way,
West Bromwich, B70 7AW
T 0121 525 5969
E lyngcomm@btconnect.com
CE Mr Christopher Withnall BA, FCIH
Ch Mrs Wendy Bodenham
Total Staff 0
Region West Midlands
Owned or managed 86
Rt 86 **GN** 86
Tenant Type % Family 75%
Single 25%

Lytham St Annes Lions Club HA Ltd
○ Charitable HA
TSA Reg ✗
C/o C Holt, No.1 Westwood Mews,
Lytham St Annes, Lancashire,
FY8 5QE
T 01253 782515
Sec Mr Colin Holt MBE
Ch Mr Ralph B Morgan
Total Staff 0
Region North West
Owned or managed 8
Rt 8 **OP** 8
Tenant Type % Older 100%

Lytham St Annes War Memorial HA Ltd
○ Charitable HA
TSA Reg ✓
309 Church Road, Lyntham St Annes,
Lancashire, FY8 3PJ
T 01253 782515
Sec Jacqueline Wright
Ch Mr Russell C Woods
Total Staff 2
Region North West
Owned or managed 114
Rt 114 **OP** 114
Tenant Type % Older 100%

Mm

Mace Housing Co-op Ltd
★ Co-operative Society
TSA Reg ✗
The Print House, 18 Ashwin Street,
London, Greater London, E8 3DL
T 020 7254 9560
E info@macehousing.org.uk
W www.mace-housing.org.uk
CE Mr Rowland Ekperi
Sec Ms Gabriela Estifamos

Ch Ms Margaret Shenton
Total Staff 6
Region London
Owned or managed 274
Rt 274 **GN** 274
Tenant Type % Family 30%
Single 70%

MacIntyre HA Ltd
○ Charitable HA
TSA Reg ✓
Katherine's House, Dunstable Street,
Ampthill, Bedfordshire, MK45 2JP
T 01525 844400
E macintyre.ha@aragon-housing.co.uk
W www.macintyreha.co.uk
CE Ms Aileen Evans
Sec Ms Aileen Evans
Ch Mr Nicholas Dimbleby
Total Staff 15
Regions East of England + London,
South East, East Midlands,
West Midlands
Owned or managed 479
Rt 476 **GN** 12 **Sup** 464 **NSO** 3
Tenant Type % Single 100%
Parent Association Grand Union
Housing Group Ltd

Magna HA Ltd
○ Charitable HA
TSA Reg ✓
Hollands House, Poundbury Road,
Dorchester, Dorset, DT1 1SW
T 01305 216000
E hollands@magna.org.uk
W www.magna.org.uk
CE Mr Graham Colls
Sec Ms Debby Wheatley
Ch Mr Donald Rushton
Total Staff 192
Region South West
Owned or managed 6734
Rt 6117 **GN** 4475 **Sup** 192 **OP** 1450
SO 409 **NSO** 208 **Tot lets** 690
GN bs 4445
Tenant Type % Family 44%
Older 31% **Single** 25%
Development Total 414
NBA 232 **NBC** 182
Parent Association
Magna Housing Group Ltd

Magna Housing Group Ltd
■ Non-Charitable HA
TSA Reg ✓
Hollands House, Poundbury Road,
Dorchester, Dorset, DT1 1SW
T 01305 216000
E firstname.lastname@magna.org.uk
W www.magna.org.uk
CE Mr Graham Colls
Sec Ms Debby Wheatley
Ch Mr Donald Rushton

Total Staff 0
Region South West
Subsidary Association(s)
Magna HA Ltd; Magna West
Somerset HA Ltd

Magna West Somerset HA Ltd
○ Charitable HA
TSA Reg ✓
St Peter's House, Bridge Street,
Williton, Somerset, TA4 4NR
T 01984 635100
E westsom@magna.org.uk
W www.magnaws.org.uk
CE Mr Graham Colls
Sec Ms Debby Wheatley
Ch Mr Donald Rushton
Total Staff 87
Region South West
Owned or managed 2322
Rt 2200 **GN** 1702 **Sup** 85 **OP** 413
SO 97 **NSO** 25 **Tot lets** 256
GN bs 1699
Tenant Type % Family 30%
Older 43% **Single** 27%
Development Total 157
Rt 55 **GN** 55 **NBA** 79 **NBC** 78
Parent Association
Magna Housing Group Ltd

Maldon HA Ltd
☆ Charitable Company
TSA Reg ✓
Fairfield House, 33 Fambridge Road,
Maldon, Essex, CM9 6AD
T 01621 840247
E maldonha@btconnect.com
W www.maldonha.co.uk
CE Mrs Gillian Davison
Sec Mrs Gillian Davison
Ch Mr Terry Collin
Total Staff 11
Region East of England
Owned or managed 58
Rt 58 **OP** 58
Tenant Type % Older 100%

Manchester & District HA
○ Charitable HA
TSA Reg ✓
Your Housing Group, Thomson
House, Faraday Street, Birchwood
Park, Warrington, WA3 6GA
T 01925 236400
W www.yourhousinggroup.co.uk
CE Mr Brian Cronin
Sec Mrs Bronwen Rapley
Ch Mrs Kathy Cowell
Total Staff 0
Regions North West +
East Midlands
Owned or managed 10090

Rt 8844 **GN** 6660 **Sup** 276 **OP** 1908
SO 1246 **Tot lets** 1207 **GN bs** 6017
Tenant Type % Family 38%
Older 19% **Single** 43%
Development Total 36
Rt 79 **GN** 24 **OP** 55 **NBA** 25
NBC 11
Parent Association
Your Housing Group
Subsidiary Association(s)
Partington HA

Manchester Care & Repair Ltd
☆ Charitable Company
TSA Reg ✗ 🖤
Unit 14, Empress Buildings,
380 Chester Road, Manchester,
Lancashire, M16 9EA
T 0161 872 5500
E mail@careandrepair-manchester.org.uk
W www.careandrepair-manchester.org.uk
CE Ms Maggie Walker
Sec Ms Maggie Walker
Ch Mr Mark Longhill
Total Staff 48
Region North West

Manchester Jewish HA Ltd
○ Charitable HA
TSA Reg ✓ 🖤
85 Middleton Road, Crumpsall,
Manchester, Lancashire, M8 4JY
T 0161 740 0001
E info@mjha.org.uk
W www.mjha.org.uk
CE Mr John Gryckiewicz
Sec Mr John Gryckiewicz
Ch Ms Lucette Tucker &
Mr David Marks
Total Staff 11
Region North West
Owned or managed 102
Rt 102 **GN** 1 **Sup** 11 **OP** 90
Tenant Type % Older 89%
Single 11%

Manningham HA Ltd
○ Charitable HA
TSA Reg ✓ 🔑 🖤 🏠
Bank House, 30 Manor Row,
Bradford, West Yorkshire, BD1 4QE
T 01274 771144
E admin@manninghamha.co.uk
W www.manninghamhousing.co.uk
CE Mr Ansar Ali
Sec Mr Masoud Khan
Ch Mr Greg Robinson
Total Staff 52
Region Yorkshire & Humberside
Owned or managed 1333
Rt 1270 **GN** 1198 **Sup** 48 **OP** 24

SO 63 **Tot lets** 187 **GN bs** 1198
Tenant Type % Family 87%
Older 4% **Single** 9%
Development Total 74
Rt 50 **GN** 50 **NBA** 37 **NBC** 37

Mansfield Road (Nottingham) Baptist HA Ltd
○ Charitable HA
TSA Reg ✓ 🖤
45 Fox Grove Court, Nottingham
Road, Basford, Nottingham,
Nottinghamshire, NG5 1JA
T 0115 942 1508
E info@mrbha.org
W www.mrbha.org
CE Ms Jacqueline Ward
Sec Mrs S E Bye
Ch Mr Alan Joddrell
Total Staff 13
Region East Midlands
Owned or managed 110
Rt 110 **OP** 110
Tenant Type % Older 100%

Marches HA Ltd
○ Charitable HA
TSA Reg ✓ 🚚 🏠 🔑 🖤 🏠
Benedict Court, Southern Avenue,
Leominster, Herefordshire, HR6 0QF
T 01568 610100
E home@marchesha.co.uk
W www.marchesha.co.uk
CE Mr Philip Green
Sec Mr Philip Green
Ch Mr Stuart Chapman
Total Staff 86
Region West Midlands
Owned or managed 2861
Rt 2727 **GN** 2147 **Sup** 14 **OP** 566
SO 134 **Tot lets** 263 **GN bs** 1755
Tenant Type % Family 72%
Older 25% **Single** 3%
Development Total 124
NBA 67 **NBC** 57
Parent Association
Jephson Homes HA Ltd

Marlborough & District HA Ltd
○ Charitable HA
TSA Reg ✓
126 High Street, Marlborough,
Wiltshire, SN8 1LZ
T 01672 512163
Sec A Deuchar
Ch Mr Ken Culley
Total Staff 2
Region South West
Owned or managed 24
Rt 24 **GN** 24
Tenant Type % Older 100%

Martlet Homes Ltd
○ Charitable HA
TSA Reg ✓ 🖥 🖥 🚚 🏠 🔑 🏠 🏠
Martlet House, Southern Gate,
Chichester, West Sussex, PO19 8SG
T 01243 788794
E info@hydemartlet.co.uk
W www.hyde-housing.co.uk
CE Ms Jane Ball
Sec Mr John Edwards
Ch Ms C Holloway
Total Staff 329
Region South East
Owned or managed 10931
Rt 10423 **GN** 10009 **Sup** 1 **OP** 413
SO 497 **NSO** 11 **Tot lets** 366
GN bs 4917
Tenant Type % Family 40%
Older 45% **Single** 15%
Development Total 125
NBA 66 **NBC** 59
Parent Association Hyde HA Ltd

Mary Morris International Residence Ltd
○ Charitable HA
TSA Reg ✓
24 Shire Oak Road, Headingley,
Leeds, West Yorkshire, LS6 2DE
T 0113 284 4600
E info@unipol.org.uk
W www.marymorris.com
CE Ms Ann M Thompson
Ch Ms Jacqui Brown
Total Staff 7
Region Yorkshire & Humberside
Owned or managed 245
NSO 245
Tenant Type % Family 13%
Single 87%

Masonic HA
○ Charitable HA
TSA Reg ✓ 🖤
7 Banstead Road, Purley,
Surrey, CR8 3EB
T 020 8668 9861
E info@eldonhousing.co.uk
Sec Elizabeth F Range
Ch Mr Martin Clarke
Total Staff 13
Regions London + South East,
East Midlands, West Midlands,
East of England
Owned or managed 179
Rt 179 **OP** 179
Tenant Type % Older 100%

Maynard Co-operative HA Ltd
★ Co-operative Society
TSA Reg ✓ 🏠
131 Loughborough Road, Leicester, Leicestershire, LE4 5LQ
T 0116 257 6800
E tim.clarke@asra.org.uk
W www.maynardcoop.org.uk
CE Miss Nicola Parlby
Sec Mr S Gaffar
Ch Mr Alam Navsa
Total Staff 0
Region East Midlands
Owned or managed 114
Rt 114 GN 114
Tenant Type % Family 80%
Older 5% Single 15%

mcch Society Ltd
○ Charitable HA
TSA Reg ✗ 🏠 🔑 ♦ 🐦
One Hermitage Court, Hermitage Lane, Maidstone, Kent, ME16 9NT
T 01622 722400
E contactus@mcch.org.uk
W www.mcch.org.uk
CE Mr Peter Thompson
Sec Mr Peter Thompson
Ch Ann Cooke
Total Staff 1609
Regions South East + London
Owned or managed 126
Rt 125 Sup 125 SO 1 Tot lets 187
GN bs 0
Tenant Type % Single 100%
Development Total 88
Rt 28 Sup 28 NBA 76 NBC 12

Mercers Company HA Ltd
○ Charitable HA
TSA Reg ✗ 🐦
Mercers' Hall, Ironmonger Lane, London, Greater London, EC2V 8HE
T 020 7726 4991
E mail@mercers.co.uk
W www.mercers.co.uk
Sec Ms Katherine Payne
Ch The Honourable Henry Palmer
Total Staff 0
Region London
Tenant Type % Older 100%

Mercian HA Ltd
○ Charitable HA
TSA Reg ✓ 🔑 🐦 ◊
Gee Business Centre, Holborn Hill, Aston, Birmingham, West Midlands, B7 5JR
T 0121 322 7373
E enquiries@mercian.org.uk
W www.mercian.org.uk
CE Mr Kevin Devlin
Sec Ms Deborah Upton

Ch Mr Colin Small
Total Staff 0
Region West Midlands
Owned or managed 3496
Rt 2598 GN 2276 Sup 103 OP 219
SO 898 Tot lets 379 GN bs 2047
Tenant Type % Family 54%
Older 19% Single 27%
Parent Association Circle

Meres and Mosses HA
○ Charitable HA
TSA Reg ✓ 📠 🔑 🐦 ◊
Talbot House, High Street, Wem, Shropshire, SY4 5AA
T 01939 238840
E enquiries@mmha.org.uk
W www.mmha.org.uk
CE Mr Martin Holland
Sec Miss Jen Hayball
Ch Mr Gordon Hodgkiss
Total Staff 32
Region West Midlands
Owned or managed 2294
Rt 2269 GN 2078 OP 191 SO 25
Tot lets 166 GN bs 2078
Tenant Type % Family 50%
Older 35% Single 15%
Parent Association
Shropshire Housing Ltd

Merlin Housing Society Ltd
○ Charitable HA
TSA Reg ✓ 🖥 📠 🔑 ♦ 🐦
Building 1, Riverside Court, Bowling Hill, Chipping Sodbury, Bristol, South Gloucestershire, BS37 6JX
T 01454 821100
E enquiries@merlinhs.co.uk
W www.merlinhs.co.uk
CE Mr Roy Irwin
Sec Mr Andrew Ledger
Ch Andrew Frayling
Total Staff 322
Region South West
Owned or managed 8325
Rt 7815 GN 6419 Sup 1359 OP 37
SO 510 Tot lets 785 GN bs 6419
Tenant Type % Family 30%
Older 57% Single 13%

Merton Priory Homes
○ Charitable HA
TSA Reg ✓ 🖥 🔑 ◊
The Grange, 1 Central Road, Morden, Surrey, SM4 5PQ
T 0300 500 3000
E contactmph@circle.org.uk
W www.circle.org.uk/merton-priory-home
CE Mrs Pauline Ford
Sec Ms Deborah Upton
Ch Ms Jennifer Mills
Total Staff 200

Region London
Owned or managed 8852
Rt 6311 GN 6236 OP 75 SO 2541
Tot lets 364 GN bs 6236
Tenant Type % Family 47%
Older 25% Single 36%
Parent Association Circle

Methodist Homes HA
○ Charitable HA
TSA Reg ✓ 🐦 ◊
Epworth House, Stuart Street, Derby, Derbyshire, DE1 2EQ
T 01332 296200
E enquiries@mha.org.uk
W www.mha.org.uk
CE Mr Roger Davies
Sec Mr David Hayward
Ch Mr Norman Mann
Total Staff 42
Regions East Midlands + London, South East, South West, West Midlands, Yorkshire & Humberside, North East, North West
Owned or managed 771
Rt 766 Sup 474 OP 292 NSO 5
Tenant Type % Older 100%
Parent Association MHA

Metropolitan
☆ Charitable Company
TSA Reg ✓ ♦ 🐦 ◊
Cambridge House, 109 Mayes Road, Wood Green, London, Greater London, N22 6UR
T 020 8829 8000
E info@mhp-online.org.uk
W www.mhp-online.co.uk
CE Mr Mark Austin
Ch Barbara Roche
Total Staff 683
Regions London + Yorkshire & Humberside
Owned or managed 395
Rt 395 GN 13 Sup 382
Tenant Type % Single 100%
Parent Association Metropolitan

Metropolitan
○ Charitable HA
TSA Reg ✓ 🖥 🖥 📠 🏠 🔑 ♦ 🐦 ◊
Cambridge House, 109 Mayes Road, Wood Green, London, N22 6UR
T 020 3535 3000
E info@mhp-online.co.uk
W www.mhp-online.co.uk
CE Mr Brian Johnson
Sec Mrs Kristina Ingate
Ch Barbara Roche
Total Staff 1696
Regions London + South East, East Midlands, West Midlands, East of England, Yorkshire & Humberside

Owned or managed 36330
Rt 28778 GN 22939 Sup 2542
OP 3297 SO 6942 NSO 610
Tot lets 3604 GN bs 19940
Tenant Type % Family 33%
Older 26% Single 41%
Development Total 1175
Rt 503 GN 503 LCHO 122 NBA 814
NBC 361
Subsidiary Association(s) Clapham
Park Homes; Granta Housing Society
Ltd; Metropolitan; Spirita

MHA
☆ Charitable Company
TSA Reg ✓ ◊
Epworth House, Stuart Street,
Derby, Derbyshire, DE1 2EQ
T 01332 296200
E enquiries@mha.org.uk
W www.mha.org.uk
CE Mr Roger Davies
Sec Mr David Hayward
Ch Mr Keith Salisbury
Total Staff 140
Region East Midlands
Owned or managed 86
Rt 86 GN 3 OP 83
Tenant Type % Older 100%
Subsidiary Association(s) Methodist
Homes HA

MHS Homes Ltd
■ Non-Charitable HA
TSA Reg ✗ ▯ ▧ ▢ ◢ ♦ ◊
Broadside, Leviathan Way,
Chatham, Kent, ME4 4LL
T 01634 354000
E contactus@mhs.org.uk
W www.mhshomes.co.uk
CE Mr Ashley Hook
Sec Mr Carl Dewey
Ch Mr Ashley West
Total Staff 265
Regions South East + South West
Owned or managed 7482
Rt 7285 GN 6672 Sup 36 OP 577
SO 25 NSO 172 Tot lets 623
GN bs 6451
Tenant Type % Family 66%
Older 18% Single 16%
Development Total 61
NBC 61
Subsidiary Association(s) Heart of
Medway HA Ltd

Michael Blanning Trust HA Ltd
TSA Reg ✗ ▧
Shakespeares Solicitors, 37 Temple
Street, Birmingham, B2 5DJ
T 0121 237 3000
E keith.james@shakespeares.co.uk
Sec Mr Keith James
Ch Mr Keith James

Total Staff 0
Region West Midlands
Tenant Type % Older 100%

Midland Heart Ltd
○ Charitable HA
TSA Reg ✓ ▮ ▯ ▢ ◢ ♦ ▧
20 Bath Row, Birmingham,
West Midlands, B15 1LZ
T 0345 602 0540
E customer.servicecentre@
midlandheart.org.uk
W www.midlandheart.org.uk
CE Mrs Ruth Cooke
Sec Mr Andrew Foster
Ch Lord Bill Morris
Total Staff 1821
Regions West Midlands + South
East, East Midlands, East of England
Owned or managed 30745
Rt 26192 GN 21555 Sup 1863
OP 2774 SO 2610 NSO 1943
Tot lets 5732 GN bs 21227
Tenant Type % Family 45%
Older 25% Single 30%
Development Total 383
Rt 1412 GN 1065 Sup 139 OP 208
LCHO 190 NBA 21 NBC 362

Midlands Rural Housing & Village Development Assn Ltd
■ Non-Charitable HA
TSA Reg ✗ ◊
Whitwick Business Centre, Whitwick
Business Park, Stenson Road,
Coalville, Leicestershire, LE67 4JP
T 01530 278080
E midlandsrural@midlandsrh.org.uk
W www.midlandsruralhousing.org.uk
CE Mr Craig Felts
Sec Mrs Joanne Tilley
Ch Mr Derrick Dyas
Total Staff 19
Region East Midlands
Parent Association
East Midlands Housing Group

Mill Street Housing Society Ltd
○ Charitable HA
TSA Reg ✗ ▧
Fordington Hill House, High Street,
Fordington, Dorchester, Dorset,
DT1 1LZ
T 01305 261622
E mill.street@hotmail.co.uk
Sec Mr David Greenwood
Ch Mr Rupert J A Edwards
Total Staff 2
Region South West
Owned or managed 86
Rt 86 OP 40
Tenant Type % Family 50%
Older 45% Single 5%

Millat Asian HA Ltd
○ Charitable HA
TSA Reg ✓ ▧ ▣
58 Victoria Road, College Fields,
Mitcham, Surrey, CR4 3JA
T 020 8640 6413
E info@maha.org.uk
W www.maha.org.uk
CE Mr Mahmudul Islam
Sec Mr Jakir Alam Choudhary
Ch Mr Salim Ahmed
Total Staff 3
Region London
Owned or managed 103
Rt 103 GN 87 OP 16
Tenant Type % Family 76%
Older 20% Single 3%

Minster General HA Ltd
○ Charitable HA
TSA Reg ✓ ◢ ▧ ◊
Jubilee House, 92 Lincoln Road,
Peterborough, Cambridgeshire,
PE1 2SN
T 01733 349800
E info@minsterha.co.uk
W www.minster.hyde-housing.co.uk
CE Mr Steve Wilson
Sec Mr John Edwards
Ch Mr Derrick Biggs
Total Staff 51
Regions East of England + East
Midlands
Owned or managed 1747
Rt 1589 GN 1175 Sup 24 OP 390
SO 158 Tot lets 0 GN bs 1087
Tenant Type % Family 46%
Older 30% Single 24%
Parent Association
Hyde HA Ltd

Mitali HA Ltd
○ Charitable HA
TSA Reg ✓ ◊ ▣
148 Cambridge Heath Road, London,
Greater London, E1 5QJ
T 020 7780 2222
E office@mitaliha.org.uk
W www.mitaliha.org.uk
CE Mr Gabriel Codjoe
Sec Mr Richard Reger
Total Staff 3
Region London
Owned or managed 632
Rt 632 GN 632
Tenant Type % Family 100%
Parent Association Network
Housing Group Ltd

Mitre HA Ltd
○ Charitable HA
TSA Reg ✓ 🔑
c/o Eden HA, Blain House, Bridge
Lane, Penrith, Cumbria, CA11 8QU
T 01768 861400
E enquiry@edanha.org.uk
CE Mr John Clasper
Sec Mr Adrian Pritchard
Ch Dr Colin Hill
Total Staff 0
Region North West
Owned or managed 143
Rt 129 GN 129 SO 14 Tot lets 0
GN bs 0
Tenant Type % Family 40%
Older 40% Single 20%

Moat Homes Ltd
○ Charitable HA
TSA Reg ✓ 🔲 🔲 🚚 🔶 🔑 ⚲ ◊
Mariner House,
Galleon Boulevard, Crossways,
Dartford, Kent, DA2 6QE
T 0845 359 6300
E info@moat.co.uk
W www.moat.co.uk
CE Greg Taylor
Sec Jan Quirke
Ch Rosamund Blomfield-Smith
Total Staff 369
Regions South East + London,
South West, East of England
Owned or managed 16183
Rt 10749 GN 9279 Sup 214 OP 1256
SO 5337 NSO 97 Tot lets 1294
GN bs 8527
Tenant Type % Family 64%
Older 18% Single 18%
Development Total 1478
Rt 731 GN 731 LCHO 674
NBA 1214 NBC 264
Subsidiary Association(s)
Moat Housing Group

Moat Housing Group
■ Non-Charitable HA
TSA Reg ✓ ⚲ ◊
Mariner House,
Galleon Boulevard, Crossways,
Dartford, Kent, DA2 6QE
T 0845 359 6300
E customer@moat.co.uk
W www.moat.co.uk
CE Greg Taylor
Sec Ebele Akojie
Ch Tariq Cader
Total Staff 418
Region South East
Owned or managed 23
NSO 23
Parent Association
Moat Homes Ltd

Mole Valley HA Ltd
○ Charitable HA
TSA Reg ✓ 🚚 🔶 🔑 🤝 ◊
Regent House, Station Approach,
Dorking, Surrey, RH4 1TF
T 01306 505555
E info@mvha.org.uk
W www.mvha.org.uk
CE Mr David Searle
Sec Ms Deborah Upton
Ch Mr Alan Catterick
Total Staff 153
Region South East
Owned or managed 3930
Rt 3511 GN 2962 OP 549 SO 419
Tot lets 265 GN bs 2962
Tenant Type % Family 32%
Older 57% Single 11%
Development Total 48
NBA 39 NBC 9
Parent Association Circle

Monmouth Road Housing Co-operative Ltd
★ Co-operative Society
TSA Reg ✓
34 Monmouth Road, London,
Greater London, W2 4UT
Total Staff 0
Region London
Owned or managed 19
Rt 5 GN 5 NSO 14
Tenant Type % Family 40%
Older 20% Single 40%

Moorlands Housing
○ Charitable HA
TSA Reg ✓ 🚚 🔶 🔑 🤝 ◊
Your Housing Group, Thomson
House, Faraday Street, Birchwood
Park, Warrington, WA3 6GA
T 01925 236400
W www.yourhousinggroup.co.uk
CE Mr Brian Cronin
Sec Mrs Bronwen Rapley
Ch Bridget Johnson
Total Staff 0
Regions West Midlands +
North West
Owned or managed 3473
Rt 3420 GN 2573 Sup 17 OP 830
SO 53 Tot lets 299 GN bs 2014
Tenant Type % Family 45%
Older 26% Single 28%
Development Total 6
Rt 144 GN 144 NBA 6
Parent Association
Your Housing Group

Mossbank Homes Ltd
○ Charitable HA
TSA Reg ✓ 🔑 ◊
101 Great Western Street,
Moss Side, Manchester, Lancashire,
M14 4AA
T 0161 474 8340
E info@mossbank.org.uk
W www.mossbank.org.uk
CE Mr Rob Ferguson
Sec Mr Vince Ormrod
Ch Mr Reuben Flynn
Total Staff 12
Region North West
Owned or managed 1239
Rt 1128 GN 1128 SO 111 Tot lets 89
GN bs 1128
Tenant Type % Family 69%
Older 23% Single 8%
Parent Association
Mosscare Housing Ltd

Mosscare Housing Ltd
○ Charitable HA
TSA Reg ✓ 🔶 🔑 🤝 ◊
101 Gt Western Street, Moss Side,
Manchester, Lancashire, M14 4AA
T 0161 226 4211
E information@mosscare.org.uk
W www.mosscare.org.uk
CE Mr Rob Ferguson
Sec Mr Vince Ormrod
Ch Mr Frank Jones
Total Staff 155
Region North West
Owned or managed 3554
Rt 3418 GN 3028 Sup 257 OP 133
SO 136 Tot lets 394 GN bs 3028
Tenant Type % Family 77%
Older 13% Single 10%
Development Total 88
Rt 79 GN 79 NBA 58 NBC 30
Subsidiary Association(s)
Mossbank Homes Ltd

Mount Carmel
○ Charitable HA
TSA Reg ✗ 🤝
12 Aldrington Road, Streatham,
London, Greater London, SW16 1TH
T 020 8769 7674
E mountcarmeluk@yahoo.co.uk
W www.mountcarmel.org.uk
CE Ms Ruth Allonby
Sec Ms Ruth Allonby
Ch Bill Hughes
Total Staff 11
Region London
Tenant Type % Single 100%

Mount Green HA Ltd
○ Charitable HA
TSA Reg ✓ 🏠 🔑 🐝
33 Bridge Street, Leatherhead,
Surrey, KT22 8BN
T 01372 379555
E customerservices@mountgreen.
org.uk
W www.mountgreen.org.uk
CE Mr Nick Ronald
Sec Mr Nick Ronald
Ch Mr Stephen Bromley
Total Staff 32
Regions South East + London
Owned or managed 1238
Rt 1132 **GN** 750 **Sup** 24 **OP** 358
SO 106 **Tot lets** 154 **GN bs** 714
Tenant Type % Family 56%
Older 30% **Single** 14%
Development Total 60
Rt 42 **GN** 42 **LCHO** 24 **NBA** 4
NBC 56

Muir Group HA Ltd
○ Charitable HA
TSA Reg ✓ 🖵 🏠 🔑 🐝
Old Government House, Dee Hills
Park, Chester, Cheshire, CH3 5AR
T 0300 123 1222
E info@muir.org.uk
W www.muir.org.uk
CE Mr John Bellis
Sec Mr John Bellis
Ch Mr David Booth
Total Staff 185
Regions North West + South East,
East Midlands, West Midlands, East
of England, Yorkshire & Humberside
Owned or managed 5097
Rt 4568 **GN** 3428 **Sup** 420 **OP** 720
SO 520 **NSO** 9 **Tot lets** 521
GN bs 3380
Tenant Type % Family 44%
Older 18% **Single** 38%
Development Total 244
NBA 135 **NBC** 109

MuirCroft HA Ltd
○ Charitable HA
TSA Reg ✓
Muir House, Beaulieu Road, Dibden
Purlieu, Southampton, Hampshire,
SO45 4NY
T 023 8084 9481
E info@muircroft.co.uk
W www.muircroft.co.uk
CE Mrs Helen Barber
Sec Mrs Helen Barber
Ch Mr Trevor Hanmore
Total Staff 8
Region South East
Owned or managed 101
Rt 101 **OP** 101
Tenant Type % Older 100%

Mulberry Housing Co-op United
★ Co-operative Society
TSA Reg ✓
Coin Street Community Builders Ltd,
108 Stamford Street, London, SE1
9NH
T 020 7021 1600
Sec Mrs Tina Worms
Ch Mr Simon Roice
Total Staff 1
Region London
Owned or managed 56
Rt 56 **GN** 56
Tenant Type % Family 84%
Older 5% **Single** 11%

Nn

Nacro Community Enterprises Ltd
☆ Charitable Company
TSA Reg ✓ 🌢 🐝
Park Place, 10/12 Lawn Lane,
London, Greater London, SW8 1UD
T 020 7840 7200
W www.nacro.org.uk
CE Mr Kevin Lockyer
Sec Ms Liz Walker
Ch Ms Kerry Pollard
Total Staff 516
Regions London + East Midlands,
West Midlands, East of England,
North West
Owned or managed 1059
Rt 1059 **GN** 20 **Sup** 1039
Tenant Type % Single 100%

National Council of YMCAs
☆ Charitable Company
TSA Reg ✓ 🌢 🐝
Northern Office, 80 Demesne
Road, Alexandra Park, Manchester,
Lancashire, M16 8PH
T 01564 730229
W www.ymca.org.uk
CE Mr Ian Green
Sec Ms Jackie Walker
Ch Mr Tim Waldron
Total Staff 446
Regions London + South East,
South West, East Midlands,
West Midlands, East of England,
Yorkshire & Humberside,
North East, North West
Owned or managed 952
Rt 952 **GN** 35 **Sup** 917
Tenant Type % Single 100%

Nehemiah United Churches HA Ltd
○ Charitable HA
TSA Reg ✓ 🔑 🐝 🏚
5 Beacon Court, Birmingham Road,
Great Barr, Birmingham,
West Midlands, B43 6NN
T 0121 358 0966
E contact@nehemiah-ucha.co.uk
W www.nehemiah-ucha.co.uk
CE Mr Llewellyn Graham
Sec Mr Llewellyn Graham
Ch Kwadwo Owusu-Darko
Total Staff 36
Region West Midlands
Owned or managed 987
Rt 980 **GN** 705 **Sup** 38 **OP** 237 **SO** 5
NSO 2 **Tot lets** 0 **GN bs** 0
Tenant Type % Family 49%
Older 28% **Single** 23%

Network for Change Ltd
○ Charitable HA
TSA Reg ✗ 🐝
150-152 London Road, Leicester,
Leicestershire, LE2 1ND
T 0116 247 0335
E info@networkforchange.org.uk
W www.networkforchange.org.uk
CE Gabby Briner
Sec Gabby Briner
Ch Ms Averil Coutinho
Total Staff 10
Region East Midlands
Owned or managed 20
Rt 20 **Sup** 20
Tenant Type % Family 9%
Older 14% **Single** 77%

Network Housing Group Ltd
○ Charitable HA
TSA Reg ✓ 🌢
Olympic Office Centre,
8 Fulton Road, Wembley, Middlesex,
HA9 0NU
T 020 8900 0185
E network@networkhg.org.uk
W www.networkhg.org.uk
CE Mrs Helen Evans
Sec Mr Richard Reger
Ch Mr Andy Watson
Total Staff 111
Region London
Subsidary Association(s)
Community Trust Housing;
London Strategic Housing Ltd;
Mitali HA Ltd; Network Stadium HA
Ltd; Riversmead HA Ltd; Willow
Housing and Care Ltd

Network Stadium HA Ltd
○ Charitable HA
TSA Reg ✓ ▢ ▦ 🏠 🔑 🤝 ♦
Olympic Office Centre,
8 Fulton Road, Wembley, Middlesex,
HA0 0NU
T 0300 373 3000
E stadium@stadiumha.org.uk
W www.stadiumha.org.uk
CE Eusebio Barata
Sec Mr Richard Reger
Ch Mr Charles Humphry
Total Staff 125
Regions London + South East,
East of England
Owned or managed 9711
Rt 7927 GN 6955 Sup 720 OP 252
SO 1772 NSO 12 Tot lets 904
GN bs 5498
Tenant Type % Family 42%
Older 20% Single 38%
Development Total 655
NBA 378 NBC 277
Parent Association
Network Housing Group Ltd

New Charter Homes Ltd
✪ Not-for-Profit Company
TSA Reg ✓ ▦ ▢ ▦ 🏠 🤝 ♦
Cavendish 249, Cavendish Street,
Ashton-Under-Lyne, Lancashire,
OL6 7AT
T 0161 331 2000
E contact@newcharter.co.uk
W www.newcharter.co.uk
CE Mr Ian Munro
Sec Mr Martin Frost
Ch Mr Geoff Loughlin
Total Staff 0
Region North West
Owned or managed 14873
Rt 14861 GN 14105 Sup 83 OP 673
NSO 12
Tenant Type % Family 38%
Older 48% Single 14%
Development Total 61
Rt 128 GN 128 NBA 39 NBC 22
Parent Association New Charter
Housing Trust Ltd

New Charter Housing Trust Ltd
✪ Not-for-Profit Company
TSA Reg ✓ ▦ ♦ ♦
Cavendish 249, Cavendish Street,
Ashton-Under-Lyne, Lancashire,
OL6 7AT
T 0161 331 2000
E contact@newcharter.co.uk
W www.newcharter.co.uk
CE Mr Ian Munro
Sec Mr Martin Frost
Ch Cllr Ged Cooney
Total Staff 856

Region North West
Subsidiary Association(s) Aksa HA
Ltd; Gedling Homes; New Charter
Homes Ltd

New Forest Villages HA Ltd
○ Charitable HA
TSA Reg ✓
P O Box 190, Pitmore Lane,
Lymington, Hampshire, SO41 6WS
T 01590 681122
E margaret.nfvha@btconnect.com
CE Mrs Margaret Brooks
Sec Mrs Margaret Brooks
Ch Miss Rachel Smith
Total Staff 1
Region South East
Owned or managed 48
Rt 48 GN 45 OP 3
Tenant Type % Family 60%
Older 20% Single 20%

New Foundations HA Ltd
○ Charitable HA
TSA Reg ✓ 🏠
238 Burnley Road East, Waterfoot,
Rossendale, Lancashire, BB4 9DQ
T 01706 835333
E john@newfoundations.co.uk
W www.newfoundations.co.uk
CE Ms Vicki Taylor
Sec Ms Vicki Taylor
Ch Mrs Judith Whitehead
Total Staff 3
Regions North West + London,
South East, South West, West
Midlands, North East
Owned or managed 149
Rt 140 GN 14 Sup 126 NSO 9
Tenant Type % Single 100%
Development Total 8
NBA 8

New Fylde Housing Ltd
■ Non-Charitable HA
TSA Reg ✓ ▦ 🏠 🔑 ♦
Sumner House, 21 King Street,
Leyland, PR25 2LW
T 01772 450600
W www.progressgroup.org.uk
CE Ms Jacqui De-Rose
Sec Mr Eric Hughes
Ch Mr David Morris
Total Staff 46
Region North West
Owned or managed 2141
Rt 2070 GN 1488 Sup 152 OP 430
SO 69 NSO 2 Tot lets 295
GN bs 1448
Tenant Type % Family 52%
Older 30% Single 18%
Development Total 113
Rt 9 GN 1 Sup 8 NBA 62 NBC 51
Parent Association

Progress Housing Group Ltd

New Linx Housing Trust
❏ Charitable Trust
TSA Reg ✓ ▢ ▦ 🏠 🔑 ♦
Keily House, Gresley Road, Louth,
Lincolnshire, LN11 8FG
T 01507 355000
E customerservices@
newlinxhousingtrust.co.uk
W www.newlinxhousingtrust.co.uk
CE Mr Jack Whyman
Sec Mr Brian Desmond
Ch Mr Brian Burnett
Total Staff 174
Regions East Midlands +
West Midlands
Owned or managed 7068
Rt 6602 GN 5823 Sup 100 OP 679
SO 377 NSO 89 Tot lets 663
GN bs 5368
Tenant Type % Family 55%
Older 42% Single 35%
Development Total 118
NBA 32 NBC 86
Parent Association
Waterloo Housing Group Ltd

New Outlook HA Ltd
○ Charitable HA
TSA Reg ✓ 🤝 🤝
Mill House, Mill Lane, Bromsgrove
Street, Halesowen, West Midlands,
B63 3JP
T 0121 602 6511
E admin@noha.org.uk
W www.newoutlookha.org
CE Ms Maureen Bradley
Ch Mr Anthony McCool
Total Staff 69
Region West Midlands
Owned or managed 52
Rt 52 GN 2 OP 50
Tenant Type % Older 66%
Single 34%

New Progress HA Ltd
○ Charitable HA
TSA Reg ✓ ▦ 🏠 🔑 🤝 ♦
Sumner House, 21 King Street,
Leyland, Lancashire, Lancashire,
PR25 2LW
T 01772 450600
E enquiries@newprogress.co.uk
W www.newprogress.co.uk
CE Mr Bernie Keenan
Ch Mr Stuart Miller
Total Staff 88
Region North West
Owned or managed 3983
Rt 3764 GN 2790 Sup 39 OP 935
SO 132 NSO 87 Tot lets 610
GN bs 2766
Tenant Type % Family 51%

Older 34% Single 15%
Development Total 60
NBA 45 NBC 15
Parent Association
Progress Housing Group Ltd

New Prospects Association Ltd
○ Charitable HA
TSA Reg ✗ 🦡
Centre House, 33 Front Street,
Monkseaton, Whitley Bay,
Tyne And Wear, NE25 8AQ
T 0191 251 7737
E ellen.vick@new-prospects.org
W www.newprospects.org.uk
CE Ms Ellen Vick
Sec Mr Alan Ross
Ch Mr Paul Hutchinson
Total Staff 215
Region North East
Owned or managed 24
Rt 24 **Sup** 24
Tenant Type % Single 100%

New Venture Housing Co-op Ltd
★ Co-operative Society
TSA Reg ✓
23 Venturecourt, 3 Horncastle Road,
Lee, London, Greater London,
SE12 9LJ
T 020 8851 8142
Sec Mrs Vivien Merry
Ch Mr Tony Francis
Total Staff 0
Region London
Owned or managed 27
Rt 27 **OP** 27
Tenant Type % Older 100%

New World HA Ltd
○ Charitable HA
TSA Reg ✓ 📷 🔧
8 Grange Mills, Weir Road, Balham,
London, Greater London,
SW12 0NE
T 020 8675 0320
E info@newha.co.uk
W www.newha.co.uk
CE Mr Ian Weightman
Sec Mr Elinam Attipoe
Ch Richard Robinson
Total Staff 6
Region London
Owned or managed 352
Rt 352 **GN** 339 **OP** 13
Tenant Type % Family 80%
Older 3% Single 17%
Development Total 20
NBC 20

Newlon Housing Trust
❑ Charitable Trust
TSA Reg ✓ 🖥 🔳 📷 🔧 ◊
4 Daneland Walk, Hale Village,
London, N17 9FE
T 020 7613 8000
E info@newlon.org.uk
W www.newlon.org.uk
CE Mr Mike Hinch
Sec Ms Barbara Duff
Ch Ms Sarah Ebanja
Total Staff 126
Region London
Owned or managed 6602
Rt 4704 **GN** 4135 **Sup** 420 **OP** 149
SO 1054 **NSO** 844 **Tot lets** 332
GN bs 3559
Tenant Type % Family 61%
Older 14% Single 25%
Development Total 871
Rt 588 **GN** 588 **LCHO** 239
NBA 538 NBC 333
Subsidiary Association(s)
Access Homes HA Ltd; Outward

Nexus (Midlands) HA (2005) Ltd
○ Charitable HA
TSA Reg ✓ 🦡 ◊
Apex 2, Apex Park, Wainwright
Road, Worcester, Worcestershire,
WR4 9FN
T 01905 613526
E nexus@wmhousing.co.uk
W www.wmhousing.co.uk
CE Mrs Pat Brandum
Sec Miss Zoe Moncrieff
Ch Mr Graham Myatt
Total Staff 57
Region West Midlands
Owned or managed 2388
Rt 2388 **GN** 2085 **Sup** 90 **OP** 213
Tenant Type % Family 72%
Older 11% Single 17%
Parent Association
WM Housing Group

Norcare Ltd
☆ Charitable Company
TSA Reg ✗ 🦡 ◊
Portman House, Portland Road,
Shieldfield, Newcastle Upon Tyne,
Tyne And Wear, NE2 1AQ
T 0191 261 2228
E norcare@norcare-ltd.com
W www.norcare.co.uk
CE Mrs Susan Bickerton
Sec Mrs Dianne Fleming
Ch Rod Jones
Total Staff 80
Region North East
Owned or managed 115
Rt 115 **Sup** 115
Tenant Type % Family 10%

Single 90%
Parent Association
Fabrick Housing Group Ltd

North Camden Housing Co-op Ltd
★ Co-operative Society
TSA Reg ✓
Unit 33, Bickerton House, 25
Bickerton Road, London,
Greater London, N19 5JT
T 020 7272 1219
E office@nchc.org.uk
W www.nchc.org.uk
Sec Ms Marianne Rouvier-Angeli
Ch Mr Richard Brayshay
Total Staff 3
Region London
Owned or managed 106
Rt 106 **GN** 106
Tenant Type % Family 29%
Older 6% Single 65%

North Devon Homes Ltd
✪ Not-for-Profit Company
TSA Reg ✓ 🔳 🔧
Westacott Road, Barnstaple, Devon,
EX32 8TA
T 01271 312500
E enquiries@ndh-ltd.co.uk
W www.yourlocallandlord.com
CE Mr Martyn Gimber
Sec Ms Nasreen Hussain
Ch Mr Nick Lewis
Total Staff 110
Region South West
Owned or managed 3215
Rt 3113 **GN** 2520 **Sup** 10 **OP** 583
SO 94 **NSO** 8 **Tot lets** 464
GN bs 2506
Tenant Type % Family 29%
Older 61% Single 10%

North Hertfordshire Homes Ltd
○ Charitable HA
TSA Reg ✓ 🖥 🔳 📷 🔧 † 🦡
Rowan House, Avenue One,
Letchworth Garden City,
Hertfordshire, SG6 2WW
T 01462 704100
E customer.services@nhh.org.uk
W www.nhh.org.uk
CE Kevin Thompson
Sec Kevin Thompson
Ch Gordon Johnston
Total Staff 326
Region East of England
Owned or managed 9006
Rt 8269 **GN** 7326 **Sup** 125 **OP** 818
SO 727 **NSO** 10 **Tot lets** 816
GN bs 7265
Tenant Type % Family 47%
Older 25% Single 28%

Development Total 321
Rt 150 GN 38 Sup 77 OP 35
NBA 248 NBC 73

North Lincolnshire Homes Ltd
☆ Charitable Company
TSA Reg ✓
Meridian House, Normanby Road,
Scunthorpe, South Humberside,
DN15 8QZ
T 01724 279900
E enquiries@nlhomes.org.uk
W www.nlhomes.org.uk
CE Mr Andrew Orrey
Sec Mr Steve Wardrope
Ch Mr Tony Lightfoot
Total Staff 283
Region Yorkshire & Humberside
Owned or managed 9746
Rt 9746 GN 9160 OP 586
Tenant Type % Family 69%
Older 31%
Development Total 6
NBA 6

North London Muslim HA Ltd
◯ Charitable HA
TSA Reg ✓
15b - 15c Urban Hive,
Theydon Road, Upper Clapton,
London, Greater London, E5 9BQ
T 020 8815 4200
E info@nlmha.com
W www.nlmha.com
CE Mr Ahmed Mapara
Sec Nafisa Patel
Ch Ashraf Hakim
Total Staff 12
Region London
Owned or managed 619
Rt 619 GN 619
Tenant Type % Family 83%
Older 7% Single 10%

North Star Housing Group Ltd
■ Non-Charitable HA
TSA Reg ✓
Endeavour House, St. Marks Court,
Stockton-On-Tees, Cleveland,
TS17 6QN
T 01642 796300
E info@northstarhg.co.uk
W www.northstarhg.co.uk
CE Mrs Angela Lockwood
Sec Mr Peter Lenehan
Ch Mr Jed Lester
Total Staff 28
Region North East
Subsidiary Association(s) Endeavour
HA ; Teesdale HA Ltd

North West Housing Services Ltd
■ Non-Charitable HA
TSA Reg ✗
19 Devonshire Road, Princes Park,
Liverpool, Merseyside, L8 3TX
E info@nwhousing.org
W www.nwhousing.org
CE Mr Syed Maqsood
Sec Mr Kevin Wan
Ch Mr Brian O'Hare
Total Staff 0
Region North West

Northamptonshire Rural HA Ltd
◯ Charitable HA
TSA Reg ✓
Whitwick Business Centre,
Stenson Road, Coalville,
Leicestershire, LE67 4JP
T 01530 278080
E midlandsrural@midlandsrh.org.uk
W www.northamptonshirerha.org.uk
Sec Mr Craig Felts
Ch Mr Christopher Sparrow
Total Staff 0
Region East Midlands
Owned or managed 536
Rt 477 GN 477 SO 59 Tot lets 57
GN bs 296
Tenant Type % Family 87%
Older 12% Single 1%

Norwich Housing Society Ltd
◯ Charitable HA
TSA Reg ✓
13 Bracondale, Norwich, Norfolk,
NR1 2AL
T 01603 625078
E reception@norwichhousingsociety.
co.uk
W www.norwichhousingsociety.org
CE Mr Nicholas Bagshaw
Sec Mr Nicholas Bagshaw
Ch Mr David Robinson
Total Staff 10
Region East of England
Owned or managed 290
Rt 284 GN 22 OP 262 NSO 6
Tenant Type % Family 6%
Older 90% Single 4%

Notting Hill Home Ownership HA Ltd
■ Non-Charitable HA
TSA Reg ✓
Bruce Kenrick House, 2 Killick Street,
London, N1 9FL
T 020 8357 5000
E cst@nhhg.org.uk
W www.nottinghillhousing.org.uk
CE Ms Kate Davies
Sec Mr Andrew Nankivell

Ch Mr Paul Hodgkinson
Total Staff 590
Regions London + South East,
South West, East of England
Owned or managed 6980
Rt 80 GN 80 SO 5870 NSO 1030
Tot lets 0 GN bs 7
Tenant Type % Family 50%
Older 7% Single 43%
Development Total 1154
 LCHO 1160 NBA 803 NBC 351
Parent Association Notting Hill
Housing Trust

Notting Hill Housing Trust
◯ Charitable HA
TSA Reg ✓
Bruce Kenrick House, 2 Killick Street,
London, N1 9FL
T 020 8357 5000
E online@nhhg.org.uk
W www.nottinghillhousing.org.uk
CE Ms Kate Davies
Sec Mr Andrew Nankivell
Ch Mr Paul Hodgkinson
Total Staff 987
Regions London + South East,
East of England
Owned or managed 22439
Rt 20618 GN 18828 Sup 970 OP 820
SO 379 NSO 1442 Tot lets 2068
GN bs 16208
Tenant Type % Family 55%
Older 23% Single 22%
Development Total 1854
NBA 1173 NBC 681
Subsidiary Association(s) Notting
Hill Home Ownership HA Ltd

Nottingham Community (2nd) HA Ltd
■ Non-Charitable HA
TSA Reg ✓
12-14 Pelham Road, Sherwood Rise,
Nottingham, Nottinghamshire,
NG5 1AP
T 0800 013 8555
E info@ncha.org.uk
W www.ncha.org.uk
CE Mr Mike Andrews
Sec Mr Steve Walker
Ch Dr Nigel Nice
Total Staff 0
Region East Midlands
Owned or managed 16
Rt 3 GN 3 SO 13 Tot lets 0 GN bs 0
Tenant Type % Family 100%
Parent Association Nottingham
Community HA Ltd

Nottingham Community HA Ltd
○ Charitable HA
TSA Reg ✓
🖿 📧 500 ⬠ 🔑 🔧 ♦ 🤝 ♨
12-14 Pelham Road, Nottingham, Nottinghamshire, NG5 1AP
T 0845 650 1201
E info@ncha.org.uk
W www.ncha.org.uk
CE Mr Mike Andrews
Sec Mr Paul Higginbotham
Ch Dr Nigel Nice
Total Staff 856
Region East Midlands
Owned or managed 7988
Rt 7356 **GN** 6213 **Sup** 584 **OP** 559
SO 632 **Tot lets** 1381 **GN bs** 5834
Tenant Type % Family 47%
Older 11% **Single** 42%
Development Total 739
NBA 410 **NBC** 329
Subsidiary Association(s)
Nottingham Community (2nd) HA Ltd

Nottingham Jewish HA Ltd
○ Charitable HA
TSA Reg ✗ 🤝 🤝
c/o Hollybrook, Old Melton Road, Normanton-on-the-Wolds, Nottingham, Nottinghamshire, NG12 5NN
T 07764 222028
E laurence@flitterman.co.uk
Sec Mrs Stacey Friedman
Ch Mrs Stephanie Besbrode
Total Staff 0
Region East Midlands
Tenant Type % Older 100%

Nottinghamshire YMCA
☆ Charitable Company
TSA Reg ✓ 🤝
4 Shakespeare Street, Nottingham, Nottinghamshire, NG1 4FG
T 0115 956 7600
E admin@nottsymca.org
W www.nottsymca.com
CE Mr William Wakefield
Sec Mrs Gill Turnbull
Ch Mrs Diane Bialek
Total Staff 120
Region East Midlands
Owned or managed 273
Rt 273 **GN** 146 **Sup** 127
Tenant Type % Single 100%

Oo

Oak Foundation
○ Charitable HA
TSA Reg ✓ 🔑 🤝 ♨
Brook House, Ouse Walk, Huntingdon, Cambridgeshire, PE29 3QW
T 01480 428701
E info@luminus.org.uk
W www.luminus.org.uk
CE Dr Chan Abraham
Sec Dr Chan Abraham
Ch Mr David Vessey
Total Staff 21
Region East of England
Owned or managed 632
Rt 622 **GN** 3 **Sup** 84 **OP** 535 **SO** 5
NSO 5 **Tot lets** 106 **GN bs** 622
Tenant Type % Family 2%
Older 93% **Single** 5%
Parent Association Luminus Group

Ocean Housing Group Ltd
✪ Not-for-Profit Company
TSA Reg ✓ ♨
Stennack House, Stennack Road, Holmbush, St Austell, Cornwall, PL25 3SW
T 01726 874450
E enquiries@oceanhousing.com
W www.oceanhousing.com
CE Mr David Renwick
Sec Mr Kevin Pearce
Ch Mr Dennis Spilsbury
Total Staff 23
Region South West
Subsidiary Association(s)
Ocean Housing Ltd

Ocean Housing Ltd
○ Charitable HA
TSA Reg ✓ 📧 YTHO ⬠ 🔑 ♨
Stennack House, Stennack Road, Holmbush, St. Austell, Cornwall, PL25 3SW
T 01726 874450
E enquiries@oceanhousing.com
W www.oceanhousing.com
CE Mr David Renwick
Sec Ms Frances Turner
Ch Mr Simon Hembury
Total Staff 57
Region South West
Owned or managed 4159
Rt 3807 **GN** 3028 **Sup** 22 **OP** 757
SO 352 **Tot lets** 315 **GN bs** 3001
Tenant Type % Family 66%
Older 20% **Single** 14%
Development Total 117
Rt 99 **GN** 99 **LCHO** 82 **NBA** 77

NBC 40
Parent Association
Ocean Housing Group Ltd

Ockley HA Ltd
○ Charitable HA
TSA Reg ✓ 🔑
Elmers Farmhouse, Ockley, Surrey, RH5 5TQ
T 01306 627569
Sec Mrs Deb Herbert
Ch Mrs Veryan Pryke
Total Staff 0
Region South East
Owned or managed 19
Rt 15 **GN** 3 **OP** 12 **SO** 4 **Tot lets** 0
GN bs 0
Tenant Type % Family 47%
Older 40% **Single** 13%

Octavia Housing
○ Charitable HA
TSA Reg ✓ ⬠ 🔧 ♦ 🤝
Emily House, 202-208 Kensal Road, London, Greater London, W10 5BN
T 020 8354 5500
E enquiries@octaviahousing.org.uk
W www.octaviahousing.org.uk
CE Mr Grahame Hindes
Sec Mr Colin Hughes
Ch Mr Andrew Herbert
Total Staff 296
Region London
Owned or managed 4106
Rt 3693 **GN** 3438 **Sup** 231 **OP** 24
SO 399 **NSO** 14 **Tot lets** 202
GN bs 3278
Tenant Type % Family 43%
Older 22% **Single** 35%
Development Total 143
Rt 223 **GN** 138 **Sup** 85 **LCHO** 24
NBA 88 **NBC** 55

Odu-Dua HA Ltd
○ Charitable HA
TSA Reg ✓ ⬠
84-88 Kingsgate Road, West Hampstead, London, Greater London, NW6 4LA
T 020 7625 1799
E admin@odu-dua.org
W www.odu-dua.org
CE Miss Lara Oyedele
Sec Miss Lara Oyedele
Ch Mr John Oke
Total Staff 7
Region London
Owned or managed 201
Rt 201 **GN** 201
Tenant Type % Family 75%
Older 5% **Single** 20%

Odyssey Care Ltd
○ Charitable HA
TSA Reg ✗ 🖤
1 Smiths Yard, Summerley Street,
London, Greater London,
SW18 4HR
T 020 7062 8860
E info@odyssey-csft.org
W www.odysseycare.org
CE Miss Ingrid Vlam
Total Staff 0
Region London
Tenant Type % Single 100%

Ogilby Housing Society Ltd
○ Charitable HA
TSA Reg ✗
Estate Office, Greenways Court,
Butts Green Road, Hornchurch,
Essex, RM11 2JL
T 01708 475115
CE Mr Richard Sibley
Sec Mrs J Kidd
Total Staff 6
Regions East of England +
London, South East
Owned or managed 114
Rt 114 **GN** 114
Tenant Type % Family 20%
Older 20% **Single** 60%

Old Ben Homes Ltd
☆ Charitable Company
TSA Reg ✓ 🖤
3 The Old Hall, Church Road,
Lilleshall, Shropshire, TF10 9JA
T 01952 677257
E oldben1@btconnect.com
CE Mrs Christine Kinnersley
Sec Mrs Christine Kinnersley
Ch Mr David Blundell
Total Staff 6
Regions West Midlands + South East
Owned or managed 78
Rt 78 **OP** 78
Tenant Type % Older 100%

Old Etonian HA Ltd
○ Charitable HA
TSA Reg ✓
Rugby Chambers, 2 Rugby Street,
London, Greater London,
WC1N 3QU
T 020 7440 9440
E enquiries@teachershousing.org.uk
W www.teachershousing.org.uk
CE Ms Sian Llewellyn
Sec Ms Sian Llewellyn
Ch Mr Thomas Mitcheson
Total Staff 1
Region London
Owned or managed 53
Rt 53 **GN** 53
Tenant Type % Family 81%
Single 19%

Old Ford HA
☆ Charitable Company
TSA Reg ✓ 🚐 🄳 🔑 🔥
4th Floor, Solar House, 1
-9 Romford Road, London, E15 4LJ
T 020 3583 1500
E old.ford@circle.org.uk
W www.oldford.org.uk
CE Ms June Morton
Sec Ms Deborah Upton
Ch Mr Alan Riddell
Total Staff 158
Region London
Owned or managed 4972
Rt 3977 **GN** 3933 **Sup** 14 **OP** 30
SO 896 **NSO** 99 **Tot lets** 481
GN bs 3155
Tenant Type % Family 45%
Older 35% **Single** 20%
Development Total 748
Rt 336 **GN** 336 **NBA** 421 **NBC** 327
Parent Association Circle

Old Oak HA Ltd
☆ Charitable Company
TSA Reg ✓ 🔑 🔥
Old Oak House, 43-45 Erconwald St,
London, Greater London, W12 0BP
T 020 8743 5486
E oldoakqueries@familymosaic.co.uk
CE Mr David Leach
Ch Lisa Homan
Total Staff 11
Region London
Owned or managed 617
Rt 607 **GN** 607 **SO** 10 **Tot lets** 30
GN bs 0
Parent Association
Family Mosaic Housing

Omid HA Ltd
○ Charitable HA
TSA Reg ✗ 🖤 🏠
45 Queen's Walk, London,
Greater London, W5 1TL
T 020 8248 7701
E omid@ha.fednet.org.uk
CE Mr Shahram Aghili
Sec Mr Shahram Aghili
Ch Mr A Pourghazi
Total Staff 0
Region London
Tenant Type % Family 10%
Single 90%

One Housing Group Ltd
○ Charitable HA
TSA Reg ✓
🔲 🔲 🚐 🚐 🄳 🔑 🔥 🖤
100 Chalk Farm Road,
London, NW1 8EH
T 020 8821 5100
E info@onehousinggroup.co.uk
W www.onehousinggroup.co.uk
CE Mick Sweeney
Sec Ms Louisa Loizou
Ch Mr Anthony Mayer
Total Staff 876
Regions London + South East,
East of England
Owned or managed 12084
Rt 10524 **GN** 8763 **Sup** 1678 **OP** 83
SO 1519 **NSO** 41 **Tot lets** 1252
GN bs 8676
Tenant Type % Family 42%
Older 12% **Single** 46%
Development Total 1224
Rt 856 **GN** 631 **Sup** 121 **OP** 104
LCHO 441 **NBA** 760 **NBC** 464

One Vision Housing Ltd
○ Charitable HA
TSA Reg ✓ 🔲 🔲 🔑 🔥
Atlantic House, Dunnings Bridge
Road, Bootle, Merseyside, L30 4TH
T 0300 365 1111
E enquiries@ovh.org.uk
W www.ovh.org.uk
CE Mr Roy Williams
Sec Mrs Tracey Liggett
Ch Mr Darren Hardy
Total Staff 240
Region North West
Owned or managed 11571
Rt 10998 **GN** 9398 **Sup** 132 **OP**
1468 **SO** 557 **NSO** 16 **Tot lets** 1007
GN bs 9398
Tenant Type % Family 55%
Older 16% **Single** 29%
Subsidiary Association(s)
Pine Court HA Ltd

Optima Community Association
☆ Charitable Company
TSA Reg ✓ 🄳 🔑 🖤 🔥
St Thomas House, 80 Bell Barn Road,
Birmingham, West Midlands, B15 2AF
T 0121 687 3111
E info@optima.org.uk
W www.optima.org.uk
CE Mr Simon Kimberley
Sec Mr John Lellow
Ch Dr Peter Taylor
Total Staff 83
Region West Midlands
Owned or managed 3953
Rt 3710 **GN** 3388 **Sup** 9 **OP** 313
SO 243 **Tot lets** 186 **GN bs** 1861
Tenant Type % Family 27%
Older 21% **Single** 52%
Development Total 95
NBA 54 **NBC** 41
Parent Association
WM Housing Group

Orbit Group Ltd
○ Charitable HA
TSA Reg ✓ 🏠 🔑 🌱 ♨
Garden Court, Harry Weston Road, Binley Business Park, Binley, Coventry, West Midlands, CV3 2SU
T 024 7643 8000
E info@orbit.org.uk
W www.orbit.org.uk
CE Mr Paul Tennant
Sec Mr Richard Wright
Ch Liz Potter
Total Staff 1387
Regions West Midlands + London, South East, South West, East Midlands, East of England
Owned or managed 3486
Rt 183 GN 183 SO 3303 Tot lets 44
GN bs 0
Tenant Type % Family 47%
Older 19% Single 34%
Development Total 230
Rt 224 OP 224 LCHO 675 NBC 230
Subsidiary Association(s) Orbit Heart of England; Orbit South HA Ltd

Orbit Heart of England
○ Charitable HA
TSA Reg ✓ 🏢 🖥 🗝 🏠 🔑 ♦ 🐾 ♨
10 Greenhill Street, Stratford-Upon-Avon, Warwickshire, CV37 6LG
T 0345 850 0500
E info@orbit.org.uk
W www.orbitheartofengland.org.uk
CE Mr Stewart Fergusson
Sec Mr Stewart Fergusson
Ch Mr Robin Dahlberg
Total Staff 523
Regions West Midlands + South East, South West, East Midlands, East of England
Owned or managed 15514
Rt 14616 GN 12702 Sup 444
OP 1470 SO 466 NSO 432
Tot lets 2326 GN bs 12500
Tenant Type % Family 55%
Older 35% Single 10%
Development Total 314
Rt 733 GN 568 Sup 12 OP 153
NBA 15 NBC 299
Parent Association Orbit Group Ltd

Orbit South HA Ltd
○ Charitable HA
TSA Reg ✓
🏢 🖥 🗝 🏠 🔑 🐾 ♨
Horizon House, 2nd Floor, Eclipse Park, Sittingbourne Road, Maidstone, Kent, ME14 3EN
T 0800 678 1221
E info@orbit.org.uk
W www.orbitsouth.org.uk
CE Mrs Vivien Knibbs

Sec Mrs Vivien Knibbs
Ch Mrs Fran Beckett
Total Staff 32
Regions South East + London, East Midlands, East of England
Owned or managed 16614
Rt 15551 GN 13966 Sup 324
OP 1261 SO 1063 Tot lets 2015
GN bs 13765
Tenant Type % Family 53%
Older 17% Single 30%
Development Total 715
Rt 1788 GN 1725 OP 63 NBA 383
NBC 332
Parent Association Orbit Group Ltd

Orchard (Weybridge) HA Ltd
○ Charitable HA
TSA Reg ✗
12 The Orchard, Hanger Hill, Weybridge, Surrey, KT13 9XT
Ch Mrs Rosemary Thomson
Total Staff 0
Region South East
Tenant Type % Older 100%

Orchard Housing Society Ltd
○ Charitable HA
TSA Reg ✓ 🐾
1 The Orchard, Hampstead Way, London, Greater London, NW11 6YN
T 020 8455 3223
E orchardhousing@btconnect.com
CE Mr Matthew Rutherford
Sec Mrs Joan Holton
Ch Mr John Boulter
Total Staff 2
Region London
Owned or managed 60
Rt 60 OP 60
Tenant Type % Older 100%

Oriel Housing Ltd
○ Charitable HA
TSA Reg ✓ ♨
Collins House, Bishopstoke Road, Eastleigh, Hampshire, SO50 6AD
T 0300 123 1567
E radiandirect@radian.co.uk
W www.radian.co.uk
CE Mr Lindsay Todd
Sec Mr Terry Walker
Ch Mr John Collinge
Total Staff 0
Region South East
Parent Association
Radian Group Ltd

Origin Housing Ltd
○ Charitable HA
TSA Reg ✓ 🖥 💰 🏠 🔑 🐾
St Richards House, 110 Eversholt Street, London, Greater London, NW1 1BS
T 020 7209 9209
E Ros.gunnell@originhousing.org.uk
W www.originhousing.org.uk
CE Ms Karen Wilson
Sec Ms Caroline Waterer
Ch Mr Colin Sherriff
Total Staff 237
Regions London + East of England
Owned or managed 5497
Rt 4164 GN 3492 Sup 242 OP 430
SO 371 NSO 962 Tot lets 486
GN bs 3210
Tenant Type % Family 50%
Older 29% Single 21%
Development Total 503
Rt 295 GN 295 LCHO 227
NBA 228 NBC 275

Orione Care
☆ Charitable Company
TSA Reg ✓ 🐾
13 Lower Teddington Road, Hampton Wick, Kingston-Upon-Thames, Surrey, KT1 4EU
T 020 8977 5130
E info@orionecare.org
W www.sonsofdivineprovidence.org
Sec Mr Michael Healy
Ch Rev Stephen Beale
Total Staff 99
Regions London + South East, North West
Owned or managed 90
Rt 75 GN 65 Sup 10 NSO 15
Tenant Type % Older 80%
Single 20%

Orwell HA Ltd
○ Charitable HA
TSA Reg ✓ 🏠 🔑 ♦ 🐾
Crane Hill Lodge, 325 London Road, Ipswich, Suffolk, IP2 0BE
T 01473 218818
E qwc@orwell-housing.co.uk
W www.orwell-housing.co.uk
CE Mr Stephen R Javes
Sec Mr Stephen R Javes
Ch Mr Martin Bennett
Total Staff 437
Region East of England
Owned or managed 3283
Rt 3170 GN 2372 Sup 337 OP 461
SO 91 NSO 22 Tot lets 892
GN bs 2325
Tenant Type % Family 72%
Older 23% Single 5%
Development Total 212
Rt 137 GN 137 LCHO 15 NBA 106
NBC 106

Outward

☆ Charitable Company
TSA Reg ✗ ◊
Newlon House, 4 Daneland Walk,
Hale Village, London, N17 9FE
T 020 8520 7745
W www.outward.org.uk
CE Mr Peter Little
Sec Mr Peter Little
Ch Mr Christopher Blundell
Total Staff 0
Region London
Tenant Type % Older 29%
Single 71%
Parent Association
Newlon Housing Trust

Oxbode HA Ltd

■ Non-Charitable HA
TSA Reg ✓ ⚲
9 Pullman Court, Great Western
Road, Gloucester, Gloucestershire,
GL1 3ND
T 01452 505359
E info@oxbodehousing.org.uk
W www.oxbodehousing.org.uk
CE Mr Jim Dickson
Ch Ms Kate Clemmow
Total Staff 10
Region South West
Owned or managed 707
Rt 675 GN 626 Sup 16 OP 33 SO 32
Tot lets 0 GN bs 0
Tenant Type % Family 69%
Older 22% Single 9%

Oxford Citizens HA Ltd

○ Charitable HA
TSA Reg ✓ ◎ ⚲ ◊
244 Barns Road, Oxford,
Oxfordshire, OX4 3RW
T 01865 773000
E info@ocha.org.uk
W www.ocha.org.uk
CE Mr Andrew Smith
Sec Mrs Catherine Dixon
Ch Ms Alice Copping
Total Staff 87
Region South East
Owned or managed 2806
Rt 2392 GN 1716 Sup 130 OP 546
SO 414 Tot lets 179 GN bs 1702
Tenant Type % Family 61%
Older 19% Single 20%
Development Total 64
Rt 41 GN 41 LCHO 14 NBA 35
NBC 29
Parent Association
GreenSquare Group Ltd

Oxford Overseas Students HA Ltd

○ Charitable HA
TSA Reg ✗
117 Banbury Road, Oxford,
Oxfordshire, OX2 6JX
T 01865 311277
E tim.rous@nooc.org.uk
W www.nooc.org.uk
CE Mr Timothy Rous
Sec Mrs Emma Young
Ch James Heywood
Total Staff 9
Region South East
Owned or managed 73
 NSO 73
Tenant Type % Family 10%
Single 90%

Oxted Limpsfield & District HA Ltd

○ Charitable HA
TSA Reg ✓
Crabwood, 13 Bluehouse Lane,
Oxted, Surrey, RH8 0UA
T 01883 717074
E info@crabwood.co.uk
W www.crabwood.co.uk
Sec Mrs Judy Bunn
Ch Mr David Russell
Total Staff 2
Region South East
Owned or managed 22
Rt 22 GN 22
Tenant Type % Older 100%

Pp

Padley HA Ltd

○ Charitable HA
TSA Reg ✓
T 01246 290261
E padley@norrow.demon.co.uk
W www.norrow.demon.co.uk
Sec Mrs M PH Stoch
Ch Mr K Robinson
Total Staff 2
Region Yorkshire & Humberside
Tenant Type % Family 1%
Older 99%

Paradigm Homes Charitable HA Ltd

○ Charitable HA
TSA Reg ✓
■ ☐ ⚙ ⚙ ◎ ⚲ ♦ ◊
Building 1, Glory Park Avenue,
Wooburn Green, High Wycombe,
Buckinghamshire, HP10 0DF
T 0300 303 1010
E enquiries@paradigmhousing.co.uk
W www.paradigmhousing.co.uk
CE Ms Alison Hadden
Sec Miss Julie Packham
Ch Mr Michael Gahagan
Total Staff 430
Regions South East + London,
East of England
Owned or managed 11439
Rt 9672 GN 8876 Sup 237 OP 559
SO 1534 NSO 233 Tot lets 1154
GN bs 8876
Tenant Type % Family 59%
Older 26% Single 15%
Development Total 681
NBA 406 NBC 275
Parent Association
Paradigm Housing Group Ltd

Paradigm Housing Group Ltd

■ Non-Charitable HA
TSA Reg ✓ ☐ ♦ ⚙ ◊
Building 1, Glory Park Avenue,
Wooburn Green, High Wycombe,
Buckinghamshire, HP10 0DF
T 0300 303 1010
E enquiries@paradigmhousing.co.uk
W www.paradigmhousing.co.uk
CE Ms Alison Hadden
Sec Ms Rosalind Perkins
Ch David Easson
Total Staff 436
Region South East
Owned or managed 9672
Rt 9672 GN 8876 Sup 237 OP 559
Tenant Type % Family 65%
Older 25% Single 10%
Subsidary Association(s) Paradigm
Homes Charitable HA Ltd

Paragon Community Housing Group

■ Non-Charitable HA
TSA Reg ✓ ♦ ◊
Case House, 85-89 High Street,
Walton-On-Thames, Surrey,
KT12 1DZ
T 01932 235700
E info@paragonchg.co.uk
W www.paragonchg.co.uk
CE Mr Dilip Kavi
Sec Mrs Marion Hall
Ch Mr John Cudd
Total Staff 287

Region South East
Subsidiary Association(s) Elmbridge
Housing Trust Ltd; Richmond Upon
Thames Churches HT

Park Gardens Supported Housing Ltd
○ Charitable HA
TSA Reg ✗
Ground Floor, Maville House,
Beech Avenue, Nottingham,
Nottinghamshire, NG7 7LS
T 0115 841 7711
E paul.carpenter@frameworkha.org
W www.frameworkha.org
CE Mr Andrew Redfern
Sec Mr Andrew Redfern
Ch Mr Bob McKittnick
Total Staff 0
Region East Midlands
Tenant Type % Single 100%

Park Hill Housing Co-op Ltd
★ Co-operative Society
TSA Reg ✓
13 Allard Gardens, Briarwood Road,
London, Greater London, SW4 9QA
T 020 7622 4295
E phhc@btconnect.com
Sec Mr Edward Houghton
Ch Mr Roney Fraser-Munro
Total Staff 0
Region London
Owned or managed 25
Rt 25 GN 25
Tenant Type % Family 44%
Single 56%

Parkway Green Housing Trust
☆ Charitable Company
TSA Reg ✓ ▢ ▣ 🐚 ◊
Parkway Green House,
460 Palatine Road, Manchester,
Lancashire, M22 4DJ
T 0300 111 0000
E info@parkwaygreen.co.uk
W www.parkwaygreen.co.uk
CE Mr Nigel Wilson
Sec Mr Richard Coughlan
Ch Cllr Paul Andrews
Total Staff 174
Region North West
Owned or managed 5738
Rt 5738 GN 5708 Sup 30
Tenant Type % Family 63%
Older 26% Single 11%
Development Total 30
Rt 68 GN 68 NBA 19 NBC 11
Parent Association Wythenshawe
Community Housing Group

Partington HA
■ Non-Charitable HA
TSA Reg ✗ ▦ ◊
Your Housing Group, Thomson
House, Faraday Street, Birchwood
Park, Warrington, WA3 6GA
T 01925 236400
W www.yourhousinggroup.co.uk
CE Mr Brian Cronin
Sec Mrs Bronwen Rapley
Ch Mr Fred Varden
Total Staff 0
Region North West
Owned or managed 1292
Rt 1292 GN 1292
Tenant Type % Family 51%
Older 24% Single 25%
Parent Association Manchester &
District HA

Pathways
❏ Charitable Trust
TSA Reg ✓
65 Tawny Close, London,
Greater London, W13 9LX
T 020 8579 7411
E info@yourpathways.org.uk
W www.yourpathways.org.uk
CE Mrs Maria Gledhill
Sec Mr Peter Thomas
Ch Mr Timothy Luckett
Total Staff 12
Region London
Owned or managed 137
Rt 136 OP 136 NSO 1
Tenant Type % Older 100%

Peabody
❏ Charitable Trust
TSA Reg ✓ ▣ ▢ ▣ 🔑 ♦ 🐚 ◊
45 Westminster Bridge Road,
London, Greater London, SE1 7JB
T 020 7021 4000
E company.secretary@peabody.org.uk
W www.peabody.org.uk
CE Mr Stephen Howlett
Sec Ms Susan Hickey
Ch Mr Christopher Strickland
Total Staff 627
Region London
Owned or managed 18828
Rt 15182 GN 14436 Sup 355 OP 391
SO 1257 NSO 2389 Tot lets 784
GN bs 14022
Tenant Type % Family 44%
Older 10% Single 46%
Development Total 26
 NBA 13 NBC 13
Subsidiary Association(s) CBHA

Peacehaven & Telscombe HA Ltd
○ Charitable HA
TSA Reg ✓ 🐚
Dorothy House,
127 Dorothy Avenue North,
Peacehaven, East Sussex, BN10 8DS
T 01273 587817
E info@ptha.co.uk
W www.ptha.co.uk
Sec Mrs Sandra Morris
Ch Mrs Sandra Clayton
Total Staff 10
Region South East
Owned or managed 20
Rt 20 OP 20
Tenant Type % Older 100%

Peak District Rural HA Ltd
○ Charitable HA
TSA Reg ✓ 🔑
1st Floor, 10 Cromford Mill,
Mill Road, Cromford, Matlock,
Derbyshire, DE4 3RQ
T 01629 826040
E midlandsrural@midlandsrh.org.uk
W www.peakdistrictrha.org.uk
CE Mr Craig Felts
Sec Mrs Alison Clamp
Ch Mr Sam Matthews
Total Staff 0
Regions East Midlands + West
Midlands, Yorkshire & Humberside
Owned or managed 251
Rt 213 GN 183 OP 30 SO 38
Tot lets 0 GN bs 0
Tenant Type % Family 64%
Older 26% Single 10%

Peak Valley HA Ltd
○ Charitable HA
TSA Reg ✓ ▣ 🔑 ◊
100 Hattersley Road East, Hattersley,
Hyde, Cheshire, SK14 3EQ
T 0345 270 3501
E mail@pvha.co.uk
W www.pvha.co.uk
CE Mr Philip Corris
Ch Mr Geoffrey Minshull
Total Staff 10
Region North West
Owned or managed 1508
Rt 1506 GN 1350 OP 156 SO 2
Tot lets 94 GN bs 1257
Development Total 82
NBA 41 NBC 41
Parent Association
Symphony Housing Group

Peaks & Plains Housing Trust
❑ Charitable Trust
TSA Reg ✓ ▢ 🔲 🔑
Ropewalks, Newton Street,
Macclesfield, Cheshire, SK11 6QJ
T 01625 553553
E trust@peaksplains.org
W www.peaksplains.org
CE Mr Tim Pinder
Sec Mr Greg Bones
Ch Mr David Gooda
Total Staff 225
Region North West
Owned or managed 5138
Rt 4882 GN 3354 OP 1528 SO 256
Tot lets 490 GN bs 3310
Tenant Type % Family 40%
Older 50% Single 10%

Pendleton Improved HA Ltd
◼ Non-Charitable HA
TSA Reg ✓ ◊
5th Floor, Paragon House, 48
Seymour Grove, Manchester,
Lancashire, M16 0LN
T 0161 610 1000
W www.irwellvalleyha.co.uk
CE Dr Tom Manion
Sec Angela Garvin
Ch Ms Lynne Garsden
Total Staff 0
Region North West
Parent Association Irwell Valley HA
Ltd

Penge Churches HA
○ Charitable HA
TSA Reg ✓
99 Maple Road, Penge, London,
SE20 8LN
T 020 8659 3055
E housing@pengechurchesha.org.uk
W www.pengechurchesha.org.uk
CE Ms Gill Rose
Sec Ms Gill Rose
Ch Mr Edward Lee-Smith
Total Staff 5
Region London
Owned or managed 265
Rt 261 GN 248 Sup 13 NSO 4
Tenant Type % Family 21%
Older 41% Single 38%

Pennine Housing 2000 Ltd
✪ Not-for-Profit Company
TSA Reg ✓ ▣ ▢ 🔲 ▢ 🔑 ♦ ◊
Bull Green House, Bull Green,
Halifax, HX1 2EB
T 01422 284500
E info@ph2k.org.uk
W www.ph2k.org.uk
CE Mr Tom Miskell
Sec Mr George Paterson

Ch Mr Peter Caffrey
Total Staff 354
Region Yorkshire & Humberside
Owned or managed 12471
Rt 12049 GN 11537 OP 512 SO 386
NSO 36 Tot lets 1656 GN bs 11537
Development Total 1
NBA 1
Parent Association
Together Housing Group Ltd

Penwith HA Ltd
○ Charitable HA
TSA Reg ✓ ▢ 🔲 🔑 🐦 ◊
67 Morrab Road, Penzance,
Cornwall, TR18 2QJ
T 01736 331799
E contact@penwithha.org.uk
W www.penwithha.org.uk
CE Mr Andrew Moore
Ch Mrs Gail Hunt
Total Staff 120
Region South West
Owned or managed 6940
Rt 6813 GN 6073 Sup 41 OP 699
SO 103 NSO 24 Tot lets 328
GN bs 3131
Tenant Type % Family 46%
Older 41% Single 13%
Parent Association Devon &
Cornwall Housing Ltd

People First HA Ltd
○ Charitable HA
TSA Reg ✓ 🐦
No.1 City Road, 3rd Floor,
City Road East, Manchester,
Lancashire, M15 4PN
T 0161 235 6900
E admin@peoplefirsthousing.co.uk
W www.peoplefirsthousing.co.uk
CE Mr Kulbinder Kang
Sec Mr Kulbinder Kang
Ch Mr Adrian Lohrey
Total Staff 38
Region North West
Owned or managed 292
Rt 292 GN 275 Sup 17
Tenant Type % Family 40%
Older 20% Single 40%

Peter Bedford HA Ltd
○ Charitable HA
TSA Reg ✓ 🐦
Legard Works, Legard Road,
Highbury, London, Greater London,
N5 1DE
T 020 7226 6074
E admin@peterbedford.org.uk
W www.peterbedford.org.uk
CE Debby Ounsted
Ch Mr Robert Woolf
Total Staff 63
Region London

Owned or managed 265
Rt 265 GN 64 Sup 201
Tenant Type % Family 5%
Older 10% Single 85%

Petersfield HA Ltd
○ Charitable HA
TSA Reg ✓ ▢ 🔑
32 Lavant Street, Petersfield,
Hampshire, Hampshire, GU32 3EF
T 01730 263589
E info@petersfieldhsg.co.uk
W www.petersfieldhsg.co.uk
CE Mrs Denise Rajchel
Sec Mrs Denise Rajchel
Ch Mr David Walsh
Total Staff 7
Region South East
Owned or managed 275
Rt 241 GN 237 Sup 4 SO 34
Tot lets 4 GN bs 0
Tenant Type % Family 48%
Older 19% Single 33%
Development Total 4
Rt 17 GN 17 NBA 4

Phoenix Community HA (Bellingham & Downham) Ltd
○ Charitable HA
TSA Reg ✓ ▢ 🔲 ▢ 🔑
Wren Court, 15-17 London Road,
Bromley, BR1 1DE
T 0800 028 5700
E corporate.communications@
phoenixch.org
W www.phoenixcommunityhousing.
org
CE Mr Jim Ripley
Sec Mr Chris Starke
Ch Mrs Pat Fordham
Total Staff 144
Region London
Owned or managed 6281
Rt 5472 GN 5472 SO 809
Tot lets 267 GN bs 5472
Development Total 4
NBA 4

Phoenix Futures
☆ Charitable Company
TSA Reg ✓ ♦ 🐦
3rd Floor, Asra House, 1 Long Lane,
London, Greater London, SE1 4PG
T 020 7234 9740
E info@phoenix-futures.co.uk
W www.phoenix-futures.org.uk
CE Ms Karen Biggs
Sec Mr George Lambis
Ch Mr Dick Holland
Total Staff 618
Regions London + South East
Owned or managed 59
Rt 59 Sup 59

Tenant Type % Family 11%
Single 89%

Pickering & Ferens Homes
❑ Charitable Trust
TSA Reg ✓ 🏠
Silvester House, The Maltings,
Silvester Street, Hull,
North Humberside, HU1 3HA
T 01482 223783
E info@pfh.org.uk
W www.pfh.org.uk
Ch Mr Tom Hogan
Total Staff 46
Region Yorkshire & Humberside
Owned or managed 1242
Rt 1242 OP 1242
Tenant Type % Older 100%
Development Total 54
Rt 20 OP 20 NBA 24 NBC 30

Pierhead HA Ltd
■ Non-Charitable HA
TSA Reg ✓ 🏠 🔧
9th Floor Wellington Buildings,
The Strand, Liverpool, Merseyside,
L2 0PP
T 0151 227 1001
E info@pierheadhousing.com
W www.pierheadhousing.com
CE Mr Graham Coslett
Sec Mr Graham Coslett
Ch Mr Geoffrey Freeman
Total Staff 39
Region North West
Owned or managed 1731
Rt 1500 GN 1232 Sup 87 OP 181
SO 32 NSO 199 Tot lets 170
GN bs 1232
Tenant Type % Family 30%
Older 30% Single 40%
Development Total 3
NBA 3

Pine Court HA Ltd
○ Charitable HA
TSA Reg ✓ ◊
1 Nelson Street, Liverpool,
Merseyside, L1 5DW
T 0151 709 6878
E contactus@pinecourt-housing.co.uk
W www.pinecourt-housing.org.uk
CE Mr Ian Fazakerley
Sec Mr Roy Williams
Ch Mr Philip Leong
Total Staff 3
Region North West
Owned or managed 454
Rt 454 GN 393 Sup 61
Tenant Type % Family 74%
Older 11% Single 15%
Parent Association
One Vision Housing Ltd

Pine Ridge HA Ltd.
○ Charitable HA
TSA Reg ✓
24 Pine Grove, Bushey,
Hertfordshire, WD23 2DY
T 01923 236514
E info@pineridge.org.uk
CE Mrs Lesley Culley
Sec Mrs Lesley Culley
Ch Mr Patrick Sweeney
Total Staff 3
Region East of England
Owned or managed 107
Rt 107 GN 107
Tenant Type % Family 65%
Older 31% Single 4%

Pinner House Society Ltd
○ Charitable HA
TSA Reg ✓ 🤝
Pinner House, Church Lane, Pinner,
Middlesex, HA5 3AA
T 020 8429 1255
E pinner.house@virgin.net
W www.pinnerhouse.co.uk
CE Ms Rachel Barkoff
Sec Mrs Anne Coleman
Ch Mr Francis Spencer-Cotton
Total Staff 4
Region London
Owned or managed 30
Rt 30 OP 30
Tenant Type % Older 100%

Places for People Group
✪ Not-for-Profit Company
TSA Reg ✓ ♦ ◊
305 Gray's Inn Road, London,
Greater London, WC1X 8QR
T 020 7843 3800
F 020 7843 3802
E enquiries@placesforpeople.co.uk
W www.placesforpeople.co.uk
CE Mr David Cowans
Sec Mr Chris Martin
Ch Mr Chris Phillips
Total Staff 2846
Region London
Subsidiary Association(s) Cotman
HA Ltd; Places for People Homes
Ltd; Places for People Individual
Support Ltd

Places for People Homes Ltd
■ Non-Charitable HA
TSA Reg ✓ 🖥 🗔 500 🏠 🔧 ♦ ◊
305 Gray's Inn Road, London,
Greater London, WC1X 8QR
T 020 7843 3800
F 020 7843 3802
E enquiries@placesforpeople.co.uk
W www.placesforpeople.co.uk
CE Mr David Cowans

Sec Mr Chris Martin
Ch Mr Chris Phillips
Total Staff 655
Region London
Owned or managed 51219
Rt 38510 GN 35051 Sup 978
OP 2481 SO 9268 NSO 3441
Tot lets 5128 GN bs 32220
Tenant Type % Family 37%
Older 23% Single 40%
Development Total 505
NBA 302 NBC 203
Parent Association
Places for People Group

Places for People Individual Support Ltd
○ Charitable HA
TSA Reg ✓ 🗔 🔧 ♦ 🤝 ◊ 🏠
305 Gray's Inn Road, London,
Greater London, WC1X 8QR
T 020 7843 3800
F 020 7843 3802
E enquiries@placesforpeople.co.uk
W www.placesforpeople.co.uk
CE Mr David Cowans
Sec Mr Chris Martin
Ch Mr Chris Phillips
Total Staff 768
Region London
Owned or managed 7368
Rt 7293 GN 2784 Sup 1624
OP 2885 SO 73 NSO 2
Tot lets 1321 GN bs 2784
Tenant Type % Family 3%
Older 53% Single 44%
Parent Association
Places for People Group

Plumlife Homes Ltd
■ Non-Charitable HA
TSA Reg ✓ 🔧 ◊
Southern Gate, 729 Princess
Road, West Didsbury, Manchester,
Lancashire, M20 2LT
T 0161 447 5000
E enquires@plumlife.co.uk
W www.greatplaces.org.uk
CE Mr Stephen Porter
Sec Mr Phil Elvy
Ch Mr Les Coop
Total Staff 14
Region North West
Owned or managed 408
Rt 251 GN 251 SO 157 Tot lets 0
GN bs 0
Parent Association
Great Places Housing Group

Plus Dane (Cheshire) HA Ltd
■ Non-Charitable HA
TSA Reg ✓ ⬛ ⬛ 🔑 ♦ 🤝 ◊
Shepherds Mill, Worrall Street,
Congleton, Cheshire, CW12 1DT
T 01260 281037
E alison.carey@
neighbourhoodinvestor.com
W www.neighbourhoodinvestor.com
CE Mr Mike Doran
Sec Mrs Alison Carey
Ch Mr Maurice Evans
Total Staff 529
Regions North West +
West Midlands
Owned or managed 4894
Rt 4547 **GN** 2981 **Sup** 214 **OP** 1352
SO 252 **NSO** 95 **Tot lets** 760
GN bs 2905
Tenant Type % Family 30%
Older 50% **Single** 20%
Development Total 454
Rt 159 **GN** 150 **Sup** 9 **LCHO** 77
NBA 240 **NBC** 214
Parent Association
Plus Dane Housing Group Ltd

Plus Dane (Merseyside) HA Ltd
○ Charitable HA
TSA Reg ✗ ⬛ 🔑 ♦ 🤝 ◊
Baltimore Buildings, 13-15 Rodney
Street, Liverpool, Merseyside, L1 9EF
T 0151 708 4664
E alison.carey@
neighbourhoodinvestor.com
W www.neighbourhoodinvestor.com
CE Mr Gerard Murden
Sec Mrs Alison Carey
Ch Mr George Davies
Total Staff 333
Region North West
Owned or managed 7265
Rt 6958 **GN** 6527 **Sup** 137 **OP** 294
SO 307 **Tot lets** 711 **GN bs** 6358
Tenant Type % Family 49%
Older 25% **Single** 26%
Development Total 273
Rt 312 **GN** 271 **OP** 41 **LCHO** 70
NBA 141 **NBC** 132
Parent Association
Plus Dane Housing Group Ltd

Plus Dane Housing Group Ltd
■ Non-Charitable HA
TSA Reg ✓ ♦ ◊
Baltimore Buildings, 13-15 Rodney
Street, Liverpool, Merseyside, L1 9EF
E alison.carey@
neighbourhoodinvestor.com
W www.neighbourhoodinvestor.com
CE Mr Ken Perry
Sec Mrs Alison Carey
Ch Ms Linda Minnis

Total Staff 862
Region North West
Subsidiary Association(s) Plus
Dane (Cheshire) HA Ltd; Plus Dane
(Merseyside) HA Ltd

Plymouth Community Homes
○ Charitable HA
TSA Reg ✓ ⬛ ⬜ ⬛ 🔑 ♦
Ground Floor, Princess Court, 23
Princess Street, Plymouth, Devon,
PL1 2EX
T 0800 694 3101
E governance@
plymouthcommunityhomes.co.uk
W www.plymouthcommunityhomes.
co.uk
CE Mr Clive Turner
Sec Ms Belinda Pascoe
Ch Ms Elaine Pellow
Total Staff 638
Region South West
Owned or managed 16126
Rt 14636 **GN** 14210 **OP** 426
SO 1481 **NSO** 9 **Tot lets** 780
GN bs 14210
Tenant Type % Family 47%
Older 29% **Single** 24%
Development Total 34
Rt 137 **GN** 137 **LCHO** 58 **NBA** 34

Polish Citizen's Committee HA Ltd
○ Charitable HA
TSA Reg ✓ 🤝 ⬛
55 Princes Gate, London, Greater
London, SW7 2PG
T 020 7584 6992
E citizens.committee@tiscali.co.uk
W www.antokol.co.uk
Ch Mrs Barbara Korzeniowska
Total Staff 30
Region London
Owned or managed 34
Rt 34 **OP** 34
Tenant Type % Older 100%

Polish Retired Persons HA Ltd
○ Charitable HA
TSA Reg ✓
24 Florence Road, London,
Greater London, W5 3TX
T 020 8567 1997
Sec Mrs B Jablonski
Ch Mr B B Mordas
Total Staff 0
Region London
Owned or managed 44
Rt 44 **OP** 44
Tenant Type % Older 100%

Poole Old Peoples Welfare HS Ltd
○ Charitable HA
TSA Reg ✓
11 Winchester Place, North Street,
Poole, Dorset, BH15 1NX
T 01202 673344
Sec Mr S Dean
Ch R A Lees
Total Staff 0
Region South West
Owned or managed 11
Rt 11 **OP** 11
Tenant Type % Older 100%

Poplar HARCA
☆ Charitable Company
TSA Reg ✓
⬛ 🤝 ⬛ 🔑 ♦ 🤝 ⬛
167a East India Dock Road, Poplar,
London, E14 0EA
T 020 7510 0500
E info@poplarharca.co.uk
W www.poplarharca.co.uk
CE Mr Stephen Stride, Bsc (Hons),
MCIOH
Sec Mr Stephen Stride, Bsc (Hons),
MCIOH
Ch Ms Bernadette Conroy
Total Staff 299
Region London
Owned or managed 8731
Rt 6333 **GN** 6333 **SO** 9 **NSO** 2389
Tot lets 393 **GN bs** 6306
Tenant Type % Family 61%
Older 14% **Single** 25%
Development Total 535
Rt 334 **GN** 334 **NBA** 269 **NBC** 266

Porchlight
☆ Charitable Company
TSA Reg ✗ 🤝
2nd Floor, Watling Chambers,
18-19 Watling Street, Canterbury,
Kent, CT1 2UA
T 01227 760078
E headoffice@porchlight.org.uk
W www.porchlight.org.uk
CE Mr Mike Barrett
Sec Mr Mike Barrett
Ch Mrs Anne Norris JP
Total Staff 140
Region South East
Tenant Type % Single 100%

Portal HA Ltd
○ Charitable HA
TSA Reg ✓ ⬛ ◊
Collins House, Bishopstoke Road,
Eastleigh, Hampshire, SO50 6AD
T 0300 123 1567
E radiandirect@radian.co.uk
W www.radian.co.uk
CE Mr Lindsay Todd

Sec Mr Terry Walker
Ch Tom Moloney
Total Staff 0
Regions South East + South West
Owned or managed 1073
Rt 1073 GN 999 Sup 30 OP 44
Tenant Type % Family 85%
Older 7% Single 8%
Development Total 393
NBA 381 NBC 12
Parent Association
Radian Group Ltd

Portsmouth Churches HA Ltd
○ Charitable HA
TSA Reg ✓ 👓
20 Fratton Road, Portsmouth,
Hampshire, PO1 5BX
T 023 9229 7877
E s.brotherston@btconnect.com
W www.portsmouthchurchesha.co.uk
CE Mrs Susan Brotherston
Ch Mr Harold Wonham
Total Staff 21
Region South East
Owned or managed 40
Rt 40 GN 9 Sup 31
Tenant Type % Family 50%
Single 50%

Portsmouth Rotary HA Ltd
○ Charitable HA
TSA Reg ✓
13b Grove Road South, Southsea,
Hampshire, PO5 3QR
T 023 9275 4791
W www.prha.co.uk
CE Mr Graham Cole
Sec Mr Graham Cole
Ch Mr David Marshall
Total Staff 8
Region South East
Owned or managed 141
Rt 141 GN 141
Tenant Type % Older 100%

Preston Care & Repair Ltd
○ Charitable HA
TSA Reg ✗
The Annexe, PCC Works Dept Site,
St. Pauls Road, Preston, Lancashire,
PR1 1PX
T 01772 204096
E agency@prestoncareandrepair.
fednet.org.uk
CE Ms Liz Sykes
Ch Mr Michael McCulloch
Total Staff 10
Region North West

Prestwich & North Western HA Ltd
■ Non-Charitable HA
TSA Reg ✓ 🔑
The Estate Office, 24 Rectory Green,
Prestwich, Manchester, Lancashire,
M25 1BQ
T 0161 773 5219
E info@prestwichnwha.co.uk
W www.prestwichnwha.co.uk
CE Mrs Sue Lawrence
Sec Mrs Sue Lawrence
Ch Mr Tony Barlow
Total Staff 7
Region North West
Owned or managed 194
Rt 186 GN 186 SO 8 Tot lets 13
GN bs 0
Tenant Type % Family 25%
Older 25% Single 50%

Probus Women's Housing Society Ltd
■ Non-Charitable HA
TSA Reg ✗
Gladstone House, 2 Church Road,
Liverpool, Merseyside, L15 9EG
T 0151 733 0864
E probus@hbdltd.com
W www.probus-housing.co.uk
Sec Ms Margaret Swinson
Ch Mrs Janice Miles
Total Staff 0
Regions North East + London, South
East, East of England, North West
Owned or managed 39
Rt 39 GN 39
Tenant Type % Family 90%
Single 10%

Progress Care HA Ltd
○ Charitable HA
TSA Reg ✓ 🏠 🔑 ♨
Warwick House, Kilnhouse Lane,
Lytham St. Annes, FY8 3DU
T 01772 450600
E enquiries@progessgroup.org.uk
W www.progressgroup.org.uk
CE Ms Jacqui De-Rose
Sec Mr Eric Hughes
Ch Mr Tony Harrison
Total Staff 66
Regions North West + London,
South East, South West, East
Midlands, West Midlands, East of
England, Yorkshire & Humberside,
North East
Owned or managed 3394
Rt 2790 Sup 2790 SO 30 NSO 574
Tot lets 442 GN bs 0
Tenant Type % Single 100%
Development Total 244
Rt 46 Sup 46 NBA 192 NBC 52
Parent Association
Progress Housing Group Ltd

Progress Housing Group Ltd
■ Non-Charitable HA
TSA Reg ✓ 🔑 ♦ ♨
Sumner House, 21 King Street,
Leyland, Lancashire, PR25 2LW
T 01772 450600
E enquiries@progressgroup.org.uk
W www.progressgroup.org.uk
CE Ms Jacqui De-Rose
Sec Mr Eric Hughes
Ch Janet Hale
Total Staff 268
Region North West
Owned or managed 81
 SO 54 NSO 27 Tot lets 0 GN bs 0
Subsidiary Association(s)
New Fylde Housing Ltd; New
Progress HA Ltd; Progress Care
HA Ltd

Prospect Housing and Support Services
○ Charitable HA
TSA Reg ✗ 🏠 👓
Hethersett Centre, RNIB College,
Philanthropic Road, Redhill, Surrey,
RH1 4DG
T 01737 765800
E prospect@prospectha.org.uk
W www.prospectha.org.uk
CE Ms Deborah Tosler
Sec Ms Deborah Tosler
Ch Ms Val Brandt
Total Staff 0
Regions South East + London
Owned or managed 156
Rt 156 Sup 156
Tenant Type % Single 100%
Development Total 13
NBA 9 NBC 4

Providence Row HA
○ Charitable HA
TSA Reg ✓ 👓
Providence House,
458 Bethnal Green Road, London,
Greater London, E2 0EA
T 020 7920 7300
E info@prha.net
W www.prha.net
CE Ms Fiona Humphrey
Sec Ms Fiona Humphrey
Ch Mrs Lynn Vickery
Total Staff 117
Region London
Owned or managed 626
Rt 626 GN 102 Sup 491 OP 33
Tenant Type % Family 3% Single 97%

Provincial HA Ltd
■ Non-Charitable HA
TSA Reg ✗ ◊
Armitt House, Monmouth Road, Cheadle Hulme, Cheadle, Cheshire, SK8 7EF
T 0161 486 9911
W www.equityhousing.co.uk
CE Mr David Fisher
Sec Mr David Fisher
Ch Mr Brian Ashfield
Total Staff 0
Region North West
Tenant Type % Family 10%
Older 80% **Single** 10%
Parent Association
Equity Housing Group Ltd

Purleigh Old People's HA Ltd
○ Charitable HA
TSA Reg ✗
Fairfields Church Hill, Purleigh, Chelmsford, Essex, CM3 6QG
T 01621 828100
Sec Mrs J Prestwich
Ch Mrs J Snow
Total Staff 1
Region East of England
Owned or managed 24
Rt 12 **OP** 12 **NSO** 12
Tenant Type % Older 100%

Puttenham and Wanborough Housing Society Ltd
○ Charitable HA
TSA Reg ✓
Harolds Hill, Crosswater Lane, Churt, Farnham, Surrey, GU10 2JN
T 01483 810470
CE Mr Gordon David
Sec Mrs Carolyn MacLeod
Ch Dr G D Starte
Total Staff 0
Region South East
Owned or managed 15
Rt 15 **GN** 15
Tenant Type % Family 71%
Older 29% **Single** 7%

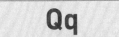

Quadrant-Brownswood Tenant Co-op Ltd
★ Co-operative Society
TSA Reg ✓
43-45 Mountgrove Road, London, Greater London, N5 2LX
T 020 7359 9360
Sec Ms Betty Connaughton
Ch Sarah Taylor

Total Staff 3
Region London
Owned or managed 141
Rt 141 **GN** 141
Tenant Type % Family 64%
Older 13% **Single** 23%

Quaker Housing Trust
☆ Charitable Company
TSA Reg ✗
Friends House, Euston Road, London, Greater London, NW1 2BJ
T 020 7663 1036
E involveme@qht.org.uk
W www.qht.org.uk
Sec Paula Harvey
Ch David Burnell
Total Staff 0
Region London

Radian Group Ltd
✪ Not-for-Profit Company
TSA Reg ✓ ♦ ◊
Collins House, Bishopstoke Road, Eastleigh, Hampshire, SO50 6AD
T 0300 123 1567
E radiandirect@radian.co.uk
W www.radian.co.uk
CE Mr Lindsay Todd
Sec Mr Terry Walker
Ch Mr Richard Hastilow
Total Staff 511
Region South East
Subsidiary Association(s)
Drum HA Ltd;
Oriel Housing Ltd; Portal HA Ltd; Radian Support Ltd; The Swaythling Housing Society Ltd; Windsor and District HA

Radian Support Ltd
○ Charitable HA
TSA Reg ✗ ♦ 🐾 ◊
Parkside House, 33 - 39 Sheet Street, Windsor, Berkshire, SL4 1BY
T 0300 123 1567
W www.radian.co.uk
CE Ms Gina Small
Sec Mr Terry Walker
Ch Mr Richard Barritt
Total Staff 496
Region South East
Owned or managed 3
Rt 3 **Sup** 3
Parent Association
Radian Group Ltd

Raglan HA Ltd
○ Charitable HA
TSA Reg ✓ ■ 🖵 📷 🔑 ♦ 🐾
Suite C, Lancaster House, Grange Business Park, Enderby Road, Leicester, Leicestershire, LE8 6EP
T 0800 011 6420
E info@raglan.org
W www.raglan.org
CE Mr Nicholas Harris
Sec Mrs Anne Harling
Ch Mr George Blunden
Total Staff 383
Regions South West + London, South East, East Midlands, West Midlands, East of England, North West
Owned or managed 11833
Rt 10572 **GN** 8851 **Sup** 183 **OP** 1538
SO 1261 **Tot lets** 1437 **GN bs** 8713
Tenant Type % Family 42%
Older 21% **Single** 37%
Development Total 108
Rt 591 **GN** 581 **Sup** 10 **LCHO** 262
NBA 54 **NBC** 54

Railway HA and Benefit Fund
❑ Charitable Trust
TSA Reg ✓ 📷
Bank Top House, Garbutt Square, Neasham Road, Darlington, County Durham, DL1 4DR
T 01325 482125
E info@railwayha.co.uk
W www.railwayha.co.uk
CE Mrs Anne Rowlands
Sec Mrs Anne Rowlands
Ch Mr Barrie Ward
Total Staff 41
Regions North East + West Midlands, Yorkshire & Humberside, North West
Owned or managed 1367
Rt 1367 **GN** 442 **OP** 925
Tenant Type % Family 18%
Older 80% **Single** 2%
Development Total 28
NBA 14 **NBC** 14

Raven Housing Trust Ltd
○ Charitable HA
TSA Reg ✓ 🖵 🐾 📷 🔑 🐾
Raven House, 29 Linkfield Lane, Redhill, Surrey, RH1 1SS
T 01737 272400
E raven@ravenht.org.uk
W www.ravenht.org.uk
CE Mr Jonathan Higgs
Sec Mr Jonathan Higgs
Ch Mr John Butler
Total Staff 188
Regions South East + London
Owned or managed 5561

Rt 5357 **GN** 4839 **Sup** 154 **OP** 364
SO 194 **NSO** 10 **Tot lets** 415
GN bs 4684
Tenant Type % Family 30%
Older 32% **Single** 38%
Development Total 210
NBA 113 **NBC** 97

Rayner House and Yew Trees Ltd
○ Charitable HA
TSA Reg ✓ 🐾
3-5 Damson Parkway, Solihull, West Midlands, B91 2PP
T 0121 705 9293
E businessmanager@raynorhouse.co.uk
W www.raynerhouseandyewtrees.co.uk
CE Ms Zoe Collis
Sec Mr Peter Scurlock
Ch Mr Peter J. Travis
Total Staff 44
Region West Midlands
Owned or managed 66
Rt 66 **OP** 66
Tenant Type % Older 100%

RCHL
○ Charitable HA
TSA Reg ✗ 🐾
Unit 2, Caxton Place, Roden Street, Ilford, Essex, IG1 2AH
T 020 8477 1800
E info@rchl.org.uk
W www.rchl.org.uk
CE Mr Paul Allen
Sec Mr Paul Allen
Ch J G Hughes
Total Staff 0
Region London
Tenant Type % Older 10%
Single 90%

Red Devon Housing Ltd
■ Non-Charitable HA
TSA Reg ✓ 🐾
Red Devon Housing Ltd, Brook House, Church Street, Dawlish, EX7 9AX
T 01626 863192
E reddevonhousing2@tiscali.co.uk
W www.reddevonhousing.co.uk
CE Ms Margaret Nicholls
Sec Mrs H Armson
Ch Ms Margaret Nicholls
Total Staff 20
Region South West
Owned or managed 38
Rt 37 **GN** 17 **Sup** 20 **NSO** 1
Tenant Type % Older 100%

Red House Farm Housing Co-op Ltd
★ Co-operative Society
TSA Reg ✓
2 Gleneagles Court, Red House Farm, Whitley Bay, NE25 9NA
CE Ms Jane Olson
Sec Ms Jane Olson
Ch Garry Lees
Total Staff 0
Region North East
Owned or managed 39
Rt 39 **GN** 39
Tenant Type % Family 62%
Older 25% **Single** 13%

Red Kite Community Housing Ltd
○ Charitable HA
TSA Reg ✓ 🖥 📻 📠 🄳 🔑
Queen Victoria Road, High Wycombe, Buckinghamshire, HP11 1BB
T 01494 76222
W www.redkitehousing.org.uk
CE Mr Trevor Morrow
Sec Mr Neil Venables
Ch Dr Jennie Ferrigno
Total Staff 120
Region South East
Owned or managed 6075
Rt 6066 **GN** 4225 **Sup** 1620 **OP** 221
SO 9 **Tot lets** 116 **GN bs** 6054
Tenant Type % Family 28%
Older 49% **Single** 23%
Development Total 6056
NBA 6056

Redditch Co-operative Homes
☆ Charitable Company
TSA Reg ✓ ◊
Britten House, Britton Street, Redditch, Worcestershire, B97 6HD
T 01527 591170
E info@rch.coop
W www.rch.coop
CE Mr Carl Taylor
Sec Miss Joanne Easton
Ch Mr William Hartnett
Total Staff 3
Region West Midlands
Owned or managed 270
Rt 270 **GN** 270
Tenant Type % Family 52%
Older 15% **Single** 33%
Parent Association
Accord HA Ltd

Redditch Friends HA
○ Charitable HA
TSA Reg ✓
37 Oxhill Close, Matchborough West, Redditch, Worcestershire, B98 0ER
T 01527 525107
E redditchfriends@btconnect.com
CE Miss Jill Davies
Sec Mr Gary Peter Brookes
Ch Mr John Colebrook
Total Staff 3
Region West Midlands
Owned or managed 46
Rt 46 **GN** 46
Tenant Type % Family 47%
Single 53%

Redditch YMCA Ltd
☆ Charitable Company
TSA Reg ✓ 📠 🐾
Church Hill Centre, Loxley Close, Redditch, Worcestershire, B98 9JG
T 01527 61643
E enquiries@redditchymca.org.uk
W www.redditchymca.org
CE Mr Duncan Berry
Sec Mr Duncan Berry
Ch Ms Jacintha Hodgson
Total Staff 105
Region West Midlands
Owned or managed 202
Rt 202 **GN** 150 **Sup** 52
Tenant Type % Family 16%
Single 84%
Development Total 34
Rt 34 **Sup** 34 **NBA** 34

Redland HA Ltd
○ Charitable HA
TSA Reg ✓ 📠 🔑
Holly House, Corbet Close, Lawrence Weston, Bristol, Avon, BS11 0TA
T 0117 938 2700
E housing.admin@redlandha.co.uk
W www.somerhousinggroup.co.uk/section_3.aspx
CE Mr Victor da Cunha
Sec Miss Philippa Armstrong
Ch Mr Roger Thomas
Total Staff 25
Region South West
Owned or managed 1551
Rt 1417 **GN** 1220 **Sup** 14 **OP** 183 **SO** 82 **NSO** 52 **Tot lets** 99 **GN bs** 1032
Tenant Type % Family 70%
Older 20% **Single** 10%
Development Total 8
NBA 4 **NBC** 4

Refuge
☆ Charitable Company
TSA Reg ✗ 👓
International House,
1 St. Katharines Way, London,
Greater London, E1W 1UN
T 020 7395 7700
E info@refuge.org.uk
W www.refuge.org.uk
CE Ms Sandra Horley
Sec Ms Sandra Horley
Ch Mr Peter Wallach
Total Staff 0
Region London
Owned or managed 270
Rt 270 Sup 270
Tenant Type % Family 100%

Regenda Ltd
○ Charitable HA
TSA Reg ✓ ☐ ⓐ 🔑 ◕ ♦
Regenda House, Enterprise Business
Park, Northgate Close, Horwich,
Bolton, Lancashire, BL6 6PQ
T 01204 814000
E info@regenda.org.uk
W www.regenda.org.uk
CE Mr Bernard Gallagher
Sec Miss Julie Vincent
Ch Mr John Thomson
Total Staff 472
Region North West
Owned or managed 9968
Rt 9968 GN 8134 Sup 927 OP 907
Tenant Type % Family 51%
Older 27% Single 22%
Development Total 121
Rt 235 GN 235 LCHO 83 NBA 13
NBC 108

Reigate Quaker HA Ltd
○ Charitable HA
TSA Reg ✓ 👓
Thomas Moore House, Reigate Road,
Reigate, Surrey, RH2 0QW
T 01737 242101
E reigatequakerha1@btconnect.com
Sec Raymond Dill
Ch Michael Higgins
Total Staff 5
Region South East
Owned or managed 74
Rt 74 Sup 60 OP 14
Tenant Type % Older 100%

Renaissance Social Housing Ltd
✪ Not-for-Profit Company
TSA Reg ✗
Suite 33, 3rd Floor, Northumbrian
Water House, 7-15 Pink Lane,
Newcastle-Upon-Tyne,
Tyne And Wear, NE1 5DW
T 0191 260 5544

E info@rshl.co.uk
W www.rshl.co.uk
CE Mr B Thompson
Sec Ms Sheila Skinner
Ch Mr B Thompson
Total Staff 0
Region Yorkshire & Humberside
Tenant Type % Single 100%

Renew Leeds Ltd
☆ Charitable Company
TSA Reg ✗
34 Regent Street, Leeds, LS2 7QN
T 0113 383 3920
E admin@renew-leeds.co.uk
W www.renew-leeds.co.uk
CE Mr Trevor Mason
Sec Mr Matthew Walker
Ch Mr Andrew Taylor
Total Staff 65
Region Yorkshire & Humberside

Reside HA
■ Non-Charitable HA
TSA Reg ✓ ⓐ 👓
Reside HA Ltd,
33 Old London Road, Kingston Upon
Thames, Surrey, KT2 6ND
T 020 8255 5220
E enquiries@residehousing.com
W www.residehousing.com
CE Mr Peter Webster
Sec Mr Dipak Patel
Ch Mr Richard Smith
Total Staff 12
Regions London + South East,
North East
Owned or managed 138
Rt 137 Sup 137 NSO 1
Tenant Type % Single 100%
Development Total 19
Rt 1 Sup 1 NBA 11 NBC 8

Retired Baptist Ministers HS Ltd
○ Charitable HA
TSA Reg ✗
26 Athelstan Road, Bournemouth,
BH6 5LY
T 01202 548890
E sgreen@rbmhs.org.uk
W www.rbmhs.org.uk
CE Mr Stewart Green
Sec Mr Stewart Green
Ch Mr F W Johnston
Total Staff 2
Regions South West + London,
South East, East Midlands, West
Midlands, East of England, North
East, North West
Tenant Type % Older 100%

Ribble Valley Homes Ltd
○ Charitable HA
TSA Reg ✓ 🖧VTHO 🔑 👓 ◊
De Lacy House, Station Road,
Clitheroe, Lancashire, BB7 2JT
T 0800 111448
E info@ribblevalleyhomes.org.uk
W www.ribblevalleyhomes.org.uk
CE Mrs Christine Grimshaw
Sec Mrs Audrey Davidson
Ch Cllr Allan Knox
Total Staff 38
Region North West
Owned or managed 1248
Rt 1167 GN 569 OP 598 SO 81
Tot lets 111 GN bs 557
Tenant Type % Family 30%
Older 60% Single 10%
Parent Association
Symphony Housing Group

Richmond Housing Partnership
○ Charitable HA
TSA Reg ✓ ☐ 🖧VTHO 🔑 👓 ◊
8 Waldegrave Road, Teddington,
Middlesex, TW11 8GT
T 0800 032 2433
E customer.services@rhp.org.uk
W www.rhp.org.uk
CE Mr David Done
Sec Mr David Done
Ch Mr John Newbury
Total Staff 237
Region London
Owned or managed 7518
Rt 7458 GN 7007 OP 451 SO 22
NSO 38 Tot lets 257 GN bs 6662
Tenant Type % Family 39%
Older 33% Single 28%
Subsidiary Association(s)
Co-op Homes (South) Ltd

Richmond Upon Thames Churches HT
○ Charitable HA
TSA Reg ✓ ⓐ 🔑 👓 ◊
13 Castle Mews, High Street,
Hampton, Surrey, TW12 2NN
T 020 8481 7277
E info@rutcht.org.uk
W www.paragonchg.co.uk
CE Mr Ian Watts
Sec Mark Rothwell
Ch Mrs Tracey Lees
Total Staff 155
Regions London + South East
Owned or managed 3528
Rt 2758 GN 2197 Sup 225 OP 336
SO 752 NSO 18 Tot lets 357
GN bs 2190
Tenant Type % Family 32%
Older 45% Single 23%
Development Total 186

NBA 101 NBC 85
Parent Association Paragon Community Housing Group

Rickmansworth Churches HA Ltd
❍ Charitable HA
TSA Reg ✓
Wensum Court, 221 High Street, Rickmansworth, Hertfordshire, WD3 1BR
T 01923 779885
E wensumcourt@aol.com
CE Mrs M Loveridge
Ch John A Walker
Total Staff 3
Region East of England
Owned or managed 26
Rt 26 **OP** 26
Tenant Type % Older 100%

Ringwood & District Old People's Housing Society Ltd
❍ Charitable HA
TSA Reg ✗
Queen Anne Cottage, The Common, Woodgreen, Fordingbridge, Hampshire, SP6 2BQ
T 01725 513862
CE Mrs Frances Bowen
Sec Mr Michael Stocken
Ch Mrs Frances Bowen
Total Staff 3
Region South East
Owned or managed 42
Rt 42 **OP** 42
Tenant Type % Older 100%

Riverlink Housing Co-op Ltd
★ Co-operative Society
TSA Reg ✗
96 Bowes Road, New Southgate, N13 4NP
T 020 8368 4995
E smallaburn@yahoo.co.uk
W www.riverlink.org.uk
Sec Mr Nigel Greenwood
Ch Kazie Dewey
Total Staff 1
Region London
Tenant Type % Family 6% **Older** 9% **Single** 85%

Riversmead HA Ltd
❍ Charitable HA
TSA Reg ✓ 📺 🏠 🔑 🤝 🜂
Riversmead House, 36 Ware Road, Hertford, Hertfordshire, SG13 7HH
T 01992 514514
E riversmead@riversmead.org.uk
W www.riversmead.org.uk
CE Mr Steve Henning
Sec Mr Paul Huckstep

Ch Kevin Brush
Total Staff 74
Regions East of England + South East
Owned or managed 4505
Rt 3849 **GN** 3348 **Sup** 16 **OP** 485
SO 643 **NSO** 13 **Tot lets** 366
GN bs 3271
Tenant Type % Family 42%
Older 46% **Single** 12%
Development Total 227
NBA 123 NBC 104
Parent Association
Network Housing Group Ltd

Rochdale Boroughwide Housing
❍ Charitable HA
TSA Reg ✓
📼 🖥️ 📺 🏠 🔑 👤 🤝
PO Box 69, The Old Post Office, The Esplanade, Rochdale, Lancashire, OL16 1AE
T 0845 070 5170
W www.rbhousing.org.uk
CE Mr Gareth Swarbrick
Sec Ms Liz Alasvand
Ch Mr Ian Agnew
Total Staff 632
Region North West
Owned or managed 13753
Rt 13743 **GN** 12838 **OP** 905 **SO** 10
Tot lets 0 **GN bs** 12796
Development Total 13711
NBA 13711

Rochford HA
❍ Charitable HA
TSA Reg ✓ 📺 🔑 🜂
Rochford HA, Chamber Court, Castle Street, Worcester, WR1 3ZQ
T 01904 334000
E enquiries.rochford@sanctuary-housing.co.uk
W www.sanctuary-housing.co.uk
CE Mr David Bennett
Sec Mr Craig Moule
Ch Mr Nigel Barron
Total Staff 27
Region East of England
Owned or managed 1842
Rt 1714 **GN** 1290 **OP** 424 **SO** 128
Tot lets 137 **GN bs** 1274
Parent Association
Sanctuary HA

Rockdale HA Ltd
❍ Charitable HA
TSA Reg ✓ 🤝
Rockdale Lodge, Rockdale Road, Sevenoaks, Kent, TN13 1JT
T 01732 458762
E enquiries@rockdale.org.uk
W www.rockdale.org.uk
CE Mrs Jill Drake

Sec Mrs Jill Drake
Ch Mrs Helen Kenny
Total Staff 63
Region South East
Owned or managed 165
Rt 137 **GN** 14 **OP** 123 **NSO** 28
Tenant Type % Older 100%

Rockingham Forest HA Ltd
❍ Charitable HA
TSA Reg ✓ 🔑
St Peter's House, 101 Wellingborough Road, Rushden, Northamptonshire, NN10 9YL
T 01933 411400
E info@rfha.org.uk
W www.rfha.org.uk
CE Ms Rosemarie Anderson
Sec Ms Rosemarie Anderson
Ch Robert Hingston
Total Staff 22
Region East Midlands
Owned or managed 813
Rt 786 **GN** 786 **SO** 6 **NSO** 21
Tot lets 0 **GN bs** 0
Tenant Type % Family 96% **Single** 4%

Roddons HA
❍ Charitable HA
TSA Reg ✓ 📺 🏠 🔑 🜂
Beacon House, 23 Hostmoor Avenue, March, Cambridgeshire, PE15 0AX
T 01354 660789
E roddonsenquiries@circle.org.uk
W www.circleanglia.org
CE Mr Christopher Smith
Sec Ms Deborah Upton
Ch Mrs Brenda Reynolds
Total Staff 123
Region East of England
Owned or managed 3915
Rt 3798 **GN** 3315 **OP** 483 **SO** 117
Tot lets 437 **GN bs** 3305
Tenant Type % Family 20%
Older 60% **Single** 20%
Development Total 121
NBA 62 NBC 59
Parent Association Circle

Rogate & Terwick HA Ltd
❍ Charitable HA
TSA Reg ✓ 🤝
East Lodge, Rogate, Petersfield, Hampshire, GU31 5EA
T 01730 821310
Sec Miss Catherine Staples
Ch Mr John Field
Total Staff 1
Region South East
Owned or managed 23
Rt 23 **GN** 23

Tenant Type % Family 16%
Older 65% Single 16%

Romford YMCA Ltd
❑ Charitable Trust
TSA Reg ✓
Rush Green Road, Romford,
Essex, RM7 0PH
T 01708 766211
E info@romfordymca.org
W www.romfordymca.org
CE Mr Dave Ball
Sec Mr Paul Setterfield
Ch Mr Andrew Dyckhoff
Total Staff 115
Regions East of England + London
Owned or managed 2
NSO 2
Tenant Type % Single 100%

Rooftop Homes Ltd
■ Non-Charitable HA
TSA Reg ✓ ◊
70 High Street, Evesham,
Worcestershire, WR11 4YD
T 01386 420800
E info@rooftopgroup.org
W www.rooftopgroup.org
CE Mr Ian Hughes
Sec Mrs Sheila Morris
Ch Nicola Inchbald
Total Staff 0
Regions West Midlands + South
West
Owned or managed 478
Rt 434 GN 388 Sup 6 OP 40
NSO 44
Tenant Type % Family 18%
Older 16% Single 66%
Parent Association
Rooftop Housing Group Ltd

Rooftop Housing Group Ltd
■ Non-Charitable HA
TSA Reg ✓ ◊
70 High Street, Evesham,
Worcestershire, WR11 4YD
T 01386 420800
E info@rooftopgroup.org
W www.rooftopgroup.org
CE Mr Ian Hughes
Sec Mrs Sheila Morris
Ch Ms Helen Burgoyne
Total Staff 164
Region West Midlands
Subsidiary Association(s) Evesham
& Pershore HA Ltd; G3 Inspiring
Individuals; Rooftop Homes Ltd

Rosebery HA Ltd
○ Charitable HA
TSA Reg ✓ 🚌 🏢 🔑
Rutland House, 57-59 South Street,

Epsom, Surrey, KT18 7PR
T 01372 814000
E customerservices@rosebery.org.uk
W www.rosebery.org.uk
CE Ms Deborah Pike
Sec Mrs Susan McBride
Ch Mrs Anna Hammond
Total Staff 35
Region South East
Owned or managed 2582
Rt 2007 GN 1657 Sup 165 OP 185
SO 575 Tot lets 171 GN bs 1644
Tenant Type % Family 50%
Older 31% Single 19%
Development Total 61
NBA 35 NBC 26

Rosemary Simmons Memorial HA Ltd
○ Charitable HA
TSA Reg ✓ 🏢 🔑 ◊
Rosemary House, Portsmouth Road,
Esher, Surrey, KT10 9AA
T 01372 461440
E housing@rsmha.org.uk
W www.rsmha.org.uk
CE Mr Paul Yates
Sec Mr Paul Yates
Ch Mr Alistair Court-Smith
Total Staff 25
Region South East
Owned or managed 516
Rt 376 GN 376 SO 140 Tot lets 0
GN bs 0
Tenant Type % Family 51%
Older 47% Single 2%
Development Total 4
Rt 39 GN 35 Sup 4 NBC 4
Subsidiary Association(s)
Fellowship Houses Trust

Ross Walk Housing Co-operative Ltd
★ Co-operative Society
TSA Reg ✓ 🏠
131 Loughborough Road, Leicester,
Leicestershire, LE4 5LQ
T 0116 257 6800
E tim.clarke@asra.org.uk
W www.rosswalkcoop.org.uk
CE Mr Sanjay Manon
Sec Mr V Thanki
Ch Mr D Pathak
Total Staff 0
Region East Midlands
Owned or managed 111
Rt 111 GN 111
Tenant Type % Family 100%

Rotary Club of Dudley HA Ltd
○ Charitable HA
TSA Reg ✓ 🕶
Rotary House, Middlepark Road,

Dudley, West Midlands, DY1 2LE
T 01384 231950
W www.dudleyrotary.org.uk/
rotaryhouse2.html
CE Mr Robert Totney
Sec Mr Anthony Dean
Ch Mr Fred Austin
Total Staff 3
Region West Midlands
Owned or managed 50
Rt 50 OP 50
Tenant Type % Older 100%

Ruskin Park House Ltd
■ Non-Charitable HA
TSA Reg ✗
The Estate Office, Ruskin Park
House, Champion Hill, London,
Greater London, SE5 8TH
T 020 7274 1066
W www.ruskinparkhouse.org.uk
CE Mr A J Foster
Sec Mr A J Foster
Ch Mr Derek Wilkinson
Total Staff 0
Region London

Russet Homes
○ Charitable HA
TSA Reg ✓ 🖥 🚌 🏢 🔑 ◊
Basted House, Harrison Road,
Borough Green, Nr Sevenoaks,
Kent, TN15 8PB
T 01732 780999
E info@russethomes.org
W www.russethomes.org
CE Mr Steven Woodcock
Sec Ms Deborah Upton
Ch Mr Andrew Hill
Total Staff 82
Region South East
Owned or managed 7121
Rt 6743 GN 6410 Sup 18 OP 315
SO 378 Tot lets 619 GN bs 6410
Tenant Type % Family 68%
Older 26% Single 6%
Development Total 25
NBA 25
Parent Association Circle

Ss

Sadeh Lok Housing Group Ltd
○ Charitable HA
TSA Reg ✓ 🔑 🕶 🏠
Trafford House, 11 Halifax Road,
Huddersfield, West Yorkshire,
HD3 3AN
T 01484 435715

E customerservices@sadehlok.co.uk
W www.sadehlok.co.uk
CE Mr Paul Dolan
Sec Mrs Susan Scargill
Ch Mr Ian Simpson
Total Staff 25
Region Yorkshire & Humberside
Owned or managed 1122
Rt 1097 GN 1034 OP 63 SO 19
NSO 6 Tot lets 0 GN bs 951
Tenant Type % Family 70%
Older 6% Single 24%

Saffron Housing Trust Ltd
☆ Charitable Company
TSA Reg ✓ 🖼 🔲 🔑 🤝
Saffron Barn, Swan Lane,
Long Stratton, Norwich, Norfolk,
NR15 2XP
T 01508 532000
E info@saffronhousing.co.uk
W www.saffronhousing.co.uk
CE Mr Adam Ronaldson
Sec Mr Stuart Tinkler
Ch Mr Michael Harrowven
Total Staff 167
Region East of England
Owned or managed 4937
Rt 4743 GN 3996 Sup 161 OP 586
SO 192 NSO 2 Tot lets 365
GN bs 3985
Tenant Type % Family 35%
Older 45% Single 20%
Development Total 185
Rt 628 GN 620 Sup 8 LCHO 20
NBA 125 NBC 60

Salvation Army HA
○ Charitable HA
TSA Reg ✓ 🔲 🤝
Barber Surgeons Hall,
1a Monkwell Square, London,
Greater London, EC2Y 5BL
T 020 7332 4800
E head.office@saha.org.uk
W www.saha.org.uk
CE Mr Nigel Parrington
Sec Mr Puneet Rajput
Ch Mr Graham Roper
Total Staff 198
Regions London + South East,
South West, East Midlands,
West Midlands, East of England,
Yorkshire & Humberside,
North East, North West
Owned or managed 3493
Rt 3417 GN 1105 Sup 2020 OP 292
NSO 76
Tenant Type % Family 10%
Older 11% Single 79%
Development Total 94
Rt 62 GN 26 Sup 36 NBA 47
NBC 47

Sanctuary HA
○ Charitable HA
TSA Reg ✓ 🔲 🔲 🔲 🔑 🌱 🤝 🔥
Chamber Court, Castle Street,
Worcester, Worcestershire,
WR1 3ZQ
T 01905 334000
E enquiry.sanctuary@sanctuary-housing.co.uk
W www.sanctuary-housing.co.uk
CE Mr David Bennett
Sec Mr Craig Moule
Ch Mr Nick Baldwin
Total Staff 8559
Regions South East + London,
South West, East Midlands,
West Midlands, East of England,
Yorkshire & Humberside,
North East, North West
Owned or managed 66355
Rt 56321 GN 43251 Sup 3811
OP 9259 SO 5337 NSO 4697
Tot lets 7359 GN bs 39921
Tenant Type % Family 30%
Older 28% Single 42%
Development Total 10840
Rt 3416 GN 2478 Sup 133 OP 805
LCHO 647 NBA 10328 NBC 512
Subsidiary Association(s)
Asra Midlands HA Ltd; Rochford HA

Saxon Weald
✪ Not-for-Profit Company
TSA Reg ✓
🔲 🔲 🔲 🔑 🤝
Saxon Weald House, 38-42
Worthing Road, Horsham,
West Sussex, RH12 1DT
T 01403 226000
E info@saxonweald.com
W www.saxonweald.com
CE Mr David Standfast
Sec Mr Norman Hill
Ch David Avery
Total Staff 176
Region South East
Owned or managed 5914
Rt 5271 GN 3732 Sup 74 OP 1465
SO 643 Tot lets 467 GN bs 3726
Tenant Type % Family 40%
Older 50% Single 10%
Development Total 594
NBA 335 NBC 259

Scimitar HA Ltd
○ Charitable HA
TSA Reg ✗
98 Park Hill, Carshalton Beeches,
Carshalton, Surrey, SM5 3RZ
T 020 8669 1172
CE Mrs Carmel Loder
Sec Mrs Carmel Loder
Ch Mr Timothy Loder

Total Staff 0
Regions London + South East
Owned or managed 6
Rt 6 GN 6
Tenant Type % Family 33%
Older 17% Single 50%

Scotscare
❑ Charitable Trust
TSA Reg ✗ 🤝
22 City Road, London,
Greater London, EC1Y 2AJ
T 020 7240 3718
E info@scotscare.com
W www.scotscare.com
CE Mr Willie Docherty
Ch Mr Wylie White
Total Staff 0
Region London
Tenant Type % Family 4%
Older 90% Single 6%

Second Step HA Ltd
○ Charitable HA
TSA Reg ✗ 🤝
9 Brunswick Square, Bristol, Avon,
BS2 8PE
T 0117 909 6630
E admin@second-step.co.uk
W www.second-step.co.uk
CE Ms Aileen Edwards
Sec Ms Aileen Edwards
Ch Mr Chris Trowell
Total Staff 163
Region South West
Owned or managed 137
Rt 137 GN 137
Tenant Type % Single 100%

Seely Hirst House
❑ Charitable Trust
TSA Reg ✗ 🤝
62 - 68 Mapperley Road,
Nottingham, Nottinghamshire,
NG3 5AS
T 0115 960 6610
E careatseely@aol.com
CE Mrs Julie Ward-Daft
Sec Mr Diane Depadova
Ch Mr M J Smith
Total Staff 59
Region East Midlands
Owned or managed 1
Rt 1 GN 1
Tenant Type % Older 100%

Self Help Community HA Ltd
○ Charitable HA
TSA Reg ✗ 🤝
12 King Square Avenue, Stokes Croft,
Bristol, Bristol, BS2 8HU
T 0117 970 5400
E housing@selfhelpha.co.uk

W www.selfhelpha.co.uk
CE Mrs Helen Razdan
Sec Mrs Helen Razdan
Ch Mr Steve Abbott
Total Staff 11
Region South West
Owned or managed 76
Rt 76 Sup 76
Tenant Type % Family 25%
Single 75%

Selwood Housing
☆ Charitable Company
TSA Reg ✓ 🖿 🌀 🅳 🔑 🐾
Bryer Ash Business Park,
Bradford Road, Trowbridge,
Wiltshire, BA14 8RT
T 01225 715715
E info@selwoodhousing.com
W www.selwoodhousing.com
CE Mr Barry Hughes
Sec Mrs Diane Hall
Ch Alison Christy
Total Staff 175
Region South West
Owned or managed 5689
Rt 5577 GN 4065 Sup 55 OP 1457
SO 108 NSO 4 Tot lets 452
GN bs 4015
Tenant Type % Family 45%
Older 33% Single 22%
Development Total 230
NBA 119 NBC 111

Sentinel HA Ltd
◯ Charitable HA
TSA Reg ✓ 🖿 🚚 🅳 🔑 🐾
56 Kingsclere Road, Basingstoke,
Hampshire, RG21 6XG
T 01256 338800
E info@sentinelha.org.uk
W www.sentinelha.org.uk
Ch Mr John Barker
Total Staff 205
Region South East
Owned or managed 8605
Rt 7582 GN 7024 Sup 23 OP 535
SO 998 NSO 25 Tot lets 1106
GN bs 6906
Tenant Type % Family 36%
Older 27% Single 37%
Development Total 931
NBA 542 NBC 389

Seven Locks Housing Ltd
☆ Charitable Company
TSA Reg ✓ 🚚 🅳 🔑 🐾 ♢
1A Anson House,
8 Compass Point, Northampton
Road, Market Harborough,
Leicestershire, LE16 9HW
T 01858 414500
E info@sevenlockshousing.co.uk
W www.sevenlockshousing.co.uk

CE Ms Deborah Bennett
Sec Mr Mike Finister-Smith
Ch Mr Stewart Harrison
Total Staff 43
Region East Midlands
Owned or managed 2198
Rt 2140 GN 1268 Sup 469 OP 403
SO 58 Tot lets 172 GN bs 1262
Tenant Type % Family 57%
Older 19% Single 24%
Development Total 4
Rt 7 GN 7 NBA 2 NBC 2
Parent Association
Acclaim Housing Group Ltd

Severn Vale Housing Society Ltd
◼ Non-Charitable HA
TSA Reg ✓ 🚚 🅳 🔑 🐾
Shannon Way, Ashchurch,
Tewkesbury, Gloucestershire,
GL20 8ND
T 01684 272727
E info@svhs.org.uk
W www.svhs.org.uk
CE Mr Hugh Aldridge
Ch Phil Roberts
Total Staff 105
Region South West
Owned or managed 3902
Rt 3238 GN 2829 OP 409 SO 170
NSO 494 Tot lets 257 GN bs 2688
Tenant Type % Family 63%
Older 27% Single 10%
Development Total 61
NBA 37 NBC 24

Severnside Housing
✪ Not-for-Profit Company
TSA Reg ✓ 🖿 🚚 🅳 🔑 🐾
Severnside House, Brassey Road,
Old Potts Way, Shrewsbury,
Shropshire, SY3 7FA
T 01743 285000
E enquiries@severnsidehousing.co.uk
W www.severnsidehousing.co.uk
CE Mrs Sarah Boden
Sec Irene Molyneux
Ch Robin Prichard
Total Staff 234
Region West Midlands
Owned or managed 5606
Rt 5308 GN 3962 Sup 702 OP 644
SO 47 NSO 251 Tot lets 338
GN bs 3962
Tenant Type % Family 16%
Older 48% Single 36%
Development Total 34
Rt 79 GN 55 Sup 12 OP 12
LCHO 32 NBA 23 NBC 11

Seymour Housing Co-operative Ltd
★ Co-operative Society
TSA Reg ✓
20a Seymour Buildings, Seymour
Place, London, Greater London,
W1H 4PP
T 020 7723 3203
E office@seymourhc.org
CE Miss Susan Page
Sec Ms Sarah Sakimoto
Ch Mr M Prigent
Total Staff 3
Region London
Owned or managed 88
Rt 88 GN 88
Tenant Type % Family 20%
Older 14% Single 66%

SHAL Housing Ltd
◯ Charitable HA
TSA Reg ✓ 🅳
2 King Square, Bridgwater, Somerset,
TA6 3DG
T 01278 444344
E information@shal.org
W www.shal.org
CE Mr John Thomson
Sec Mr John Thomson
Ch Norman Turner
Total Staff 28
Region South West
Owned or managed 668
Rt 668 GN 668
Tenant Type % Family 95% Single 5%
Development Total 12
Rt 18 GN 18 NBC 12

Shape HA
◯ Charitable HA
TSA Reg ✓
The Maltings, Riverplace, Lower
Bristol Road, Bath, BA2 1EP
T 01225 366000
E enquiries@somer.org.uk
W www.curo-group.co.uk
CE Mr Victor da Cunha
Sec Miss Philippa Armstrong
Total Staff 29
Region South West
Owned or managed 148
Rt 148 GN 22 Sup 126
Tenant Type % Family 18%
Single 82%

Shenehom HA Ltd
◯ Charitable HA
TSA Reg ✗ 🐾
31-32 Ranelagh Avenue, Barnes,
London, Greater London,
SW13 0BN
T 020 8876 2199
E info@shenehomhousing.org.uk
W www.shenehom.org.uk

CE Mr German Gentile
Sec Mrs Susan Garner
Ch Mr Robin Martin
Total Staff 7
Region London
Tenant Type % Single 100%

Shepherds Bush Housing Group
○ Charitable HA
TSA Reg ✓ 🏠 🔑
Mulliner House, Chiswick, London,
Greater London, W4 1NN
T 020 8996 4200
E group.info@sbhg.co.uk
W www.sbhg.co.uk
CE Mr Paul Doe
Sec Mrs Patricia Humberstone
Ch Mr Ellis Blackmore
Total Staff 129
Region London
Owned or managed 4487
Rt 3534 GN 3170 Sup 291 OP 73
SO 953 Tot lets 161 GN bs 3170
Tenant Type % Family 50%
Older 15% Single 35%
Development Total 38
NBA 19 NBC 19

Sherborne Close Housing Society Ltd
○ Charitable HA
TSA Reg ✓ 🕶️
C/O The Office Sherborne Close,
Dorset Road, Tunbridge Wells,
Kent, TN2 5AS
T 01892 537472
E sherborne.close@virgin.net
CE Mr Brian Hill
Sec Mr Richard Akehurst
Ch Mrs Mary Wardrop
Total Staff 3
Region South East
Owned or managed 96
Rt 94 OP 94 NSO 2
Tenant Type % Older 100%

Shian HA Ltd
○ Charitable HA
TSA Reg ✓ 🏠 🕶️ 🏠
76 Mare Street, Hackney, London,
Greater London, E8 3SG
T 020 8985 7120
E info@shian.org.uk
W www.shian.org.uk
CE Mr Leslie Laniyan
Sec Mr Leslie Laniyan
Ch Mr Aaron Whitaker
Total Staff 17
Region London
Owned or managed 477
Rt 477 GN 463 Sup 14
Tenant Type % Family 62%
Older 8% Single 30%

Development Total 25
Rt 22 GN 22 NBC 25

Shipbourne Housing Trust
○ Charitable HA
TSA Reg ✗
Waylands, Back Lane, Shipbourne,
Tonbridge, Kent, TN11 9PP
T 01732 810562
E j.playle@beamingmail.com
Sec Mr John W Playle, FRICS
Ch Mr Alan Bristow FCA
Total Staff 0
Region South East
Tenant Type % Older 100%

Shoreline Housing Partnership Ltd
☆ Charitable Company
TSA Reg ✓ 🗔 🕶️ 🏠 🔑
Shoreline House, Westgate Park,
Charlton Street, Grimsby,
South Humberside, DN31 1SQ
T 0845 849 2000
E info@shorelinehp.com
W www.shorelinehp.com
CE Mr Tony Bramley
Sec Mr Mike Walters
Ch Ms Karen Rastall
Total Staff 223
Region Yorkshire & Humberside
Owned or managed 8194
Rt 7957 GN 5647 Sup 19 OP 2291
SO 23 NSO 214 Tot lets 1160
GN bs 5625
Tenant Type % Family 79%
Older 17% Single 4%
Development Total 100
NBA 91 NBC 9

Shropshire Association for Sheltered Housing Ltd
○ Charitable HA
TSA Reg ✓
4 Saltney Close, Shrewsbury,
Shropshire, SY2 6SQ
T 01743 362195
E jshotton@btopenworld.com
CE Mr John Shotton
Sec Mr John Shotton
Ch Mr David Battisby
Total Staff 1
Region West Midlands
Owned or managed 19
Rt 19 GN 19
Tenant Type % Single 100%

Shropshire Housing Ltd
■ Non-Charitable HA
TSA Reg ✓ 💧
The Gateway, The Auction Yard,
Craven Arms, Shropshire, SY7 9BW
T 3003031190

E enquiries@shropshirehousing.org.uk
W www.shropshirehousing.org.uk
CE Mr Martin Holland
Sec Miss Jen Hayball
Ch Ms Shena Latto
Total Staff 89
Region West Midlands
Subsidiary Association(s) Meres and
Mosses HA; South Shropshire HA

Shropshire Rural HA Ltd
○ Charitable HA
TSA Reg ✓ 🏠 🕶️
The Maltings, 59 Lythwood Road,
Bayston Hill, Shrewsbury,
Shropshire, SY3 ONA
T 01743 874848
E enquiries@shropshirerural.co.uk
W www.shropshirerural.co.uk
CE Mr Bryan Powell
Sec Mrs Rachael Fullwood
Ch Cllr Heather Kidd
Total Staff 7
Region West Midlands
Owned or managed 276
Rt 275 GN 255 OP 20 NSO 1
Tenant Type % Family 87%
Older 10% Single 3%
Development Total 6
Rt 8 GN 8 NBC 6

Sidcot Friends HS Ltd
○ Charitable HA
TSA Reg ✓
Sewell House, Belmont Road,
Winscombe, Somerset, BS25 1LQ
T 01934 843746
W www.sewellhouse.org.uk
Sec Mrs Sue Mathias
Ch Mr Peter Blunt
Total Staff 15
Region South West
Owned or managed 27
Rt 27 OP 27
Tenant Type % Older 100%

Silverholme HA Ltd
○ Charitable HA
TSA Reg ✗
33A Silverholme Close, Kenton,
Harrow, Middlesex, HA3 0PJ
Sec J Lemon
Ch Mrs Gladys Irene Crotty
Total Staff 0
Region London
Tenant Type % Older 100%

Simba (Greenwich) HA Ltd
○ Charitable HA
TSA Reg ✗ 🕶️ 🏠
Suite 4, 65-66 Woodrow, London,
SE18 5DH
T 020 8855 0488

E info@simbaha.org.uk
W www.simbaha.org.uk
CE Mr Jefferson Williams
Sec Miss Sonia Vassell
Ch Mr Alwyn Lewis
Total Staff 2
Region London
Owned or managed 93
Rt 93 GN 81 Sup 12
Tenant Type % Family 35%
Single 65%

Single Homeless Project
☆ Charitable Company
TSA Reg ✗ ♦ 🐝
245 Grays Inn Road, London,
Greater London, WC1X 8QZ
T 020 7520 8660
E info@shp.org.uk
W www.shp.org.uk
CE Ms Liz Rutherfoord
Sec Ms Liz Rutherfoord
Ch Mr Jonathan Senker
Total Staff 390
Region London
Owned or managed 576
Rt 576 Sup 576
Tenant Type % Single 100%

Sir Josiah Mason's Trust
❑ Charitable Trust
TSA Reg ✓ 🐝
Mason Court, Hillborough Road,
Birmingham, West Midlands, B27 6PF
T 0121 245 1001
E enquiries@sjmt.org.uk
W www.sjmt.org.uk
CE Mr Richard Hall
Sec Mr Richard Hall
Ch Ms Annerbel Anderson
Total Staff 33
Region West Midlands
Owned or managed 165
Rt 165 OP 165
Tenant Type % Older 20%
Single 80%

SITRA
☆ Charitable Company
TSA Reg ✗
55 Bondway, 3rd Floor, London,
Greater London, SW8 1SJ
T 020 7793 4710
E post@sitra.org
W www.sitra.org.uk
CE Ms Vic Rayner
Sec Berihu Mohammed
Ch Ms Liz Rutherfoord
Total Staff 23
Region London

SLH Group
○ Charitable HA
TSA Reg ✓ 🏠 🔑 🐝
Parklands, Conleach Road, Speke,
Merseyside, L24 0TY
T 0151 285 5600
E info@slhgroup.co.uk
W www.slhgroup.co.uk
CE Ms Julie Fadden
Sec Tony Russell
Ch Mr John McHale
Total Staff 106
Region North West
Owned or managed 3628
Rt 3621 GN 3500 Sup 3 OP 118
SO 7 Tot lets 277 GN bs 3495
Tenant Type % Family 43%
Older 30% Single 27%
Development Total 3
Rt 80 GN 80 LCHO 28 NBA 3

Small Heath Park
H Co-op Ltd
★ Co-operative Society
TSA Reg ✓
15 Rochdale Walk, Small Heath,
Birmingham, West Midlands,
B10 0DF
T 0121 773 3251
E shphc15@hotmail.com
CE Mr James Deards
Sec Mr Walter Deards
Ch Mr Brian Ashby
Total Staff 2
Region West Midlands
Owned or managed 94
Rt 94 GN 94
Tenant Type % Family 40%
Older 21% Single 39%

Society of St James
☆ Charitable Company
TSA Reg ✓ 🐝
125 Albert Road South,
Southampton, Hampshire, SO14 3FR
T 023 8063 4596
E info@societyofstjames.org.uk
W www.ssj.org.uk
CE Mr Trevor Pickup
Sec Mr Trevor Pickup
Ch Mr Brian Hooper
Total Staff 174
Region South East
Owned or managed 293
Rt 293 Sup 293
Tenant Type % Family 10%
Older 8% Single 82%

Soha Housing Ltd
○ Charitable HA
TSA Reg ✓ 🔲 🚐VTHO 🏠 🔑
Royal Scot House, 99 Station Road,
Didcot, Oxfordshire, OX11 7NN
T 01235 515900

E housing@soha.co.uk
W www.soha.co.uk
CE Mr Richard Peacock
Sec Mr Richard Peacock
Ch Mr Peter Miller-Smith
Total Staff 101
Regions South East + South West
Owned or managed 5616
Rt 5044 GN 4237 Sup 29 OP 778
SO 508 NSO 64 Tot lets 304
GN bs 4200
Tenant Type % Family 20%
Older 40% Single 40%
Development Total 192
Rt 314 GN 284 OP 30 LCHO 148
NBA 1 NBC 191

Soho HA Ltd
○ Charitable HA
TSA Reg ✓ 🔑
Fourth Floor, 121 Charing Cross
Road, London, Greater London,
WC2H 0JR
T 020 7557 7400
E info@sohoha.org.uk
W www.sohoha.org.uk
CE Mr Joe Chambers
Sec Mr Rajeev Sri Murugan
Total Staff 15
Region London
Owned or managed 785
Rt 756 GN 699 Sup 38 OP 19 SO 24
NSO 5 Tot lets 0 GN bs 0
Tenant Type % Family 53%
Older 21% Single 26%

Solihull Care HA Ltd
○ Charitable HA
TSA Reg ✓ 🔑 🐝
1619 Warwick Road, Knowle, Solihull,
West Midlands, B93 9LF
T 01564 778519
W www.scha.org.uk
CE Mr Lloyd Bradshaw
Sec Mr Lloyd Bradshaw
Ch Mr David Mattocks
Total Staff 12
Region West Midlands
Owned or managed 107
Rt 101 Sup 58 OP 43 SO 6
Tot lets 10 GN bs 0
Tenant Type % Older 45%
Single 55%

Solon South West HA Ltd
○ Charitable HA
TSA Reg ✓ 🏠 🔑 🐝
1 Newfoundland Court, St Paul
Street, Bristol, Avon, BS2 8AN
T 0117 924 4071
E solon@solonswha.co.uk
W www.solonswha.co.uk
CE Mr Paul Ville
Sec Mr Paul Ville

Ch Charlie Mosse
Total Staff 32
Region South West
Owned or managed 1057
Rt 1017 **GN** 960 **Sup** 57 **SO** 40
Tot lets 274 **GN bs** 959
Tenant Type % Family 35%
Older 1% **Single** 64%
Development Total 39
NBA 36 **NBC** 3

Somer Community Housing Trust
❏ Charitable Trust
TSA Reg ✓ ▢ 🖳 ▢ 🔑 🤝
The Maltings, Riverplace, Lower
Bristol Road, Bath, BA2 1EP
T 01225 366000
E feedback@somer.org.uk
W www.curo-group.co.uk
CE Mr Victor da Cunha
Sec Miss Philippa Armstrong
Ch Mr Roger Thomas
Total Staff 248
Region South West
Owned or managed 9796
Rt 9439 **GN** 7655 **Sup** 64 **OP** 1720
SO 225 **NSO** 132 **Tot lets** 836
GN bs 7511
Tenant Type % Family 21%
Older 30% **Single** 49%
Development Total 419
NBA 244 **NBC** 175

Soroptimist (Poole) HA Ltd
○ Charitable HA
TSA Reg ✓
111 North Road, Parkstone, Poole,
Dorset, BH14 0LU
T 01202 722061
E soropoole@hotmail.com
W soroptimist-gbi.org/poole/
programme-action-projects/housing-
association/
Sec Mrs Carol Thomas
Ch Ms Catherine Dukes
Total Staff 1
Region South West
Owned or managed 20
Rt 20 **GN** 20
Tenant Type % Older 100%

South Anglia Housing Ltd
■ Non-Charitable HA
TSA Reg ✓ ▢ 🖳 ▢ 🔑 ◊
Number One Building, The
Causeway, Bishop's Stortford,
Hertfordshire, CM23 2ER
T 0845 600 1543
W www.circleanglia.org
CE Ms Tracy White
Sec Mr Stephen Robertson
Ch Murray Foster
Total Staff 0

Regions East of England + London
Owned or managed 9268
Rt 8103 **GN** 6557 **Sup** 532 **OP** 1014
SO 842 **NSO** 323 **Tot lets** 606
GN bs 5192
Tenant Type % Family 85%
Older 10% **Single** 5%
Development Total 81
Rt 77 **GN** 77 **LCHO** 48 **NBA** 56
NBC 25
Parent Association Circle

South Cheshire HS Ltd
■ Non-Charitable HA
TSA Reg ✓ 🔑
18 King Street, Newcastle-Under-
Lyme, Staffordshire, ST5 1EJ
T 01782 661818
CE Mr K A Beresford
Sec Mr D Taylor
Ch Mr K A Beresford
Total Staff 2
Region North West
Owned or managed 171
Rt 107 **GN** 107 **SO** 64 **Tot lets** 0
GN bs 0
Tenant Type % Family 35%
Older 35% **Single** 30%

South Devon Rural HA Ltd
○ Charitable HA
TSA Reg ✓ 🤝
Babbage Road, Totnes, Devon,
TQ9 5JA
T 01803 863550
E info@southdevonrural.com
W www.southdevonrural.com
CE Mr Steve Prime
Sec Mr Steve Prime
Ch Rod Hewett
Total Staff 26
Region South West
Owned or managed 237
Rt 237 **GN** 203 **Sup** 12 **OP** 22
Tenant Type % Family 25%
Older 55% **Single** 20%

South Lakes Housing
○ Charitable HA
TSA Reg ✓ 🖳 🔑
Little Aynam House, Little Aynam,
Kendal, Cumbria, LA9 7AH
T 01539 717717
W www.southlakeshousing.co.uk
CE Mr Peter Thomas
Sec Ms Lindsay Simons
Total Staff 125
Region North West
Owned or managed 3171
Rt 3166 **GN** 2722 **OP** 444 **SO** 5
Tot lets 240 **GN bs** 2719
Tenant Type % Family 53%
Older 43% **Single** 4%

South London YMCA
☆ Charitable Company
TSA Reg ✓ ▢ 🤝
Marco Polo House, 3-5 Lansdowne
Road, Croydon, Surrey, CR9 1LL
T 020 7101 9960
E enquiries@slymca.org.uk
W www.slymca.org.uk
CE Mr Jeremy Gray
Sec Mr Dennis Simmonds
Ch Mr David Fitze
Total Staff 85
Region London
Owned or managed 444
Rt 444 **Sup** 444
Tenant Type % Single 100%
Development Total 60
NBC 60

South Mildmay Tenant Co-op Ltd
★ Co-operative Society
TSA Reg ✓
The Office, 52 Mildmay Park,
London, Greater London, N1 4PR
T 020 7249 8280
CE Ms Kathryn McKenzie
Sec Mr John Jones
Ch Ms Linda Brown
Total Staff 3
Region London
Owned or managed 107
Rt 107 **GN** 107
Tenant Type % Family 51%
Older 17% **Single** 32%

South Northants Homes
○ Charitable HA
TSA Reg ✓ 🖳 ▢ 🔑 ◊
Wood Burcote House, Wood
Burcote Road, Towcester,
Northamptonshire, NN12 6TF
T 0845 460 6888
E housing@southnorthantshomes.
co.uk
W www.southnorthantshomes.co.uk
CE Mr Paul Calland
Sec Mr Paul Calland
Ch Clive Williams
Total Staff 92
Region East Midlands
Owned or managed 3071
Rt 2952 **GN** 2087 **Sup** 633 **OP** 232
SO 118 **NSO** 1 **Tot lets** 277
GN bs 2018
Tenant Type % Family 65%
Older 35%
Development Total 9
NBA 5 **NBC** 4
Parent Association
Grand Union Housing Group Ltd

South Shropshire HA
○ Charitable HA
TSA Reg ✓ 🖥️ 📠 📠 🔑 🦅 ◊
The Gateway, The Auction Yard,
Craven Arms, Shropshire, SY7 9BW
T 01588 676200
E info@sshropsha.co.uk
W www.sshropsha.co.uk
CE Mr Martin Holland
Sec Miss Jen Hayball
Ch Mr Tim Ralphs
Total Staff 125
Region West Midlands
Owned or managed 2233
Rt 2109 **GN** 1774 **Sup** 41 **OP** 294
SO 122 **NSO** 2 **Tot lets** 202
GN bs 1769
Tenant Type % Family 48%
Older 35% **Single** 17%
Development Total 80
Rt 30 **GN** 30 **NBA** 45 **NBC** 35
Parent Association
Shropshire Housing Ltd

South Staffordshire HA
○ Charitable HA
TSA Reg ✓ 📠 🦅 📠 🔑 ◊
Acton Court, Acton Gate, Stafford,
Staffordshire, ST18 9AP
T 01785 312000
E enquiries@ssha.co.uk
W www.ssha.co.uk
CE Mrs Debbie Griffiths
Sec Mr Philip Ingle
Ch Mr Rolf Levesley
Total Staff 57
Region West Midlands
Owned or managed 5957
Rt 5559 **GN** 3604 **Sup** 627 **OP** 1328
SO 398 **Tot lets** 588 **GN bs** 3567
Tenant Type % Family 38%
Older 53% **Single** 9%
Development Total 142
NBA 71 **NBC** 71
Parent Association
The Housing Plus Group Ltd

South Western Housing Society Ltd
○ Charitable HA
TSA Reg ✓ 🔑 🦅
Eastbridge House, Pill Road,
Rooksbridge, Axbridge, Somerset,
BS26 2TN
T 01934 750780
E customerservices@swhs.org.uk
W www.swhs.org.uk
CE Phil Yorke
Sec Phil Yorke
Ch Mrs Anne Robinson
Total Staff 11
Region South West
Owned or managed 526
Rt 477 **GN** 417 **OP** 60 **SO** 49

Tot lets 0 **GN bs** 3
Tenant Type % Family 65%
Older 25% **Single** 10%

South Yorkshire HA Ltd
○ Charitable HA
TSA Reg ✓ 📠 📠 🔑 🌳 🦅
43-47 Wellington Street, Sheffield,
South Yorkshire, S1 4HF
T 0114 290 0200
E enquiries@syha.co.uk
W www.syha.co.uk
CE Mr Tony Stacey
Sec Mr Tony Stacey
Ch Ms Barbara Walsh
Total Staff 440
Regions Yorkshire & Humberside +
East Midlands
Owned or managed 5495
Rt 5067 **GN** 3660 **Sup** 1105 **OP** 302
SO 277 **NSO** 151 **Tot lets** 1658
GN bs 3602
Tenant Type % Family 60%
Older 20% **Single** 20%
Development Total 305
Rt 120 **GN** 51 **Sup** 19 **OP** 50
NBA 204 **NBC** 101

Southdown HA
○ Charitable HA
TSA Reg ✓ 📠 🔑 🌳 🦅
2 Bell Lane, Lewes,
East Sussex, BN7 1JU
T 01273 405800
E info@southdownhousing.org
W www.southdownhousing.org
CE Ms Aideen Jones
Sec Ms Aideen Jones
Ch Mr Andrew Doig
Total Staff 715
Region South East
Owned or managed 597
Rt 572 **Sup** 572 **SO** 25 **Tot lets** 1
GN bs 0
Tenant Type % Single 100%
Development Total 6
Rt 6 **Sup** 6 **NBC** 6

Southern Home Ownership Ltd
■ Non-Charitable HA
TSA Reg ✓ 🔑 ◊
Fleet House, 59-61 Clerkenwell
Road, London, Greater London,
EC1M 5LA
T 0845 612 0021
E service.centre@shgroup.org.uk
W www.shgroup.org.uk
CE Mr Tom Dacey
Ch Mr Jim Hitch
Total Staff 1
Regions London + South East
Owned or managed 2380
Rt 53 **GN** 53 **SO** 2300 **NSO** 27

Tot lets 11 **GN bs** 0
Tenant Type % Family 35%
Single 65%
Parent Association
Southern Housing Group Ltd

Southern Housing Group Ltd
○ Charitable HA
TSA Reg ✓
🖥️ 📠 🦅 📠 🔑 🌳 🦅 ◊
Fleet House, 59-61 Clerkenwell
Road, London, Greater London,
EC1M 5LA
T 0845 612 0021
E info@shgroup.org.uk
W www.shgroup.org.uk
CE Mr Tom Dacey
Ch Mr Andrew McIntyre
Total Staff 827
Regions London + South East,
South West, East of England
Owned or managed 23775
Rt 21549 **GN** 18632 **Sup** 324
OP 2593 **SO** 2213 **NSO** 13
Tot lets 2271 **GN bs** 17662
Tenant Type % Family 40%
Older 35% **Single** 25%
Development Total 679
NBA 380 **NBC** 299
Subsidiary Association(s) Southern
Home Ownership Ltd

Southport Soroptimist HA Ltd
○ Charitable HA
TSA Reg ✗
32 Curzon Road, Southport, PR8 6PL
Ch Mrs Helen Beecham
Total Staff 0
Region North West
Tenant Type % Older 100%

Southwark & London Diocesan HA Ltd
○ Charitable HA
TSA Reg ✓ 📠
Trinity House, 4 Chapel Court,
Borough High Street, London,
Greater London, SE1 1HW
T 020 7089 1370
W www.southwark.anglican.org/
sldha
CE Mr Steve Joyce
Sec Mr Steve Joyce
Total Staff 6
Regions London + South East
Owned or managed 257
Rt 257 **GN** 243 **Sup** 14
Tenant Type % Family 68%
Older 2% **Single** 30%
Development Total 8
Rt 20 **GN** 20 **NBC** 8

Southway Housing Trust
○ Charitable HA
TSA Reg ✓
Aspen House, 825 Wilmslow Road, Didsbury, Manchester, Lancashire, M20 2SN
T 0161 448 4200
E connect2southway@southwayhousing.co.uk
W www.southwayhousing.co.uk
CE Ms Karen Mitchell
Sec Mr Neil Botfish
Ch Emma Richman
Total Staff 167
Region North West
Owned or managed 5893
Rt 5893 **GN** 5867 **OP** 26
Tenant Type % Family 61%
Older 23% **Single** 16%
Development Total 3
Rt 20 **GN** 20 **NBA** 3

Southwold Young Peoples HA
❏ Charitable Trust
TSA Reg ✗
Southwold House, 240 Station Road, Yate, Avon, BS37 4AQ
T 01454 325165
E sypha@btconnect.com
CE Elizabeth Fraser
Sec Mrs J Youell
Ch Mr Adrian Rush
Total Staff 9
Region South West
Owned or managed 26
Rt 26 **Sup** 26
Tenant Type % Single 100%

Sovereign HA Ltd
○ Charitable HA
TSA Reg ✓
Berkshire House, 22-24 Bartholomew Street, Newbury, Berkshire, RG14 5LL
T 0845 712 5530
E enquiries@sovereign.org.uk
W www.sovereign.org.uk
CE Ms Ann Santry
Sec Ms Valerie Lynch
Ch Mr John Simpson
Total Staff 981
Regions South East + South West
Owned or managed 33780
Rt 29056 **GN** 26002 **Sup** 312
OP 2742 **SO** 4140 **NSO** 584
Tot lets 3459 **GN bs** 25482
Tenant Type % Family 51%
Older 30% **Single** 19%
Development Total 2069
Rt 2077 **GN** 2077 **LCHO** 727
NBA 1339 **NBC** 730

Spectrum Housing Group Ltd
■ Non-Charitable HA
TSA Reg ✓
Spectrum House, Grange Road, Christchurch, Dorset, BH23 5GE
T 01425 283600
E info@spectrumhousing.co.uk
W www.spectrumhousing.co.uk
CE Mr Wayne Morris
Sec Ms Claire McKenna
Ch Mr Richard Organ
Total Staff 487
Region South West
Owned or managed 16672
Rt 13226 **GN** 10435 **Sup** 1288
OP 1503 **SO** 1260 **NSO** 2186
Tot lets 1176 **GN bs** 10083
Tenant Type % Family 29%
Older 22.25% **Single** 48.75%
Development Total 691
NBA 399 **NBC** 292

Spenborough Flower Fund Homes Ltd
○ Charitable HA
TSA Reg ✗
5 Layton Mount, Rawdon, Leeds, West Yorkshire, LS19 6PQ
T 0113 250 8332
E sffhomes@ntlworld.com
W www.sffhomes.org.uk
CE Ms Jill Husband
Sec Ms Jill Husband
Ch Mr Peter Benson
Total Staff 0
Region Yorkshire & Humberside
Owned or managed 60
Rt 60 **GN** 60
Tenant Type % Older 100%

Spire Homes (LG) Ltd
✪ Not-for-Profit Company
TSA Reg ✓
1 Crown Court, Crown Way, Rushden, Northamptonshire, NN10 6BS
T 0300 123 6611
E spirehomes@longhurst-group.org.uk
W www.spirehomes.org.uk
CE Julie Doyle
Sec Lynn Stubbs
Ch John Farrar
Total Staff 106
Region East Midlands
Owned or managed 4905
Rt 4677 **GN** 3217 **Sup** 17 **OP** 1443
SO 228 **Tot lets** 403 **GN bs** 3217
Tenant Type % Family 37%
Older 53% **Single** 9%
Development Total 75
Rt 220 **GN** 220 **LCHO** 127 **NBA** 60
NBC 15
Parent Association
Longhurst Group Ltd

Spirita
○ Charitable HA
TSA Reg ✓
Raleigh House, 68-84 Alfreton Road, Nottingham, Nottinghamshire, NG7 3NN
T 020 3535 3540
E customer_services@spirita.org.uk
W www.mhp-online.co.uk
Ch Sheila Button
Total Staff 331
Regions East Midlands + West Midlands
Owned or managed 9613
Rt 9149 **GN** 6341 **Sup** 360 **OP** 2448
SO 402 **NSO** 62 **Tot lets** 3
GN bs 3769
Development Total 398
NBA 398
Parent Association Metropolitan

Spitalfields HA Ltd
○ Charitable HA
TSA Reg ✓
78 Quaker Street, London, Greater London, E1 6SW
T 020 7392 5400
E admin@spitalfieldsha.co.uk
W www.spitalfieldsha.co.uk
CE Mr Omar Mapara
Sec Mr Jalal Uddin Chowdhury
Ch Mr Yousuf Kamali
Total Staff 15
Region London
Owned or managed 755
Rt 682 **GN** 682 **SO** 73 **Tot lets** 0
GN bs 0
Tenant Type % Family 74%
Single 26%

Spotland and Falinge HA Ltd
○ Charitable HA
TSA Reg ✓
92 Spotland Road, Rochdale, Lancashire, OL12 6PJ
T 01706 345087
E sfha@zen.co.uk
CE Mr Harry Turner
Sec Mr Harry Turner
Ch Mrs Kath Greenwood
Total Staff 1
Region North West
Owned or managed 30
Rt 30 **GN** 30
Tenant Type % Family 60%
Older 13% **Single** 27%

Springboard Two HA Ltd
■ Non-Charitable HA
TSA Reg ✓
Springboard House, 2a Claughton Road, London, Greater London, E13 9PN
T 020 8475 0033

E info@springboardha.org.uk
W www.springboardha.org.uk
CE Mr Mark Gayfer
Ch Mr Steve Woolridge
Total Staff 0
Region London
Owned or managed 68
 SO 68 Tot lets 0 GN bs 0
Tenant Type % Family 100%
Parent Association
Genesis HA

Springs Tenant Management Co-op Ltd
★ Co-operative Society
TSA Reg ✗
55 Dorset Drive, Springs Estate,
Bury, Lancashire, BL9 9DN
T 0161 764 3375
E springstmcoop@btconnect.com
CE Mr Ray Wallis
Sec Wendy Cropper
Ch Ms Carol Unsworth
Total Staff 5
Region North West
Owned or managed 315
Rt 315 GN 315
Tenant Type % Family 48%
Older 21% Single 31%

Square Building Trust Ltd
◯ Charitable HA
TSA Reg ✓
c/o Home Group Ltd,
2 Gosforth Park Way, Salters Lane,
Newcastle Upon Tyne,
Tyne And Wear, NE12 8ET
T 0191 290 7935
Sec Mr John Blakemore
Ch Mr William Southern
Total Staff 0
Region North East
Owned or managed 115
Rt 115 GN 90 Sup 25
Tenant Type % Family 19%
Older 68% Single 13%

St Andrew Housing Co-operative Ltd
★ Co-operative Society
TSA Reg ✓
13a St Andrew Street, Beverley,
East Yorkshire, HU17 0NS
T 01482 882103
E info@standrewhousing.karoo.co.uk
CE Mr Graham Teal
Sec Mr Graham Teal
Ch Mrs Maureen Marsh
Total Staff 6
Region Yorkshire & Humberside
Owned or managed 78
Rt 78 GN 41 OP 37
Tenant Type % Family 29%
Older 60% Single 11%

St Anne's Community Services
☆ Charitable Company
TSA Reg ✓ ♠ 👓
6 St Mark's Avenue, Leeds,
West Yorkshire, LS2 9BN
T 0113 243 5151
E info@st-annes.org.uk
W www.st-annes.org.uk
CE Mrs Julie Robinson
Sec Mr John Baczkowski
Ch Mrs Alison Legg
Total Staff 1340
Region Yorkshire & Humberside
Owned or managed 508
Rt 390 Sup 390 NSO 118
Tenant Type % Older 8% Single 92%

St Basils
☆ Charitable Company
TSA Reg ✓ 👓
Heath Mill Lane, Deritend,
Birmingham, West Midlands, B9 4AX
T 0121 772 2483
E info@stbasils.org.uk
W www.stbasils.org.uk
CE Ms Jean Templeton
Sec Mr Brian Adams
Ch Ms Kathy Halliday
Total Staff 193
Region West Midlands
Owned or managed 399
Rt 399 Sup 399
Tenant Type % Single 100%

St Christopher's Fellowship
☆ Charitable Company
TSA Reg ✓ 👓
1 Putney High Street, Putney,
Greater London, SW15 1SZ
T 020 8780 0800
E Info@stchris.org.uk
W www.stchris.org.uk
CE Mr Jonathan Farrow
Sec Mr Jonathan Farrow
Ch Ms Heather Barker
Total Staff 191
Region London
Owned or managed 175
Rt 175 Sup 175
Tenant Type % Single 100%

St Ignatius HA Ltd
◯ Charitable HA
TSA Reg ✗ 👓
Unit 202, Parma House,
Clarendon Road, London,
Greater London, N22 6UL
T 020 8808 0818
E paul@stignatius.org.uk
CE Mr Paul Fernandes
Ch Noble Amoateng
Total Staff 6
Region London
Tenant Type % Single 100%

St Johns College HA Ltd
◯ Charitable HA
TSA Reg ✗
Savills (L+P) Ltd, Wytham Court,
11 West Way, Botley, Oxford,
Oxfordshire, OX2 0QL
T 01865 269000
E bronaldson@savills.com
Sec Bridget Ronaldson
Ch Sir Michael Scholar
Total Staff 0
Region South East
Tenant Type % Older 100%

St Lawrence's Hospital Charity
❑ Charitable Trust
TSA Reg ✓
Bathurst Estate Office, Cirencester,
Gloucestershire, GL7 2BU
T 01285 653135
CE Mr Chris J Rowles
Ch The Earl Bathurst
Total Staff 1
Region South West
Owned or managed 22
Rt 22 GN 22
Tenant Type % Older 100%

St Lukes Housing Society Ltd
◯ Charitable HA
TSA Reg ✓ 👓
7 McMaster House, Latimer Road,
Headington, Oxford, Oxfordshire,
OX3 7PX
T 01865 769726
E saintlukeshousing@tiscali.co.uk
W www.saintlukeshousing.org.uk
CE Mrs Sandy Russell
Sec Mrs Sandy Russell
Ch Mr Jeremy Burgess
Total Staff 4
Region South East
Owned or managed 36
Rt 36 OP 36
Tenant Type % Family 12%
Older 80% Single 8%

St Martin of Tours HA Ltd
◯ Charitable HA
TSA Reg ✓ 👓
318-320 St. Pauls Road, London,
Greater London, N1 2LF
T 020 7704 3820
E enquiries@stmartinoftours.org.uk
W www.stmartinoftours.org.uk
CE Mr John Thompson
Sec Mr Philip Bowles
Ch Mr Nick Purchase
Total Staff 68
Region London
Owned or managed 109
Rt 109 Sup 109
Tenant Type % Single 100%

St Martins Housing Trust
☆ Charitable Company
TSA Reg ✗ 🐦
35 Bishopgate, Norwich, Norfolk, NR1 4AA
T 01603 667706
E enquiries@stmartinshousing.org.uk
W www.stmartinshousing.org.uk
CE Mr Derek Player
Sec Tracy Yates
Ch Mr Kevin Long
Total Staff 0
Region East of England
Tenant Type % Single 100%

St Michael Housing Society (Penzance) Ltd
◯ Charitable HA
TSA Reg ✗ 🏠
2 Orchard Court , Alverton, Penzance, Cornwall, TR18 4SX
T 01736 874960
E stmichaelhousing@hotmail.co.uk
CE Rev Keith Owen
Sec Mrs Joy George
Ch Rev Keith Owen
Total Staff 1
Region South West
Owned or managed 23
Rt 23 GN 23
Tenant Type % Family 50%
Older 45% Single 5%

St Minver CLT Ltd
☆ Charitable Company
TSA Reg ✗ 🏠
Woodlands, Maple Leaf Drive, Bodieve, Wadebridge, Cornwall, PL27 6EY
T 01208 816206
E helen.richards0@btinternet.com
Sec Mrs Helen Rawe
Ch Mr Edward Rowe
Total Staff 0
Region South West
Development Total 8
NBC 8

St Mungo Community HA
☆ Charitable Company
TSA Reg ✓ 🏠 ♦ 🐦
2nd Floor Griffin House, 161 Hammersmith Road, London, Greater London, W6 8BS
T 020 8762 5500
E info@mungos.org
W www.mungos.org
CE Charles Fraser CBE
Sec Charles Fraser CBE
Ch Mr Paul Doe
Total Staff 869
Region London
Owned or managed 1629
Rt 1629 Sup 1629

Tenant Type % Single 100%
Development Total 48
NBA 24 NBC 24

St Peter's (Saltley) HA Ltd
◯ Charitable HA
TSA Reg ✓ 🐦
Burrows Building, Bridge Road, Saltley, Birmingham, West Midlands, B8 3TE
T 0121 327 7265
E office@stpetershousing.org.uk
W www.stpetershousing.org.uk
CE Ms Jean Tompkins
Sec Ms Maureen Bradley
Ch Mr Peter Archer
Total Staff 8
Region West Midlands
Owned or managed 105
Rt 105 GN 59 OP 46
Tenant Type % Family 16%
Older 45% Single 39%

St Petroc's Society
◯ Charitable HA
TSA Reg ✗ 🐦
8 City Road, Truro, Cornwall, TR1 2JJ
T 01872 279485
E home@stpetrocs.org.uk
W www.stpetrocs.org.uk
CE Mr Steve Ellis
Sec Derek Archer
Ch Mr Geoff Tate
Total Staff 26
Region South West
Tenant Type % Single 100%

St Thomas's Housing Society Ltd
◼ Non-Charitable HA
TSA Reg ✗
2 St. Thomas Drive, East Clandon, Guildford, Surrey, GU4 7RZ
T 01483 223848
Sec Mrs L Crockford
Ch Mr Anthony Reeves
Total Staff 0
Region South East
Owned or managed 10
NSO 10
Tenant Type % Family 100%

St Vincent's HA Ltd
◯ Charitable HA
TSA Reg ✓ 🏠 🔑 🐦
First Floor, Metropolitan House, 20 Brindley Road, Manchester, Greater Manchester, M16 9HQ
T 0161 772 2120
E enquiry@svha.co.uk
W www.svha.co.uk
CE Ms Charlotte Norman
Ch Mr John Towers

Total Staff 0
Regions North West + West Midlands, Yorkshire & Humberside
Owned or managed 3350
Rt 3242 GN 2280 Sup 418
OP 544 SO 62 NSO 46
Tot lets 258 GN bs 2161
Tenant Type % Family 45%
Older 30% Single 25%
Development Total 128
Rt 135 GN 132 Sup 3 LCHO 29
NBC 128

St Vincents Family HA Ltd
◯ Charitable HA
TSA Reg ✓ 🐦
63 - 65 Herne Hill, London, Greater London, SE24 9NE
T 01825 732177
E pctaylor@svfha.com
Sec Mr R E Gates
Ch Peter Taylor
Total Staff 0
Regions London + South East
Owned or managed 42
Rt 42 GN 30 OP 12
Tenant Type % Family 33%
Older 44% Single 24%

Stafford and Rural Homes Ltd
✪ Not-for-Profit Company
TSA Reg ✓ 🖥 🚌 📷 🔑 🐦
The Rurals, 1 Parker Court, Dyson Way, Staffordshire Technology Park, Beaconside, Stafford, Staffordshire, ST18 0WP
T 01785 216601
E enquiries@sarh.co.uk
W www.sarh.co.uk
CE Ms Karen Armitage
Sec Mrs Karen Marshall
Ch Mr Kevin Upton
Total Staff 190
Region West Midlands
Owned or managed 5953
Rt 5704 GN 4252 Sup 8 OP 1444
SO 249 Tot lets 534 GN bs 4251
Tenant Type % Family 35%
Older 35% Single 30%
Development Total 30
NBA 22 NBC 8

Staffordshire HA Ltd
◯ Charitable HA
TSA Reg ✓ 🏠 🔑 🐦 ◊
308 London Road, Stoke, Staffordshire, ST4 5AB
T 01782 744533
E mailbox@staffshousing.org.uk
W www.staffshousing.org.uk
CE Mrs Diane Lea
Sec Mr Frank Hammond
Ch Ms Rhian Hughes

Total Staff 120
Region West Midlands
Owned or managed 2675
Rt 2348 GN 1831 Sup 84 OP 433
SO 167 NSO 160 Tot lets 388
GN bs 1803
Tenant Type % Family 28%
Older 38% Single 34%
Development Total 27
Rt 156 GN 139 Sup 4 OP 13
LCHO 21 NBA 15 NBC 12
Subsidiary Association(s)
Blue Mountain HA Ltd

Staincliffe HA Ltd
○ Charitable HA
TSA Reg ✗
Elbolton, Hebden Road, Grassington,
North Yorkshire, BD23 5LH
T 01756 752086
Sec Mrs Margaret Stockdale
Ch Mrs Helen Wright
Total Staff 1
Region Yorkshire & Humberside
Tenant Type % Older 100%

Stanhope Court (Worcester) HA Ltd
○ Charitable HA
TSA Reg ✓ 🐦
c/o Worcester Community Housing
Ltd, Progress House, Midland Road,
Worcester, Worcestershire,
WR5 1DU
T 01905 670200
Ch Mr Keith Layton
Total Staff 0
Region West Midlands
Owned or managed 16
Rt 16 OP 16
Tenant Type % Older 100%

Starley Housing Co-operative Ltd
★ Co-operative Society
TSA Reg ✓
17a Starley Road, Coventry,
West Midlands, CV1 3JU
T 024 7622 3111
E starley@starleyhousingcooperative.
co.uk
W www.starleyhousing.co.uk
Sec Ms Kim O'Neil
Ch Sharon O'Driscoll
Total Staff 6
Region West Midlands
Owned or managed 125
Rt 125 GN 125
Tenant Type % Family 45%
Older 9% Single 46%

Steve Biko HA
○ Charitable HA
TSA Reg ✓ 🔑 🐦 🏠
19 Devonshire Road, Princes Park,
Liverpool, Merseyside, L8 3TX
T 0151 726 2200
E info@stevebiko.co.uk
W www.stevebikoha.org
CE Ms Tracey Gore
Sec Mike Bernard
Ch Ms Alison Navarro
Total Staff 8
Region North West
Owned or managed 270
Rt 265 GN 195 Sup 70 SO 5
Tot lets 27 GN bs 271
Tenant Type % Family 30%
Older 60% Single 10%

Stoke on Trent and North Staffordshire YMCA HA
❑ Charitable Trust
TSA Reg ✗ 🐦
Edinburgh House, Harding
Road, Hanley, Stoke-On-Trent,
Staffordshire, ST1 3AE
T 01782 864500
E tracey.mears@northstaffsymca.
org.uk
W www.northstaffsymca.org.uk
CE Mr Daniel Flynn
Sec Mr Daniel Flynn
Ch Mr Michael Toohey
Total Staff 0
Region West Midlands
Tenant Type % Single 100%

Stoke-on-Trent Housing Society Ltd
■ Non-Charitable HA
TSA Reg ✓ 🏠 🔑 ◊
Kingsley, The Brampton, Newcastle,
Staffordshire, ST5 0QW
T 01782 854707
E enquiries@aspirehousing.co.uk
W www.aspirehousing.co.uk/soths
Sec Mr Raj Brightman
Ch Mr Trevor Jones
Total Staff 0
Region West Midlands
Owned or managed 462
Rt 452 GN 452 SO 10 Tot lets 85
GN bs 452
Tenant Type % Family 30%
Older 20% Single 50%
Development Total 20
Rt 20 GN 20 LCHO 10 NBA 1
NBC 19
Parent Association
Aspire Housing Ltd

Stoll
☆ Charitable Company
TSA Reg ✓ 🐦
446 Fulham Road, London,
Greater London, SW6 1DT
T 020 7385 2110
E info@stoll.org.uk
W www.stoll.org.uk
CE Mr Ed Tytherleigh
Sec Mrs Tabitha Northrup
Ch Dr Simon Chapman
Total Staff 26
Region London
Owned or managed 235
Rt 235 GN 16 Sup 219
Tenant Type % Family 4%
Older 74% Single 22%

Stonechester HA Ltd
○ Charitable HA
TSA Reg ✗
1 Belmont , Bath, Avon, BA1 5DZ
T 01225 485910
E stonechester@
westofenglandestates.co.uk
W www.westofenglandestate.co.uk
CE Mr Martin Perry
Sec Mr Martin Perry
Ch Mr Paul P F Perry
Total Staff 0
Region South West
Tenant Type % Older 100%

Stonewall HA Ltd
○ Charitable HA
TSA Reg ✗ 🐦
2a Leroy Business Centre,
436 Essex Road, Islington, London,
Greater London, N1 3QP
T 020 7359 6242
E info@stonewallhousing.org
W www.stonewallhousing.org
CE Mr Bob Green
Sec Mr Bob Green
Ch Mr Andrew Van Doorn
Total Staff 14
Region London
Tenant Type % Single 100%

Stroud Green Housing Co-operative Ltd
★ Co-operative Society
TSA Reg ✓ 🔑
Unit 1 The Mews, Albert Road,
London, Greater London, N4 3RD
T 020 7263 2716
E stroudgreencoop@gmail.com
Sec Ms Jennifer Wood
Ch Mr Wilf Murray
Total Staff 1
Region London
Owned or managed 65
Rt 63 GN 63 SO 2 Tot lets 0
GN bs 0

Tenant Type % Family 59%
Older 7% Single 34%

Suffolk Estate Co-operative Ltd
★ Co-operative Society
TSA Reg ✗ 🔑
The Housing Office,
Welshpool Street, London,
Greater London, E8 4PF
T 020 7923 3774
E info@suffolktmo.co.uk
W www.solarsuffolk.org.uk
CE Mr Griffith Quartey
Sec Miss Susanne Lechner
Ch Keith Miller
Total Staff 7
Region London
Owned or managed 389
Rt 297 GN 297 SO 92 Tot lets 0
GN bs 0
Tenant Type % Family 60%
Older 15% Single 25%

Suffolk Housing Society Ltd
○ Charitable HA
TSA Reg ✓ 📷 🔑 🤝
Old Mission House,
St Botolph's Lane, Bury St Edmunds,
Suffolk, IP33 2AX
T 01284 767224
E office@suffolkhousing.org
W www.suffolkhousing.org
CE Mr Ian Winslet
Sec Mr Steve Pugh
Ch Mr Andrew Budden
Total Staff 33
Region East of England
Owned or managed 2011
Rt 1843 GN 1450 Sup 77 OP 316
SO 148 NSO 20 Tot lets 207
GN bs 1419
Tenant Type % Family 10%
Older 42% Single 48%
Development Total 66
NBA 33 NBC 33

Sunridge HA Ltd
○ Charitable HA
TSA Reg ✗ 🤝
76 The Ridgeway, London,
Greater London, NW11 8PT
T 020 8458 3389
E sunridge.court@virgin.net
CE Mrs Pamela Peterkin
Sec Mr Edward Levy
Ch Mrs Linda Stone
Total Staff 0
Region London
Tenant Type % Older 100%

Surrey Federation Charitable HA
○ Charitable HA
TSA Reg ✗
Anthony West House,
Wheeler's Lane, Brockham,
Betchworth, Surrey, RH3 7LG
E paul@pjjohnson.com
Sec Mr John Zetter
Ch Mrs Rosemary Mote
Total Staff 0
Region South East
Owned or managed 13
Rt 13 OP 13
Tenant Type % Older 100%

Sussex Central YMCA
☆ Charitable Company
TSA Reg ✓ 🤝
Reed House, 47 Church Road, Hove,
East Sussex, BN3 2BE
T 01273 222550
E info@sussexcentralymca.org.uk
W www.hoveymca.org.uk
CE Mr David Standing
Sec Mr David Standing
Ch Mr Ian Chisnall
Total Staff 239
Region South East
Owned or managed 206
Rt 206 Sup 206
Tenant Type % Single 100%

Sussex Housing & Care
○ Charitable HA
TSA Reg ✓ 🤝
Ronald Simson House,
24 Sutton Avenue, Seaford,
East Sussex, BN25 4LG
T 0845 402 3702
E office@sussexhousing.org.uk
W www.sussexhousing.org.uk
CE Mr Martin Burke
Sec Mr Martin Burke
Ch Mr Dave Hill
Total Staff 175
Region South East
Owned or managed 585
Rt 585 OP 585
Tenant Type % Older 100%

Sussex Oakleaf HA Ltd
○ Charitable HA
TSA Reg ✓ 🤝
Norris House, Burrell Road,
Haywards Heath, West Sussex,
RH16 1TW
T 01444 459517
E info@sussexoakleaf.org.uk
W www.sussexoakleaf.org.uk
CE Mr Robert Jones
Sec Mr Robert Jones
Ch Ms Barbara Williams
Total Staff 217

Region South East
Owned or managed 50
Rt 50 Sup 50
Tenant Type % Single 100%

Sussex Overseas HS Ltd
○ Charitable HA
TSA Reg ✓ 🤝
Bishop Hannington Church Office,
Nevill Avenue, Hove, East Sussex,
BN3 7NH
T 01273 732965
E Johneputtock@aol.com
Sec Mr Maurice Willard
Ch Mr Desmond Collins
Total Staff 0
Region South East
Owned or managed 15
Rt 15 GN 15
Tenant Type % Family 33%
Older 44% Single 23%

Sutton Housing Society Ltd
○ Charitable HA
TSA Reg ✓ 🤝
1a Trickett House, 125 Brighton
Road, Sutton, Surrey, SM2 5SN
T 020 8642 1500
E info@shsoc.org.uk
W www.suttonhousingsociety.org.uk
CE Mr Christopher Turton
Sec Mr Christopher Turton
Ch Mr Andrew Jepp
Total Staff 17
Region London
Owned or managed 446
Rt 444 GN 127 Sup 23 OP 294
NSO 2
Tenant Type % Family 12%
Older 72% Single 16%

SWALLOW
☆ Charitable Company
TSA Reg ✗ 🤝
The Old Engine House, Old Pit Road,
Midsomer Norton, Bath, Avon,
BA3 4BQ
T 01761 414034
E info@swallowcharity.org
W www.swallowcharity.org
CE Ms Beverley Craney
Sec Mr Tony Quinn
Ch Mr Tim Watson
Total Staff 0
Region South West
Owned or managed 10
Rt 10 Sup 10
Tenant Type % Single 100%

Swan HA
○ Charitable HA
TSA Reg ✓
Pilgrim House, High Street, Billericay, Essex, CM12 9XY
T 0300 303 2500
E info@swan.org.uk
W www.swan.org.uk
CE Mr John Synnuck
Sec Jamie Smith
Ch Richard Frost
Total Staff 252
Regions East of England + London
Owned or managed 9758
Rt 8487 GN 8138 Sup 269 OP 80
SO 1230 NSO 41 Tot lets 720
GN bs 6290
Tenant Type % Family 87%
Older 6% Single 7%
Development Total 577
Rt 774 GN 772 Sup 2 LCHO 211
NBA 23 NBC 554

Swarthmore Housing Society Ltd
○ Charitable HA
TSA Reg ✗
31 Marsham Lane, Gerrards Cross, Buckinghamshire, SL9 8HB
T 01753 885663
E carehome@swarthmore.co.uk
CE Ms Lilli Porter
Sec Ms Jen Jackson
Ch Mrs Jane Taylor
Total Staff 0
Region South East
Tenant Type % Older 100%

Swinden HA Ltd
■ Non-Charitable HA
TSA Reg ✗
Swinden Technology Centre, Moorgate, Rotherham, South Yorkshire, S60 3AR
T 01709 820166
E martin.sturdy@corusgroup.com
Sec Mr Martin J Sturdy
Ch Mr Simon Pike
Total Staff 0
Region Yorkshire & Humberside
Owned or managed 28
Rt 14 GN 14 NSO 14
Tenant Type % Family 70%
Single 30%

Symphony Housing Group
■ Non-Charitable HA
TSA Reg ✓
12 Hanover Street, Liverpool, L1 4AA
T 0151 708 5777
E mail@contourhousing.co.uk
W www.symphonyhousing.org.uk

CE Mr Philip Gandy
Sec Mrs Audrey Davidson
Ch Mr Chris Jeffries
Total Staff 1061
Region North West
Owned or managed 4
Rt 4 GN 4
Subsidiary Association(s)
Beechwood Ballantyne; Cobalt Housing Ltd; Contour Homes; Contour Property Services Ltd; Hyndburn Homes Ltd; Liverpool Housing Trust; Peak Valley HA Ltd; Ribble Valley Homes Ltd

Synergy Housing Ltd
○ Charitable HA
TSA Reg ✓
Synergy Housing Group Ltd, Link House, 25 West Street, Poole, BH15 1LD
T 01202 308600
E firstname.lastname@synergyhousing.co.uk
W www.synergyhousing.co.uk
CE Mr Graeme Stanley
Ch Mr Mel Cook
Total Staff 360
Regions South West + South East
Owned or managed 9084
Rt 8414 GN 6487 Sup 33 OP 1894
SO 660 NSO 10 Tot lets 879
GN bs 6415
Tenant Type % Family 35%
Older 47% Single 18%
Development Total 68
NBA 41 NBC 27
Parent Association Aster Group

Tally Ho Housing Co-op Ltd
★ Co-operative Society
TSA Reg ✓
3a Moss Hall Crescent, North Finchley, London, Greater London, N12 8NY
T 020 8445 0560
Sec A Edwards
Ch S Pitcher
Total Staff 2
Region London
Owned or managed 47
Rt 40 GN 40 SO 7 Tot lets 0
GN bs 0
Tenant Type % Family 80%
Single 20%

Tamar Housing Society Ltd
○ Charitable HA
TSA Reg ✓
Mayflower House, 178 Armada Way, Plymouth, Devon, PL1 1LD
T 01752 250902
E info@tamarhs.org
W www.tamarhs.org
CE Mrs Julie Barnett
Ch Ms Caroline Theyer
Total Staff 36
Region South West
Owned or managed 496
Rt 459 GN 459 SO 37 Tot lets 0
GN bs 2
Tenant Type % Family 50%
Older 30% Single 20%

Tamarisk Housing Ltd
▲ Other
TSA Reg ✗
2B Admirals Way, Hythe, Hampshire, SO45 6RU
T 023 8084 4862
W www.tamariskhousing.org.uk
CE Mr Patrick Wallace
Ch Mr Andrew Granger
Total Staff 1
Region East Midlands

Tamil Community HA Ltd
○ Charitable HA
TSA Reg ✓
Tamil House, Unit 2, Fountayne Business Centre, Broad Lane, London, Greater London, N15 4AG
T 020 8493 7160
E info@tamilhousing.org.uk
W www.tamilhousing.org.uk
CE Mr Devan Kanthasamy
Ch Mr Sharvanandan Arnold
Total Staff 10
Region London
Owned or managed 289
Rt 289 GN 279 Sup 10
Tenant Type % Family 60%
Older 10% Single 30%

Tamworth Cornerstone HA Ltd
○ Charitable HA
TSA Reg ✓
The Old School House, Woodhouse Lane, Amington, Tamworth, Staffordshire, B77 3AE
T 01827 319918
E sheilawall@t-c-h-a.co.uk
W www.t-c-h-a.co.uk
CE Mrs Sheila Wall
Sec Mrs Susan Joyce
Ch Mr Frank Joyce
Total Staff 0
Region West Midlands
Owned or managed 32

Rt 32 Sup 32
Tenant Type % Single 100%

Tangram Housing Co-operative Ltd
★ Co-operative Society
TSA Reg ✓
76 Bankside Street, Harehills, Leeds, West Yorkshire, LS8 5AD
T 0113 248 8743
Ch Simon Brett
Total Staff 1
Region Yorkshire & Humberside
Owned or managed 37
Rt 37 GN 37
Tenant Type % Family 35%
Older 5% Single 60%

Tannery Arts Ltd
○ Charitable HA
TSA Reg ✗
Tannery Arts Ltd, Unit 12, Rich Industrial Estate, Crimscott Street, London, SE1 5TE
T 020 7729 8008
E admin@tanneryarts.org.uk
W www.tanneryarts.org.uk
Sec Mr Andrew Bick
Total Staff 0
Region London
Tenant Type % Family 30%
Single 70%

Tarka Housing Ltd
○ Charitable HA
TSA Reg ✓ 📠 🔑 ♦
Tarka House, Clovelly Road Industrial Estate, Bideford, EX39 3HN
T 01237 428080
E info@tarkahousing.org.uk
W www.tarkahousing.org.uk
CE Mr Nigel Barnard
Sec Miss Lucy Rickson
Ch David Howell
Total Staff 70
Region South West
Owned or managed 1859
Rt 1794 GN 1449 OP 345 SO 65
Tot lets 135 GN bs 1440
Parent Association
Westward Housing Group Ltd

Taunton Association for The Homeless
○ Charitable HA
TSA Reg ✗ 🕶
90-91 East Reach, Taunton, Somerset, TA1 3HF
T 01823 271326
E info@tahltd.co.uk
W www.tah.org.uk
CE Mr John Shipley
Sec Mrs Esther Bishop

Ch David Edmondson
Total Staff 44
Region South West
Owned or managed 129
Rt 129 Sup 129
Tenant Type % Single 100%

TCHG Foundation
☆ Charitable Company
TSA Reg ✗ ♦
Monson House, 1 Monson Way, Tunbridge Wells, TN1 1LQ
T 01892 514614
E foundation@tchg.org.uk
W www.tchg.org.uk
CE Mr Bob Heapy
Sec Mr Paul Cooper
Ch Mr Alan Riddell
Total Staff 0
Region South East
Parent Association
Town & Country Housing Group

TCHG Living Ltd
■ Non-Charitable HA
TSA Reg ✓ 📠 🔑 ♦
Monson House, 1 Monson Way, Tunbridge Wells, Kent, TN1 1LQ
T 0845 873 1314
E living@tchg.org.uk
W www.tchg.org.uk
CE Mr Bob Heapy
Sec Mr Paul Cooper
Ch Mr Darren Hughes
Total Staff 5
Region South East
Owned or managed 711
Rt 505 GN 505 SO 70 NSO 136
Tot lets 0 GN bs 0
Tenant Type % Family 70%
Single 30%
Parent Association
Town & Country Housing Group

Teachers' HA Ltd
○ Charitable HA
TSA Reg ✓ 🕶
Rugby Chambers, 2 Rugby Street, London, Greater London, WC1N 3QU
T 020 7440 9440
E enquiries@teachershousing.org.uk
W www.teachershousing.org.uk
CE Ms Sian Llewellyn
Sec Ms Sian Llewellyn
Ch Mr Roger Hinton
Total Staff 45
Regions London + South East, South West, West Midlands, Yorkshire & Humberside
Owned or managed 617
Rt 602 GN 335 OP 267 NSO 15
Tenant Type % Family 46%
Older 44% Single 10%

Tees Valley Housing Ltd
■ Non-Charitable HA
TSA Reg ✓ 📠 🔑 🕶 ♦
2 Hudson Quay, Windward Way, Middlesborough, Cleveland, TS2 1QG
T 01642 773600
E enquiries@fabrickgroup.co.uk
W www.teesvalley.org
CE Mr Doug Ross
Sec Mrs Heather Ashton
Ch Ms Sue Jeffrey
Total Staff 175
Regions North East + Yorkshire & Humberside
Owned or managed 4840
Rt 4154 GN 3766 Sup 164 OP 224
SO 650 NSO 36 Tot lets 636
GN bs 3609
Tenant Type % Family 36%
Older 22% Single 42%
Development Total 379
NBA 225 NBC 154
Parent Association
Fabrick Housing Group Ltd

Teesdale HA Ltd
○ Charitable HA
TSA Reg ✓ 📠 🔑 ♦
14A Redwell Court, Harmire Enterprise Park, Harmire Road, Barnard Castle, County Durham, DL12 8BN
T 01833 694400
E enquiries@teesdaleha.co.uk
W www.teesdaleha.co.uk
CE Mrs Angela Lockwood
Sec Mr Peter Lenehan
Ch Mr Jed Lester
Total Staff 12
Region North East
Owned or managed 940
Rt 930 GN 929 Sup 1 SO 10
Tot lets 0 GN bs 0
Tenant Type % Family 35%
Older 55% Single 10%
Parent Association
North Star Housing Group Ltd

Teign Housing
☆ Charitable Company
TSA Reg ✓ 📠 📠 🔑 🕶
Templar House, Collett Way, Newton Abbot, Devon, TQ12 4PH
T 01626 322722
E info@teignhousing.co.uk
W www.teignhousing.co.uk
CE Mr Mike Hanrahan
Sec Mrs Jo Reece
Ch Mr Stephen Purser
Total Staff 85
Region South West
Owned or managed 3713
Rt 3514 GN 2506 OP 1008 SO 199

Tot lets 231 **GN bs** 2504
Tenant Type % Family 40%
Older 50% **Single** 10%
Development Total 24
NBA 12 **NBC** 12

Terra Nova Developments Ltd
✪ Not-for-Profit Company
TSA Reg ✗ ◊
Southerngate, 729 Princess Road,
Manchester, Lancashire, M20 2LT
T 0161 447 5028
W www.greatplaces.org.uk
CE Mr Stephen Porter
Sec Mr Phil Elvy
Total Staff 0
Region North West
Parent Association
Great Places Housing Group

Thame & District HA Ltd
◯ Charitable HA
TSA Reg ✓ 🕶
Pearce Court, Windmill Road,
Thame, Oxfordshire, OX9 2DJ
T 01844 212564
E office@tdha.co.uk
W www.tdha.co.uk
CE Mrs Angie Menary
Ch Mr Nigel Tonge
Total Staff 8
Region South East
Owned or managed 111
Rt 96 **OP** 96 **NSO** 15
Tenant Type % Older 100%

Thames Reach HA Ltd
◯ Charitable HA
TSA Reg ✗ ♦ 🕶
Elmfield House, 5 Stockwell Mews,
London, Greater London, SW9 9GX
T 020 7702 4260
E enquiries@thamesreach.org.uk
W www.thamesreach.org.uk
CE Mr Jeremy Swain
Sec Mr Jeremy Swain
Ch Mr Kenneth Olisa
Total Staff 291
Region London
Owned or managed 423
Rt 423 **Sup** 423

Thames Valley Charitable HA Ltd
◯ Charitable HA
TSA Reg ✓ ■ ▢ 🔟 ◨ 🔑 ◊
Premier House, 52 London Road,
Twickenham, Middlesex, TW1 3RP
T 020 8607 0607
E info@tvha.co.uk
W www.tvha.co.uk
CE Ms Geeta Nanda

Sec Mrs Tish Etter
Ch Jane Staveley
Total Staff 0
Regions London + South East,
South West
Owned or managed 12092
Rt 5024 **GN** 5006 **OP** 18 **SO** 4958
NSO 2110 **Tot lets** 349 **GN bs** 5006
Tenant Type % Family 70%
Older 25% **Single** 5%
Development Total 830
Rt 288 **GN** 288 **NBA** 557 **NBC** 273
Parent Association
Thames Valley HA Ltd

Thames Valley HA Ltd
■ Non-Charitable HA
TSA Reg ✓ ▢ ◨ 🔑 ◊
Premier House, 52 London Road,
Twickenham, Middlesex, TW1 3RP
T 020 8607 0607
E info@tvha.co.uk
W www.tvha.co.uk
CE Ms Geeta Nanda
Sec Mrs Tish Etter
Ch John Garrity
Total Staff 215
Regions London + South East
Owned or managed 5452
Rt 5066 **GN** 5048 **OP** 18 **SO** 350
NSO 36 **Tot lets** 0 **GN bs** 2
Tenant Type % Family 70%
Older 14% **Single** 16%
Development Total 105
Rt 66 **Sup** 51 **OP** 15 **LCHO** 250
NBA 105
Subsidiary Association(s)
Thames Valley Charitable HA Ltd

The Abbeyfield Society
☆ Charitable Company
TSA Reg ✓ ◨ 🔑 ♦ 🕶
Abbeyfield House, 53 Victoria Street,
St Albans, Hertfordshire, AL1 3UW
T 01727 857536
E post@abbeyfield.com
W www.abbeyfield.com
CE Mr Paul Allen
Sec Mrs Natasha Singarayer
Ch Mr John Robinson
Total Staff 1698
Regions East of England +
London, South East, South West,
East Midlands, West Midlands,
Yorkshire & Humberside,
North East, North West
Owned or managed 1389
Rt 1276 **OP** 1276 **SO** 4 **NSO** 109
Tot lets 403 **GN bs** 0
Tenant Type % Older 100%
Single 100%
Development Total 12
NBA 7 **NBC** 5

The ACT Foundation
☆ Charitable Company
TSA Reg ✗
61 Thames Street, Windsor,
Berkshire, SL4 1QW
T 01753 753900
E info@theactfoundation.co.uk
W www.theactfoundation.co.uk
CE Mr Denis Taylor
Sec Mr James M Kerr
Ch Mr Michael A Street, OBE
Total Staff 15
Region South East
Owned or managed 15
NSO 15
Tenant Type % Family 100%

The Cambridge Pringle Group Ltd
☆ Charitable Company
TSA Reg ✗ 🕶
c/o The Company Secretary, 23
Orwell House, Cowley Road,
Cambridge, Cambridgeshire,
CB4 0PP
T 01223 223822
W www.cambridgepringlegroup.
org.uk
Sec Mr Robert Powell
Ch Mr Colin Marshall
Total Staff 6
Region East of England
Owned or managed 14
Rt 14 **GN** 14
Tenant Type % Single 100%

The Cambridgeshire Cottage HS Ltd
◯ Charitable HA
TSA Reg ✓
2 High Street, Grantchester,
Cambridge, Cambridgeshire,
CB3 9NF
T 01223 844777
E mail@tcchs.co.uk
CE Mr Michael Oldfield
Sec Mr Michael Oldfield
Ch Ms Diane Bramwell
Total Staff 2
Region East of England
Owned or managed 69
Rt 66 **GN** 66 **NSO** 3
Tenant Type % Family 47%
Older 21% **Single** 32%

The Community Housing Group
✪ Not-for-Profit Company
TSA Reg ✓ ♦ ◊
3 Foley Grove, Foley Business Park,
Stourport Road, Kidderminster,
Worcestershire, DY11 7PT
T 01562 733000
E information@communityhg.com

W www.communityhg.com
CE Mr Ray Brookes
Sec Mr David Knowlton
Ch Mrs Jenny Evans
Total Staff 449
Region West Midlands
Tenant Type % Family 39%
Older 37% Single 24%
Subsidiary Association(s) Wyre
Forest Community Housing Ltd;
Wyre Forest Sheltered Housing Ltd

The Friendly Almshouses
❏ Charitable Trust
TSA Reg ✗
167 Stockwell Park Road, London,
Greater London, SW9 0TL
T 020 7274 7176
E office@friendlyalmshouses.org
W www.friendlyalmshouses.org
Ch Ms Clare Wardle
Total Staff 4
Region London
Owned or managed 30
Rt 30 Sup 30
Tenant Type % Single 100%

The Gloucester Charities Trust
❏ Charitable Trust
TSA Reg ✓ 🐾
Gloucester Charities Trust,
Century House, 100 London Road,
Gloucester, GL1 3PL
T 01452 500429
E info@gloschar.org.uk
W www.gloucestercharitiestrust.co.uk
CE Mrs Kathryn Lewis
Ch Mrs Sheila Paterson
Total Staff 24
Region South West
Owned or managed 130
Rt 130 Sup 130
Tenant Type % Older 100%

The Guinness Partnership
❏ Charitable Trust
TSA Reg ✓ ▣ ❒ 🔲 🖭 🔑 ♦ ◊
17 Mendy Street, High Wycombe,
Buckinghamshire, HP11 2NZ
T 01494 535823
E info@guinness.org.uk
W www.guinnesspartnership.com
CE Mr Simon Dow
Sec Mr Paul Oldroyd
Total Staff 2105
Regions South East + London,
South West, East Midlands,
West Midlands, East of England,
North East, North West
Owned or managed 54042
Rt 47757 GN 40808 Sup 886
OP 6063 SO 5742 NSO 543
Tot lets 6030

Tenant Type % Family 50%
Older 20% Single 30%
Development Total 933
Rt 836 GN 676 Sup 11 OP 149
LCHO 97 NBA 25 NBC 907
Subsidiary Association(s)
Guinness HA;
Guinness Care & Support Ltd;

The Hallsands HS Ltd
❍ Charitable HA
TSA Reg ✗
20 Victoria Road, Topsham,
Exeter, Devon, EX3 0EU
T 01392 879135
E gsimey@blueyonder.co.uk
CE Mr G R S Simey
Sec Mr G R S Simey
Ch A J B Mildmay-White
Total Staff 3
Region South West
Tenant Type % Family 50%
Older 50%

The Havebury Housing Partnership
✪ Not-for-Profit Company
TSA Reg ✓ ❒ 🔲 🖭 🔑 🐾
Havebury House, Western Way,
Bury St Edmunds, Suffolk, IP33 3SP
T 0300 330 0900
E office@havebury.com
W www.havebury.com
CE Mrs Karen Mayhew
Sec Mr Paul Edwards
Ch Donald McKenzie
Total Staff 179
Region East of England
Owned or managed 6168
Rt 5897 GN 5408 Sup 39 OP 450
SO 240 NSO 31 Tot lets 501
GN bs 5363
Tenant Type % Family 35%
Older 52% Single 13%
Development Total 57
Rt 281 GN 253 Sup 2 OP 26
LCHO 13 NBA 30 NBC 27

The Housing Plus Group Ltd
■ Non-Charitable HA
TSA Reg ✓ ◊
Acton Court, Acton Gate, Stafford,
Staffordshire, ST18 9AP
T 01785 312312
E enquiries@housing-plus.co.uk
W www.housing-plus.co.uk
CE Mrs Debbie Griffiths
Sec Mr Philip Ingle
Ch Dr. Mary Griffiths FCIH
Total Staff 180
Region West Midlands
Subsidiary Association(s) South
Staffordshire HA

The Industrial Dwellings Society (1885) Ltd
❍ Charitable HA
TSA Reg ✓ 🖭 🔑 🐾
5th floor, Ockway House, 41
Stamford Hill, London, Greater
London, N16 5SR
T 020 8800 9606
E housing@ids.org.uk
W www.ids.org.uk
CE Mr Paul Westbrook
Sec Mr Paul Westbrook
Ch Mr Jonathan Davies
Total Staff 52
Region London
Owned or managed 1451
Rt 1417 GN 1225 Sup 3 OP 189
SO 26 NSO 8 Tot lets 89
GN bs 1139
Tenant Type % Family 49%
Older 27% Single 24%
Development Total 32
NBA 32

The King Street Housing Society Ltd
❍ Charitable HA
TSA Reg ✓ 🐾
89 King Street, Cambridge,
Cambridgeshire, CB1 1LD
T 01223 312294
E info@kingstreeths.org.uk
W www.kingstreeths.org.uk
CE Mr Craig Glasper
Sec Mr Craig Glasper
Ch Ms Diane Ware
Total Staff 21
Region East of England
Owned or managed 791
Rt 414 GN 385 Sup 8 OP 21 SO 189
NSO 188 Tot lets 0 GN bs 0
Tenant Type % Family 70%
Older 15% Single 15%

The Leicester Young Men's Christian Association
☆ Charitable Company
TSA Reg ✓ 🐾
7 East Street, Leicester,
Leicestershire, LE1 6EY
T 0116 255 6507
E housing@leicesterymca.co.uk
W www.leicesterymca.com
CE Mr Paul Brown
Sec Mr Paul Brown
Ch Mr Neil Griffiths
Total Staff 75
Region East Midlands
Owned or managed 91
Rt 91 GN 8 Sup 83
Tenant Type % Single 100%

The London Housing Foundation
☆ Charitable Company
TSA Reg ✗ ◊
5th Floor, 57a Great Suffolk Street, London, Greater London, SE1 0BB
T 020 7934 0177
W www.lhf.org.uk
CE Mr Donald Wood
Sec Mr Derek Joseph
Ch Mr Donald Wood
Total Staff 2
Region London
Subsidiary Association(s)
Bramah House Ltd

The Margery Maplethorpe Trust
❑ Charitable Trust
TSA Reg ✗
33 Somersham, Welwyn Garden City, Hertfordshire, AL7 2PZ
T 01707 327303
E astonstuart@aol.com
Sec Mr Stuart Aston, MRICS
Total Staff 0
Region East of England
Tenant Type % Older 100%

The North Eastern YWCA Trustees Ltd
☆ Charitable Company
TSA Reg ✓
Jesmond House, Clayton Road, Newcastle Upon Tyne, Tyne And Wear, NE2 1UJ
T 0191 281 5466
E finance@neywca.co.uk
W www.neywca.co.uk
CE Ms Janet Smith
Sec Ms Janet Smith
Ch Mr Ernest Duncan
Total Staff 28
Region North East
Owned or managed 225
Rt 225 GN 225
Tenant Type % Single 100%

The Papworth Trust
☆ Charitable Company
TSA Reg ✓ ◳ ✎ ♦ 🐾
Bernard Sunley Centre, Papworth Everard, Cambridge, Cambridgeshire, CB23 3RG
T 01480 357200
E info@papworth.org.uk
W www.papworth.org.uk
CE Mr Adrian Bagg
Sec Mr Tony Osborne
Ch Mr Robert Hammond
Total Staff 510
Region East of England
Owned or managed 653
Rt 651 GN 173 Sup 478 SO 2
Tot lets 62 GN bs 593
Tenant Type % Family 35%
Older 30% Single 35%
Development Total 4
Rt 13 Sup 13 NBA 4

The Parkview Society Ltd
○ Charitable HA
TSA Reg ✗ 🐾
35a Highweek Village, Highweek, Newton Abbot, Devon, TQ12 1QG
T 01626 332630
E email@parkviewsociety.org.uk
W www.parkviewsociety.org.uk
CE Mr Graham Pollock
Sec Mr Graham Pollock
Ch Mr Ron Hancock
Total Staff 70
Region South West
Tenant Type % Single 100%

The Radcliffe Housing Society Ltd
○ Charitable HA
TSA Reg ✓ 🐾
Radcliffe House, Homefield Road, Riverhead, Sevenoaks, Kent, TN13 2DU
T 01732 459144
E enquiries@radcliffehs.org
W www.radcliffehs.org
CE Mr Nigel Wood
Sec Mr Nigel Wood
Ch Mr David Pamment
Total Staff 8
Regions South East + London
Owned or managed 311
Rt 303 GN 245 OP 58 NSO 8
Tenant Type % Family 70%
Older 20% Single 10%

The Richard HA Ltd
○ Charitable HA
TSA Reg ✗
The Red House, Windmill Lane, Ashurst Wood, East Grinstead, RH19 3SZ
T 01342 328385
E raggydoll45@aol.com
Sec Mrs Rosemary Greener
Ch Miss Angela Cole
Total Staff 1
Region South East
Tenant Type % Single 100%

The Richmond Fellowship
☆ Charitable Company
TSA Reg ✓ ♦ 🐾
80 Holloway Road, London, N7 8JG
T 020 7697 3300
E communications@ richmondfellowship.org.uk
W www.richmondfellowship.org.uk

CE Mr Derek Caren
Ch Mr Peter Corley
Total Staff 923
Regions London + South East, South West, East of England, Yorkshire & Humberside, North East, North West
Owned or managed 646
Rt 646 Sup 646
Tenant Type % Single 100%

The Riverside Group Ltd
○ Charitable HA
TSA Reg ✓
🏠 ☐ 🚐 ◳ ✎ ♦ 🐾 ◊
2 Estuary Boulevard, Estuary Commerce Park, Liverpool, L24 8RF
T 0845 111 0000
E info@riverside.org.uk
W www.riverside.org.uk
CE Ms Carol Matthews
Sec Ms Lynn F McCracken
Ch Cllr Paul Brant
Total Staff 2665
Regions North West + London, South East, South West, East Midlands, West Midlands, East of England, Yorkshire & Humberside, North East
Owned or managed 50428
Rt 47009 GN 37548 Sup 4444
OP 5017 SO 2355 NSO 1064
Tot lets 10472 GN bs 35815
Tenant Type % Family 37%
Older 35% Single 28%
Development Total 1153
Rt 143 GN 143 LCHO 62 NBA 629
NBC 524
Subsidiary Association(s)
The St Michael's Housing Trust

The Royal Air Forces Association Housing Ltd
○ Charitable HA
TSA Reg ✓ 🐾
Stanmore House, Washington Road, Storrington, Pulborough, West Sussex, RH20 4RA
T 01903 744701
E rafahousing@hotmail.com
W www.rafa.org.uk
CE Mr Rod Martin
Sec Mrs J Easton
Ch Mr Mike Snell
Total Staff 2
Region South East
Owned or managed 32
Rt 32 OP 32
Tenant Type % Older 100%

The Sheppard Trust
☆ Charitable Company
TSA Reg ✗
12 Lansdowne Walk, London,
Greater London, W11 3LN
T 020 7727 5500
E chiefexec@sheppardtrust.org
W www.sheppardtrust.org
CE Mr David Cash
Sec Mr David Cash
Ch Mr Andrew Daws
Total Staff 6
Region London
Owned or managed 29
Rt 29 OP 29
Tenant Type % Older 100%

The St Michael's Housing Trust
❏ Charitable Trust
TSA Reg ✓ 🐾 ◊
2 Estuary Boulevard, Estuary
Commerce Park, Liverpool,
Merseyside, L24 8RF
T 0845 112 7722
E info@riverside.org.uk
W www.riverside.org.uk
CE Ms Carol Matthews
Sec Ms Lynn F McCracken
Ch Cllr Paul Brandt
Total Staff 0
Regions North West +
East Midlands
Owned or managed 13
Rt 13 Sup 13
Tenant Type % Single 100%
Parent Association
The Riverside Group Ltd

The Swaythling Housing Society Ltd
◼ Non-Charitable HA
TSA Reg ✓ 🖥 ⬜ 📷 🔑 🐾 ◊
Collins House, Bishopstoke Road,
Eastleigh, Hampshire, SO50 6AD
T 0300 123 1567
E info@radian.co.uk
W www.radian.co.uk
CE Mr Lindsay Todd
Sec Mr Terry Walker
Ch Mr John Collinge
Total Staff 88
Regions South East + South West
Owned or managed 17013
Rt 15461 GN 13996 Sup 234
OP 1231 SO 1400 NSO 152
Tot lets 775 GN bs 4814
Tenant Type % Family 96%
Older 3% Single 1%
Development Total 468
NBA 265 NBC 203
Parent Association
Radian Group Ltd

The Trees Group
◯ Charitable HA
TSA Reg ✗
165 Glenfield Road, Leicester,
Leicestershire, LE3 6DP
T 0116 299 4466
E info@thetreegroup.org.uk
W www.thetreesgroup.org.uk
CE Mr John Montague
Sec Mr David Brazier
Ch Mr Robert Ian Kennedy
Total Staff 70
Region East Midlands

The Villages HA Ltd
◼ Non-Charitable HA
TSA Reg ✓ 🔑 🐾 ◊
16 The Croft, Stockbridge Village,
Liverpool, Merseyside, L28 1NR
T 0151 480 1313
E info@villages.org.uk
W www.villages.org.uk
CE Mr Vernon Jackson
Sec Mr Vernon Jackson
Ch Mr Andrew Greenhill
Total Staff 105
Region North West
Owned or managed 2781
Rt 2744 GN 2525 Sup 8 OP 211
SO 37 Tot lets 248 GN bs 2437
Tenant Type % Family 36%
Older 7% Single 57%
Subsidary Association(s)
Villages Community HA Ltd

The Wrekin Housing Group Ltd
✪ Not-for-Profit Company
TSA Reg ✓ ◊
Colliers Way, Old Park, Telford,
Shropshire, TF3 4AW
T 01952 217100
E enquiries@wrekinhousingtrust.
org.uk
W www.wrekinhousingtrust.org.uk
CE Mr John Broadhead
Sec Mr Chris Horton
Ch Mrs Anne Ward
Total Staff 0
Region West Midlands
Subsidary Association(s)
CHOICES HA Ltd; The Wrekin
Housing Trust

The Wrekin Housing Trust
❏ Charitable Trust
TSA Reg ✓
🖥 ⬜ 🚚 YTHO 📷 🔑 ♦ 🐾 ◊
Colliers Way, Old Park, Telford,
Shropshire, TF3 4AW
T 01952 217100
E customer.contactcentre@
wrekinhousingtrust.org.uk
W www.wrekinhousingtrust.org.uk

CE Mr John Broadhead
Sec Mr Chris Horton
Ch Mrs Anne Ward
Total Staff 511
Region West Midlands
Owned or managed 12222
Rt 11086 GN 9774 Sup 60 OP 1252
SO 1134 NSO 2 Tot lets 1311
GN bs 9729
Tenant Type % Family 41%
Older 30% Single 29%
Development Total 497
Rt 1526 GN 1187 Sup 339 NBA 341
NBC 156
Parent Association
The Wrekin Housing Group Ltd

Thera Trust
☆ Charitable Company
TSA Reg ✗ ♦ 🐾 ◊
The West House, Alpha Court,
Swingbridge Road, Grantham,
Lincolnshire, NG31 7XT
T 0300 303 1280
E office@thera.co.uk
W www.thera.co.uk
CE Ms Jennifer Garrigan
Sec Mr Simon Conway
Ch Mr Bill Carter
Total Staff 2364
Regions East Midlands + South West
Owned or managed 61
Rt 61 Sup 61
Tenant Type % Single 100%
Subsidary Association(s)
Forward Housing SW

Theydon Trusts Ltd
◯ Charitable HA
TSA Reg ✗
Epping Hall, St John's Road, Epping,
Essex, CM16 5JU
T 01992 577532
Sec Michael R Chapman
Ch Mrs R Benjamin
Total Staff 1
Region East of England
Tenant Type % Older 80%
Single 20%

Thorlands Housing Management Society Ltd
★ Co-operative Society
TSA Reg ✗
The Harry Caddick Community
Centre, 63 Lilford Road, Camberwell,
London, Greater London, SE5 9HN
T 020 7326 7070
E enquiries@thorlands.org.uk
W www.thorlands.org.uk
CE Mr Max Donaldson
Sec Ms Elaine Francis
Ch Mr John Frankland
Total Staff 0

Region London
Tenant Type % Family 60%
Older 20% Single 20%

Thorngate Almshouse Trust
❏ Charitable Trust
TSA Reg ✓ 🐀
Administration Office, Clare
House, Melrose Gardens, Gosport,
Hampshire, PO12 3BZ
T 023 9251 0028
E info@thorngatealms.org.uk
CE Mrs Anne Taylor
Ch Mr Donald J Lucas
Total Staff 75
Region South East
Owned or managed 153
Rt 112 OP 112 NSO 41
Tenant Type % Older 100%

Three Oaks Homes Ltd
○ Charitable HA
TSA Reg ✓ 🚐 🏠 🔑 🐀
Blaby District Council, Council
Offices, Desford Road, Narborough,
Leicester, Leicestershire, LE19 2EP
T 0300 123 1878
E enquiries@toh.org.uk
W www.toh.org.uk
CE Mr Bruce Kerr
Sec Mrs Joanne Tilley
Ch Mr Colin Norman
Total Staff 63
Region East Midlands
Owned or managed 2367
Rt 2265 GN 1005 Sup 4 OP 1256
SO 102 Tot lets 160 GN bs 938
Tenant Type % Family 31%
Older 59% Single 10%
Development Total 30
NBA 30
Parent Association
East Midlands Housing Group

Three Rivers HA Ltd
■ Non-Charitable HA
TSA Reg ✓ 🏠 🔑 🐀 ♨
Three Rivers House, Abbeywoods
Business Park, Pity Me, Durham,
County Durham, DH1 5TG
T 0191 384 1122
E customer.services@
threerivershousing.co.uk
W www.threerivershousing.co.uk
CE Mr Paul Tanney
Sec Mr Mike Axe
Ch Hilary Parker
Total Staff 153
Region North East
Owned or managed 3147
Rt 2859 GN 2439 Sup 356 OP 64
SO 288 Tot lets 549 GN bs 2332
Tenant Type % Family 38%
Older 31% Single 31%

Development Total 257
NBA 143 NBC 114
Parent Association
Four Housing Group

Three Valleys Housing Ltd
✪ Not-for-Profit Company
TSA Reg ✓ 🖥 🚐 🔑 🐀 ♨
Three Valleys House, Bramley
Road, Long Eaton, Nottingham,
Nottinghamshire, NG10 3SX
T 0800 389 8083
E info@threevalleyshousing.com
W www.threevalleyshousing.com
CE Ms Sue Coulson
Sec Mrs Joanne Tilley
Ch Mr Bob Hingston
Total Staff 170
Region East Midlands
Owned or managed 5331
Rt 5205 GN 3360 OP 1845 SO 126
Tot lets 423 GN bs 3360
Tenant Type % Family 42%
Older 48% Single 10%
Parent Association
East Midlands Housing Group

Thrive Homes Ltd
○ Charitable HA
TSA Reg ✓ 🚐 🔑
Building 3, Hatters Lane, Watford,
Hertfordshire, WD18 8YG
T 0800 917 6077
E enquiries@thrivehomes.org.uk
W www.thrivehomes.org.uk
CE Mrs Elspeth Mackenzie
Sec Mr Tony Walker
Ch Richard Laval
Total Staff 106
Region East of England
Owned or managed 4184
Rt 3736 GN 3142 OP 594 SO 447
NSO 1 Tot lets 220 GN bs 3142

Together Housing Group Ltd
✪ Not-for-Profit Company
TSA Reg ✓ ♨
Park View House, Woodvale Office
Park, Woodvale Road, Brighouse,
West Yorkshire, HD6 4AB
T 01484 824300
E enquiries@togetherhousing.co.uk
W www.togetherhousing.co.uk
CE Mr Tom Miskell
Sec Mr George Paterson
Ch Mr Laurence Loft
Total Staff 47
Region Yorkshire & Humberside
Subsidiary Association(s) Chevin
HA Ltd; Green Vale Homes Ltd;
Harewood Housing Society Ltd;
Housing Pendle; Pennine Housing
2000 Ltd; Twin Valley Homes Ltd

Together: Working for Wellbeing
☆ Charitable Company
TSA Reg ✗ 🐀
12 Old Street, London, Greater
London, EC1V 9BE
T 020 7780 7300
E contactus@together-uk.org
W www.together-uk.org
Sec Mrs Anne Oates
Ch Anthony Sheehan
Total Staff 0
Region London
Tenant Type % Family 1%
Older 10% Single 89%

Tor Homes
☆ Charitable Company
TSA Reg ✓ 🚐 🏠 🔑 🐀 ♨
Tor House, St Peters Quay,
Totnes, Devon, TQ9 5SH
T 01803 869600
E info@torhomes.com
W www.dchgroup/tor.com
CE Mr Howard Toplis
Sec Mr Andrew Tonkin
Ch Graham Facks-Martin, MBE
Total Staff 182
Region South West
Owned or managed 3768
Rt 3309 GN 2774 OP 535 SO 459
Tot lets 398 GN bs 2774
Tenant Type % Family 75%
Older 15% Single 10%
Development Total 165
NBA 94 NBC 71
Parent Association
Devon & Cornwall Housing Ltd

Touchstone - Leeds Ltd
☆ Charitable Company
TSA Reg ✗ 🐀
Touchstone House, 2-4 Middleton
Crescent, Beeston, Leeds,
West Yorkshire, LS11 6JU
T 0113 271 8277
E office@touchstone-leeds.co.uk
W www.touchstone-leeds.co.uk
CE Ms Alison Lowe
Ch Dr Virginia Minogue
Total Staff 0
Region Yorkshire & Humberside
Tenant Type % Family 8% Single 92%

Tower Hamlets Community Housing Ltd
☆ Charitable Company
TSA Reg ✓ 🏠 🔑
285 Commercial Road, Stepney,
London, Greater London, E1 2PS
T 020 7780 3070
E thch@thch.org.uk
W www.thch.org.uk
CE Mr Michael Tyrrell

Sec Mr Michael Tyrrell
Ch Mr Roger Booth
Total Staff 85
Region London
Owned or managed 3110
Rt 1918 **GN** 1918 **SO** 91 **NSO** 1101
Tot lets 98 **GN bs** 1918
Tenant Type % Family 50%
Older 36% **Single** 23%
Development Total 40
Rt 123 **GN** 123 **LCHO** 54 **NBA** 22
NBC 18

Town & Country Housing Group
○ Charitable HA
TSA Reg ✓ ▢ ▣ ▢ ⚷ ◊
Monson House, Monson Way,
Tunbridge Wells, Kent, TN1 1LQ
T 0845 873 1321
E info@tchg.org.uk
W www.tchg.org.uk
CE Mr Bob Heapy
Sec Mr Paul Cooper
Ch Mr Francis Salway
Total Staff 159
Regions South East + London
Owned or managed 8434
Rt 7831 **GN** 7283 **Sup** 68 **OP** 480
SO 588 **NSO** 15 **Tot lets** 851
GN bs 7179
Tenant Type % Family 39%
Older 1% **Single** 60%
Development Total 537
Rt 669 **GN** 601 **Sup** 68 **LCHO** 148
NBA 319 **NBC** 218
Subsidiary Association(s)
TCHG Foundation; TCHG Living Ltd

Trafford Housing Trust
☆ Charitable Company
TSA Reg ✓ ▢ ▣ ▢ ⚷ ♦
Sale Point, 126-150 Washway Road,
Sale, Cheshire, M33 6AG
T 0300 777 7777
E tht@traffordhousingtrust.co.uk
W www.traffordhousingtrust.co.uk
CE Mr Matthew Gardiner
Sec Ms Christine Little
Ch Mr Bernard Knight
Total Staff 330
Region North West
Owned or managed 9628
Rt 9223 **GN** 6551 **Sup** 20 **OP** 2652
SO 405 **Tot lets** 672 **GN bs** 6551
Tenant Type % Family 37%
Older 34% **Single** 29%
Development Total 20
NBA 16 **NBC** 4

Transform Housing and Support
☆ Charitable Company
TSA Reg ✓ ▣ ▰ ▰
Bradmere House, Brook Way,
Leatherhead, Surrey, KT22 7NA
T 01372 387100
E info@transformhousing.org.uk
W www.transformhousing.org.uk
CE Mr Paul Mitchell
Sec Mr Ratna Sukumaran
Ch Mrs Elizabeth Kennedy
Total Staff 109
Regions South East + London
Owned or managed 585
Rt 585 **GN** 1 **Sup** 584
Tenant Type % Family 8% **Older** 1%
Single 91%
Development Total 3
Rt 11 **Sup** 11 **NBA** 3

Trent & Dove Housing
○ Charitable HA
TSA Reg ✓ ▢ ▣ ▢ ⚷
Trinity Square, Horninglow Street,
Burton-On-Trent, Staffordshire,
DE14 1BL
T 01283 528528
E enquiries@trentanddove.org
W www.trentanddove.org
CE Mr Ron Dougan
Sec Mrs Barbara Richardson
Ch Mr John Jackson
Total Staff 160
Regions West Midlands + East
Midlands
Owned or managed 5726
Rt 5299 **GN** 4534 **Sup** 9 **OP** 756
SO 427 **Tot lets** 567 **GN bs** 4481
Tenant Type % Family 40%
Older 25% **Single** 35%
Development Total 253
Rt 400 **GN** 370 **OP** 30 **LCHO** 4
NBA 171 **NBC** 82

Trident Charitable HA Ltd
○ Charitable HA
TSA Reg ✓ ◊
239 Holliday Street, Birmingham,
West Midlands, B1 1SJ
T 0121 633 4633
W www.trident-ha.org.uk
CE Mr John Morris
Sec Noel Grace
Ch Mr Mike Pritty
Total Staff 0
Region West Midlands
Owned or managed 12
Rt 12 **Sup** 12
Tenant Type % Single 100%
Parent Association
Trident HA Ltd

Trident HA Ltd
○ Charitable HA
TSA Reg ✓ ▣ ⚷ ▰ ◊
239 Holliday Street, Birmingham,
West Midlands, B1 1SJ
T 0121 633 4633
E reception@trident-ha.org.uk
W www.trident-ha.org.uk
CE Mr John Morris
Sec Noel Grace
Ch Mr Mike Pritty
Total Staff 88
Regions West Midlands +
East Midlands
Owned or managed 3106
Rt 2585 **GN** 1590 **Sup** 649 **OP** 346
SO 399 **NSO** 122 **Tot lets** 748
GN bs 1590
Tenant Type % Family 38%
Older 10% **Single** 52%
Development Total 61
NBA 61
Subsidiary Association(s) Trident
Charitable HA Ltd

Tristar Homes Ltd
TSA Reg ✓ ▰ ▢ ⚷ ♦ ◊
Tristar House, Lockheed Court,
Preston Farm Industrial Estate,
Stockton-On-Tees, Cleveland,
TS18 3SH
T 0300 111 1000
E customerservices@tristarhomes.
co.uk
W www.tristarhomes.co.uk
Total Staff 375
Region North East
Owned or managed 10543
Rt 10251 **GN** 10251 **SO** 292
Tot lets 1249 **GN bs** 10185
Parent Association Vela Group

Tung Sing HA Ltd
○ Charitable HA
TSA Reg ✓ ⚷ ▰ ◊ ▣
Your Housing Group, Thomson
House, Warrington, WA3 6GA
T 01925 236400
W www.yourhousinggroup.co.uk
CE Mr Abdul Malik-Ahad
Sec Mrs Bronwen Rapley
Ch Mr Paul Carhart
Total Staff 0
Region North West
Owned or managed 637
Rt 624 **GN** 475 **OP** 149 **SO** 13
Tot lets 34 **GN bs** 0
Tenant Type % Family 46%
Older 26% **Single** 28%
Parent Association
Your Housing Group

Tuntum HA Ltd

○ Charitable HA

TSA Reg ✓ ▣ 🗝 👓 🏠

90 Beech Avenue, New Basford, Nottingham, Nottinghamshire, NG7 7LW

T 0115 916 6066

E admin@tuntum.co.uk

W www.tuntum.co.uk

CE Mr Richard Renwick, MBE

Sec Mr Richard Renwick, MBE

Ch Ms Audra Wynter

Total Staff 65

Region East Midlands

Owned or managed 1362

Rt 1309 **GN** 1160 **Sup** 92 **OP** 57

SO 53 **Tot lets** 163 **GN bs** 1012

Tenant Type % Family 66%

Older 11% **Single** 23%

Development Total 198

Rt 33 **GN** 33 **LCHO** 19 **NBA** 143

NBC 55

Turning Point

☆ Charitable Company

TSA Reg ✓ ♠ 👓

Standon House, 21 Mansell Street, London, Greater London, E1 8AA

T 020 7481 7600

E info@turning-point.co.uk

W www.turning-point.co.uk

CE Lord Victor Adebowale, CBE

Sec Lord Victor Adebowale, CBE

Ch Sarah Wood

Total Staff 2629

Regions London + West Midlands, East of England, Yorkshire & Humberside, North East, North West

Owned or managed 156

Rt 156 **Sup** 156

Tenant Type % Single 100%

Twenty-Fifth Avenue Ltd

❑ Charitable Trust

TSA Reg ✗

Room 222 Island Business Centre, 18-36 Wellington Street, London, Greater London, SE18 6PF

T 020 3556 3030

E info@twentyfifthavenue.co.uk

W www.twentyfifthavenue.co.uk

Sec Festus Osawaru

Ch Mr Charles Osaghae

Total Staff 0

Region London

Twin Valley Homes Ltd

✪ Not-for-Profit Company

TSA Reg ✓ 🖵 🏢 ▣ 🗝 ♦ 👓 ◊

Prospect House, Wharf Street, Blackburn, Lancashire, BB1 1JD

T 01254 269000

E info@twinvalleyhomes.com

W www.twinvalleyhomes.com

CE Mr Ian Clark

Sec Mr Kevin Ruth

Ch Mr Alan Cotton

Total Staff 359

Region North West

Owned or managed 8217

Rt 7805 **GN** 7075 **Sup** 40 **OP** 690

SO 376 **NSO** 36 **Tot lets** 873

GN bs 7075

Tenant Type % Family 50%

Older 30% **Single** 20%

Development Total 17

Rt 136 **GN** 86 **OP** 50 **LCHO** 78

NBC 17

Parent Association

Together Housing Group Ltd

Two Castles HA Ltd

○ Charitable HA

TSA Reg ✓ ▣ 🗝 👓

3 Paternoster Row, Carlisle, Cumbria, CA3 8TT

T 01228 541161

E mailbox@twocastles.org.uk

W www.twocastles.org.uk

CE Mrs Stephanie Murphy

Sec Miss Gill Boyd

Ch Mr Michael Johnson

Total Staff 93

Regions North West + Yorkshire & Humberside, North East

Owned or managed 3417

Rt 2678 **GN** 2025 **Sup** 51 **OP** 602

SO 739 **Tot lets** 368 **GN bs** 1977

Tenant Type % Family 38%

Older 34% **Single** 28%

Development Total 125

Rt 250 **GN** 212 **OP** 38 **NBA** 65 **NBC** 60

Two Piers Housing Co-op Ltd

★ Co-operative Society

TSA Reg ✓

14 Oriental Place, Brighton, East Sussex, BN1 2LJ

T 01273 328108

E twopiers@co-op.org

W www.twopiers.coop

Sec Ms Helen Bartlett

Ch Mr Liam Reilly

Total Staff 0

Region South East

Owned or managed 68

Rt 68 **GN** 68

Tenant Type % Family 12%

Single 88%

Two Rivers Housing

☆ Charitable Company

TSA Reg ✓ 🏢 ▣ 🗝 ◊

7/3 Vantage Point Business Village, Mitcheldean, Gloucestershire, GL17 0DD

T 0800 316 0897

E customerservices@2rh.org.uk

W www.tworivershousing.org.uk

CE Mr Garry King

Sec Mr Garry King

Ch Dr David Garnett

Total Staff 134

Regions South West + West Midlands

Owned or managed 3808

Rt 3710 **GN** 2555 **OP** 1155 **SO** 98

Tot lets 343 **GN bs** 2540

Tenant Type % Family 31%

Older 42% **Single** 28%

Development Total 73

Rt 97 **GN** 97 **LCHO** 12 **NBA** 39

NBC 34

Subsidiary Association(s)

Two Rivers Initiatives Ltd

Two Rivers Initiatives Ltd

○ Charitable HA

TSA Reg ✗ ◊

7/3 Vantage Point Business Village, Mitcheldean, Gloucestershire, GL17 0DD

T 0800 316 0897

E customerservices@2rh.org.uk

W www.tworivershousing.org.uk

CE Mr Garry King

Sec Mr Garry King

Ch Ms Jean Birkett

Total Staff 0

Region South West

Parent Association

Two Rivers Housing

Two Saints Ltd

○ Charitable HA

TSA Reg ✓ 👓

35 Waterside Gardens, Fareham, Hampshire, PO16 8SD

T 01329 234600

E twosaints@twosaints.org.uk

W www.twosaints.org.uk

CE Ms Louise Barnden

Sec Ms Louise Barnden

Ch Mr Mike McKenzie

Total Staff 230

Region South East

Owned or managed 465

Rt 465 **Sup** 465

Tenant Type % Single 100%

Tyne HA Ltd

○ Charitable HA

TSA Reg ✓

St Silas Church Building, Clifford Street, Byker, Newcastle-Upon-Tyne, Tyne And Wear, NE6 1PG

T 0191 265 8621

E info@tynehousing.org.uk

W www.tynehousing.org.uk

CE Mr Maurice Condie
Sec Mr Maurice Condie
Ch Mr Geoff Cook
Total Staff 85
Region North East
Owned or managed 277
Rt 277 Sup 277
Tenant Type % Family 2% Single 98%

Uu

Uckfield & District HA Ltd
○ Charitable HA
TSA Reg ✓ 🕶
St Saviours, Framfield Road, Uckfield,
East Sussex, TN22 5AS
T 01825 762378
CE Mr Graham Neilly
Sec Mr Graham Neilly
Ch Mr Graham Neilly
Total Staff 1
Region South East
Owned or managed 16
Rt 16 OP 16
Tenant Type % Older 100%

Umbrella Housing Group Ltd
○ Charitable HA
TSA Reg ✓ 🕶
11a Unthank Road, Norwich,
Norfolk, NR2 2PA
T 01603 618527
Sec Mr John Ward
Ch Prue Smith
Total Staff 0
Region East of England
Owned or managed 36
Rt 36 GN 1 Sup 35
Tenant Type % Single 100%

United HA Ltd
○ Charitable HA
TSA Reg ✓ 🔑 🕶 🏠
3rd Floor, New Bond House, Bond
Street, Bristol, Avon, BS2 9AG
T 0117 942 4600
E recep@unitedha.org.uk
W www.unitedha.org.uk
CE Derek Cash
Ch Ms Jenny Vernon
Total Staff 26
Region South West
Owned or managed 1022
Rt 992 GN 953 Sup 13 OP 26 SO 30
Tot lets 47 GN bs 929
Tenant Type % Family 78%
Older 3% Single 19%

Unity HA Ltd
○ Charitable HA
TSA Reg ✓ 🏠 🔑 🕶 🏠
113-117 Chapeltown Road, Leeds,
West Yorkshire, LS7 3HY
T 0113 200 7700
E uha@unityha.co.uk
W www.unityha.co.uk
CE Mr Ali Akbor
Sec Mr Ali Akbor
Ch Ms Karen Morley
Total Staff 25
Region Yorkshire & Humberside
Owned or managed 1066
Rt 1019 GN 931 Sup 11 OP 77
SO 47 Tot lets 65 GN bs 931
Tenant Type % Family 81%
Older 7% Single 12%
Development Total 1
NBA 1

Vv

Vale of Aylesbury Housing Trust
☆ Charitable Company
TSA Reg ✓ 🖥 🚚 🏠 🔑 🕶
Fairfax House, 69 Buckingham Street,
Aylesbury, Buckinghamshire,
HP20 2NJ
T 01296 732600
E info@vaht.co.uk
W www.vaht.co.uk
CE Mr Matthew Applegate
Sec Ms Linda Foster
Ch Mr Richard Stanway-Williams
Total Staff 211
Region South East
Owned or managed 8012
Rt 7301 GN 5219 Sup 11 OP 2071
SO 702 NSO 9 Tot lets 584
GN bs 5200
Tenant Type % Family 40%
Older 47% Single 13%
Development Total 140
Rt 184 GN 184 LCHO 15 NBA 71
NBC 69

Vectis HA Ltd
○ Charitable HA
TSA Reg ✓ 🏠 🔑
30 Chapel Street, Newport,
Isle Of Wight, PO30 1PZ
T 01983 525985
E enquiries@vectishousing.co.uk
W www.vectishousing.co.uk
CE Mr Paul Hann
Sec Mr Paul Hann
Ch Mr George Hibberd
Total Staff 9
Region South East

Owned or managed 367
Rt 361 GN 361 SO 6 Tot lets 27
GN bs 301
Tenant Type % Family 50%
Older 30% Single 20%
Development Total 2
Rt 12 GN 12 NBA 2

Vela Group
✪ Not-for-Profit Company
TSA Reg ✓ ♠ ♨
Greenbank, Waldon Street,
Hartlepool, Cleveland, TS24 7QS
T 0300 111 1000
E name.lastname@velagroup.co.uk
W www.velagroup.co.uk
CE Mrs Cath Purdy
Sec Ms Linda Minns
Ch Mr Mike Clark
Total Staff 387
Region North East
Subsidiary Association(s)
Housing Hartlepool Ltd;
Tristar Homes Ltd

Venture HA Ltd
○ Charitable HA
TSA Reg ✓ 🏠 🕶
Venture House, 212h Boaler Street,
Liverpool, Merseyside, L6 6AE
T 0151 261 2100
E info@ventureha.co.uk
W www.vha.org.uk
CE Mr John Tolen
Sec Mr John Tolen
Ch Dr John Swaffield
Total Staff 37
Region North West
Owned or managed 1313
Rt 1308 GN 1157 Sup 73 OP 78
NSO 5
Tenant Type % Family 44%
Older 20% Single 36%
Development Total 18
NBA 15 NBC 3

Victoria Park Homes (1965) Ltd
○ Charitable HA
TSA Reg ✓ 🔑
3 Hope Close, Wallace Road,
London, Greater London, N1 2YS
E anne.housing@fishlife.org.uk
CE Ms Anne Cartwright
Sec Ms Anne Cartwright
Ch Jane Thorington Hassell
Total Staff 0
Region London
Owned or managed 26
Rt 11 GN 11 SO 13 NSO 2
Tot lets 0 GN bs 0
Tenant Type % Family 33%
Single 67%

Victory Housing Trust
☆ Charitable Company
TSA Reg ✓ 🏠 🏠 🔑 🐦
Tom Moore House, Cromer Road,
North Walsham, Norfolk,
NR28 0NB
T 0845 300 6648
E info@victoryhousing.co.uk
W www.victoryhousing.co.uk
CE John Archibald
Sec Mr Stephen Read
Ch Mr John Wollocombe
Total Staff 82
Region East of England
Owned or managed 4898
Rt 4811 GN 4318 OP 493 SO 38
NSO 49 Tot lets 355 GN bs 4318
Tenant Type % Family 40%
Older 50% Single 10%
Development Total 135
NBA 72 NBC 63

Villages Community HA Ltd
◯ Charitable HA
TSA Reg ✓ 🐦 ♠
16 The Croft, Stockbridge Village,
Knowsley, Merseyside, L28 1NR
T 0151 480 1313
E info@villages.org.uk
W www.villages.org.uk
CE Mr Vernon Jackson
Sec Mr Serge Botcherby
Ch Mr David Shortall
Total Staff 105
Region North West
Owned or managed 165
Rt 165 GN 89 Sup 8 OP 68
Tenant Type % Family 21%
Older 67% Single 79%
Parent Association
The Villages HA Ltd

Viridian Housing
◯ Charitable HA
TSA Reg ✓ 🏠 🏠 🔑 ♠ 🐦
Colwell House, 376 Clapham Road,
London, SW9 9AR
T 0330 123 0220
E communications@viridianhousing.
org.uk
W www.viridianhousing.org.uk
CE Mr Matthew Fox
Sec Mr Kerry Tromanhauser
Ch Hattie Llewelyn-Davies
Total Staff 1425
Regions London + South East, East
Midlands, West Midlands
Owned or managed 15960
Rt 9877 GN 7531 Sup 544 OP 1802
SO 889 NSO 5194 Tot lets 869
GN bs 7489
Tenant Type % Family 43%
Older 45% Single 12%
Development Total 154

Rt 537 GN 234 OP 303 LCHO 298
NBA 50 NBC 104

Wakefield and District Housing
☆ Charitable Company
TSA Reg ✓
🏠 🏠 🏠 🔑 ♠ 🐦
Wakefield & District Housing,
Merefield House, Whistler Drive,
Castleford, WF10 5HX
T 01977 724444
E onecall@wdh.co.uk
W www.wdh.co.uk
CE Mr Kevin Dodd
Sec Mr Lee Sugden
Ch Mr Ken Taylor
Total Staff 1428
Region Yorkshire & Humberside
Owned or managed 31372
Rt 31273 GN 29193 OP 2080 SO 99
Tot lets 3047 GN bs 29068
Tenant Type % Family 36%
Older 48% Single 16%
Development Total 425
Rt 231 GN 231 NBA 298 NBC 127

Walsall Housing Group Ltd
☆ Charitable Company
TSA Reg ✓ 🏠 🏠 🏠 🏠 🔑 ♦
100 Hatherton Street, Walsall,
West Midlands, WS1 1AB
T 0300 555 6666
E frontofhouse.enquiries@whgrp.
co.uk
W www.whg.uk.com
CE Mr Gary Fulford
Sec Miss Jane Preece
Ch Mr Paul Murray
Total Staff 628
Region West Midlands
Owned or managed 19590
Rt 19031 GN 19031 SO 555 NSO 4
Tot lets 1509 GN bs 18847
Tenant Type % Family 27%
Older 57% Single 16%
Development Total 13
Rt 204 GN 204 NBA 9 NBC 4

Walterton & Elgin Community Homes Ltd
◯ Charitable HA
TSA Reg ✓
416 Harrow Road, London,
Greater London, W9 2HX
T 020 7266 3347
E admin@wech.org.uk
W www.wech.co.uk

CE Mr Andrew Watson
Sec Ms Julie Bundy
Ch Mr Jon Cotterell
Total Staff 15
Region London
Owned or managed 445
Rt 445 GN 445
Tenant Type % Family 40%
Older 40% Single 20%

Waltham Forest HA Ltd
◯ Charitable HA
TSA Reg ✓ 🐦
31 Church Hill, Walthamstow,
London, E17 3RU
T 020 8524 6987
E info@wfha.org.uk
CE Mrs Linda Milton
Sec Mr Martin Isaacs
Ch Mr Ben Furr
Total Staff 18
Region London
Owned or managed 345
Rt 345 GN 135 Sup 23 OP 187
Tenant Type % Family 37%
Older 58% Single 5%

Wandle HA Ltd
◯ Charitable HA
TSA Reg ✓ 🏠 🏠 🔑 🐦
Second Floor, Minerva House,
Montague Close, London,
Greater London, SE1 9BB
T 020 8682 1177
E information@wandle.com
W www.wandle.com
CE Ms Sara Thakkar
Sec Helen Elderfield
Ch Philip Sturrock
Total Staff 117
Region London
Owned or managed 6610
Rt 5658 GN 5292 Sup 296 OP 70
SO 921 NSO 31 Tot lets 468
GN bs 5187
Tenant Type % Family 70%
Older 15% Single 15%
Development Total 230
Rt 209 GN 209 LCHO 54 NBA 132
NBC 98

Wansbeck Homes Ltd
■ Non-Charitable HA
TSA Reg ✓ 🏠 🏠 ♠
Beaminster Way East, Kingston Park,
Newcastle Upon Tyne,
Tyne And Wear, NE3 2ER
T 0844 800 3800
E enquiries@wansbeckhomes.co.uk
W www.bernicia.com
Sec Mr Bill Heads
Ch David Futers
Total Staff 202
Region North East

Owned or managed 5252
Rt 5252 GN 3522 Sup 8 OP 1722
Tenant Type % Family 49%
Older 33% Single 18%
Parent Association
Bernicia Group Ltd

Warbleton HA Ltd
○ Charitable HA
TSA Reg ✗
Osborne House, Rushlake Green,
Heathfield, East Sussex, TN21 9QL
T 01435 830309
Sec Mr Rob Robinson
Ch Mr David Clifford
Total Staff 0
Region South East
Tenant Type % Older 100%

Wargrave on Thames HA Ltd
○ Charitable HA
TSA Reg ✓
Elizabeth Court, Victoria Road,
Wargrave, Reading, Berkshire,
RG10 8BP
T 0118 940 6116
E elizabeth.court1@btconnect.com
CE Mrs P Roynon
Sec Mr Nicholas Sharp
Ch Mrs P Roynon
Total Staff 1
Region South East
Owned or managed 46
Rt 46 OP 46
Tenant Type % Older 1%

Warrington HA Ltd
■ Non-Charitable HA
TSA Reg ✓ 🏠 🔑 🐎
The Gateway, 89 Sankey Street,
Warrington, Cheshire, WA1 1SR
T 01925 246810
E admin@wha.org.uk
W www.wha.org.uk
CE Mr Alan Kemp
Sec Ms Kirsty Capper
Ch Mr Paul Hammond
Total Staff 44
Region North West
Owned or managed 1262
Rt 1187 GN 951 Sup 79 OP 157
SO 75 Tot lets 101 GN bs 951
Tenant Type % Family 50%
Older 20% Single 30%
Development Total 22
NBA 16 NBC 6

Warwickshire Rural HA Ltd
○ Charitable HA
TSA Reg ✓ 🔑
Whitwick Business Centre,
Stenson Road, Coalville,
Leicestershire, LE67 4JP

T 01530 278080
E midlandsrural@midlandsrh.org.uk
W www.warwickshirerha.org.uk
Sec Mr Craig Felts
Ch Mr Derrick Dyas
Total Staff 0
Region West Midlands
Owned or managed 532
Rt 440 GN 440 SO 92 Tot lets 50
GN bs 411
Tenant Type % Family 70%
Older 10% Single 20%

Waterloo HA Ltd
○ Charitable HA
TSA Reg ✓ 🏠 🔑 🐎 ♨
Waterloo House, 76 Boldmere Road,
Sutton Coldfield, West Midlands,
B73 5TJ
T 0121 355 4501
E info@waterloo.org.uk
W www.waterlooha.org.uk
CE Mr David Pickering
Sec Mr Brian Desmond
Ch Mr Jeff Sharnock
Total Staff 116
Region West Midlands
Owned or managed 6029
Rt 4232 GN 3874 OP 358 SO 1323
NSO 474 Tot lets 363 GN bs 3836
Tenant Type % Family 34%
Older 43% Single 23%
Development Total 76
NBA 76
Parent Association
Waterloo Housing Group Ltd

Waterloo Housing Group Ltd
○ Charitable HA
TSA Reg ✓ ♨
80 The Parade, Oadby, Leicester,
LE2 5BF
T 0116 220 5555
E info@waterloo.org.uk
W www.waterloo.org.uk
CE Mr David Pickering
Sec Mr Brian Desmond
Ch Mr Dennis Sleath
Total Staff 156
Region East Midlands
Subsidiary Association(s) de
Montfort Housing Society Ltd; New
Linx Housing Trust; Waterloo HA
Ltd

Watermoor House Residential Home
○ Charitable HA
TSA Reg ✗
Watermoor House, Watermoor
Road, Cirencester, Gloucestershire,
GL7 1JR
T 01285 654864
W www.watermoorhouse.org

CE Mrs Ruth Halstead
Sec Mrs Valerie Pallister
Ch Dr Susan Owen
Total Staff 42
Region South West
Owned or managed 38
Rt 38 GN 38
Tenant Type % Older 100%

Watford Community Housing Trust
○ Charitable HA
TSA Reg ✓ 🏠 🚌 🐎 🔑 🐎
Gateway House, 59 Clarendon Road,
Watford, Hertfordshire, WD17 1LA
T 01923 209000
E enquiries@wcht.org.uk
W www.wcht.org.uk
CE Ms Tina Barnard
Sec Ms Tina Barnard
Ch Mrs Diane Lee
Total Staff 171
Region East of England
Owned or managed 5263
Rt 4825 GN 4286 OP 539 SO 424
NSO 14 Tot lets 279 GN bs 4193
Tenant Type % Family 61%
Older 26% Single 13%
Development Total 24
NBA 12 NBC 12

WATMOS Community Homes
○ Charitable HA
TSA Reg ✓ 🏠 🐎
29 Stafford Street, Walsall, West
Midlands, WS2 8DG
T 01922 471910
E info@watmos.org.uk
W www.watmos.org.uk
CE Ms Ursula Barrington
Sec Mr Kul Bains
Total Staff 27
Regions West Midlands + London
Owned or managed 3050
Rt 2697 GN 2697 NSO 353
Tenant Type % Family 38%
Older 28% Single 34%
Development Total 957
NBA 957

Waveney & Yare HA Ltd
■ Non-Charitable HA
TSA Reg ✗ 🐎
Gaol Lane, Off Newgate, Beccles,
Suffolk, NR34 9SJ
T 01502 715858
E jonblankley@btconnect.com
CE Mr Jonathan Blankley
Sec Mr Jonathan Blankley
Ch Mr Ronald Walding
Total Staff 1
Region East of England
Owned or managed 224
Rt 224 GN 206 OP 18

Tenant Type % Family 57%
Older 29% Single 14%
Development Total 2
NBA 2

Waverley Eighth Co-operative HA
★ Co-operative Society
TSA Reg ✓
33 Shaftesbury Road, London,
Greater London, N19 4QW
T 020 7272 2981
Sec Birgit Voss
Ch Dan Taubman
Total Staff 0
Region London
Owned or managed 26
Rt 26 GN 26
Tenant Type % Family 20%
Older 60% Single 20%

Weaver Horizons Ltd
▲ Other
TSA Reg ✗ ◊
Gadbrook Point, Rudheath Way
, Gadbrook Park, Northwich,
Cheshire, CW9 7LL
T 01606 813300
W www.weaverhorizons.co.uk
CE Mr Steve Jennings
Sec Miss Joanne Watkins
Ch Mr Steve Nettleton
Total Staff 0
Region North West
Parent Association
Weaver Vale Housing Trust

Weaver Vale Housing Trust
☆ Charitable Company
TSA Reg ✓ ▢ 🖼 ▢ ✎ ♦ 🐾 ◊
Gadbrook Point, Rudheath Way,
Gadbrook Park, Northwich,
Cheshire, CW9 7LL
T 01606 813300
E enquiries@wvht.co.uk
W www.wvht.co.uk
CE Mr Steve Jennings
Sec Mr Andrew White
Ch Mr James Boyd
Total Staff 367
Region North West
Owned or managed 6384
Rt 6225 GN 4217 Sup 16 OP 1992
SO 159 Tot lets 465 GN bs 4217
Tenant Type % Family 51%
Older 29% Single 20%
Development Total 102
Rt 22 GN 22 NBA 52 NBC 50
Subsidiary Association(s)
Weaver Horizons Ltd

Wednesfield HA Ltd
■ Non-Charitable HA
TSA Reg ✗ ▢ ✎
Idsall Court, Broadway, Shifnal,
Shropshire, TF11 8AZ
T 01952 463603
E wha-ltd@btconnect.com
CE Mr Peter Hurlstone
Sec Ella Bamford
Ch Leonard Woodhams
Total Staff 2
Region West Midlands
Owned or managed 96
Rt 94 GN 33 OP 61 SO 2
Tot lets 15 GN bs 94
Tenant Type % Family 12%
Older 78% Single 10%
Development Total 1
NBA 1

Weller Streets Housing Co-operative Ltd
★ Co-operative Society
TSA Reg ✓
Riverside Mersey South, 69 Argyle
Street, Birkenhead, Merseyside,
CH41 6AB
T 0845 111 0000
Sec Linda Huyton
Ch Ms Patricia Nelson
Total Staff 0
Region North West
Owned or managed 67
Rt 67 GN 67
Tenant Type % Family 60%
Older 40%

Wellingborough Homes Ltd
☆ Charitable Company
TSA Reg ✓ 🖼 ▢ ✎ 🐾
9f Silver Street, Wellingborough,
Northamptonshire, NN8 1BQ
T 01933 234450
E customer.services@whomes.org
W www.wellingboroughhomes.org
CE Mr Dave Willis
Sec Mr Michael Heekin
Ch Mr Tim Davy
Total Staff 107
Region East Midlands
Owned or managed 4687
Rt 4508 GN 4247 OP 261 SO 179
Tot lets 331 GN bs 4206
Tenant Type % Family 43%
Older 45% Single 12%
Development Total 53
NBA 35 NBC 18

Welwyn Garden City HA Ltd
○ Charitable HA
TSA Reg ✓ ▢ ✎ 🐾
10 Parkway, Welwyn Garden City,
Hertfordshire, AL8 6HG
T 01707 390044
E admin@wgcha.co.uk
W www.wgcha.co.uk
CE Mr Reg Bek
Sec Mr Reg Bek
Ch Mrs Gillian Vaughan
Total Staff 69
Region East of England
Owned or managed 365
Rt 358 GN 85 Sup 20 OP 253 SO 7
Tot lets 57 GN bs 0
Tenant Type % Family 2%
Older 95% Single 3%
Development Total 3
Rt 4 GN 4 LCHO 11 NBC 3

West Cornwall HA Ltd
○ Charitable HA
TSA Reg ✗ 🐾
Chynance, Alexandra Road,
Penzance, Cornwall, TR18 4LY
T 01736 365195
E tnsgribble21@btinternet.com
CE Ms Susan Gribble
Sec Ms Sue Murdoch
Ch Mr Russell Whitlock
Total Staff 0
Region South West
Tenant Type % Older 100%

West Devon Homes Ltd
☆ Charitable Company
TSA Reg ✓ 🖼 ▢ ✎ 🐾
The Quay, Plymouth Road,
Tavistock, Devon, PL19 8AB
T 01822 813770
E enquiries@wdh.org.uk
W www.wdh.org.uk
CE Mr Howard Toplis
Sec Mr Howard Toplis
Ch Mr Paul Love
Total Staff 49
Region South West
Owned or managed 1616
Rt 1574 GN 1369 Sup 3 OP 202 SO
38 NSO 4 Tot lets 115 GN bs 1369
Development Total 8
NBA 4 NBC 4

West Eleven Housing Co-op
★ Co-operative Society
TSA Reg ✗
16 Lancaster Road, London, Greater
London, W11 1QP
T 020 7792 0966
Sec Mr Geoff Branch
Total Staff 0
Region London
Tenant Type % Family 20%
Older 2% Single 80%

West Hampstead Housing Co-operative Ltd
★ Co-operative Society
TSA Reg ✓ 🦾
82 Kingsgate Road, London,
Greater London, NW6 4LA
T 020 7328 8956
W www.whhc.net
Sec Richard Gibson
Ch Robin Prenderville
Total Staff 1
Region London
Owned or managed 91
Rt 91 GN 91
Tenant Type % Family 51%
Single 49%

West Kent HA
◯ Charitable HA
TSA Reg ✓
🗆 🚌 🏦 D 🔑 🦾
101 London Road, Sevenoaks,
Kent, TN13 1AX
T 01732 749400
E enquiries@wkha.org.uk
W www.westkent.org
CE Mr Frank Czarnowski
Sec Mr Craig Reynolds
Ch Mr Alan Knight
Total Staff 234
Region South East
Owned or managed 6475
Rt 5983 GN 5037 Sup 52 OP 894
SO 492 Tot lets 502 GN bs 5003
Tenant Type % Family 50%
Older 45% Single 5%
Development Total 538
Rt 189 GN 133 OP 56 LCHO 60
NBA 325 NBC 213

West London YMCA
☆ Charitable Company
TSA Reg ✓ 🦾
45 St. Mary's Road, London,
Greater London, W5 5RG
T 0300 111 1500
E charan.nagah@londonymca.org
W www.westlondonymca.org
CE Ms Clare Scott Booth
Sec Ms Clare Scott Booth
Ch Mr Richard Sarson
Total Staff 197

Region London
Owned or managed 422
Rt 422 Sup 422
Tenant Type % Family 8% Single 92%

West Mercia Homes Ltd
◯ Charitable HA
TSA Reg ✓ 🗆 🏦 🔑 🦾 ◊
Barnsley Hall, Barnsley Hall Road,
Bromsgrove, Worcestershire,
B61 0TX
T 01527 556400
E homes@wmhousing.co.uk
W www.wmhousing.co.uk
CE Mrs Pat Brandum
Sec Miss Zoe Moncrieff
Ch Miss P Kirby
Total Staff 0
Regions West Midlands +
South West
Owned or managed 6773
Rt 5296 GN 4527 Sup 262 OP 507
SO 1460 NSO 17 Tot lets 678
GN bs 4278
Tenant Type % Family 80%
Older 7% Single 13%
Development Total 293
NBA 164 NBC 129
Parent Association
WM Housing Group

West of England Friends HS Ltd
◯ Charitable HA
TSA Reg ✓ 🦾
Avenue House, 5 Cotham Park
North, Bristol, Avon, BS6 6BH
T 0117 989 2020
W www.friendshousingbristol.org.uk
CE Mr Michael Tuckwell
Sec Mrs Karen Parkin
Ch Mr Michael Tuckwell
Total Staff 32
Region South West
Owned or managed 48
Rt 48 GN 8 OP 40
Tenant Type % Older 100%

Westcountry HA Ltd
◯ Charitable HA
TSA Reg ✓ 🏦 🔑 🕴 🦾 ◊
Hatfield House, Hatfield Road,
Torquay, Devon, TQ1 3HF
T 01803 200300
E info@westcountryha.org.uk
W www.westcountryha.org.uk
CE Ms Karen Ayling
Sec Miss Lucy Rickson
Ch Ian McDougall
Total Staff 300
Region South West
Owned or managed 4990
Rt 3862 GN 2938 Sup 440 OP 484
SO 1104 NSO 24 Tot lets 544

GN bs 2935
Tenant Type % Family 71%
Older 14% Single 15%
Development Total 305
NBA 166 NBC 139
Parent Association
Westward Housing Group Ltd

Westfield HA Ltd
◯ Charitable HA
TSA Reg ✓ 🏦
Minto Centre, Nilsson Drive,
Westfield, Workington,
Cumbria, CA14 5BD
T 01900 602906
E enquiries@westfieldha.org.uk
W www.westfieldha.org.uk
CE Mr Graham Howarth
Sec Mr Graham Howarth
Ch Mrs Joan Minto
Total Staff 11
Region North West
Owned or managed 506
Rt 506 GN 506
Tenant Type % Family 51%
Older 37% Single 12%
Development Total 4
NBA 4

Westlea HA
◯ Charitable HA
TSA Reg ✓
🗆 🚌 🏦 D 🔑 🕴 🦾 ◊
Methuen Park, Bath Road,
Chippenham, Wiltshire, SN14 0GU
T 01249 465465
E enquiries@westlea.org.uk
W www.westlea.co.uk
CE Mrs Ann Cornelius
Sec Mrs Catherine Dixon
Ch Derek Cash
Total Staff 265
Region South West
Owned or managed 7342
Rt 6828 GN 6225 Sup 263 OP 340
SO 470 NSO 44 Tot lets 923
GN bs 6157
Tenant Type % Family 54%
Older 28% Single 18%
Development Total 543
Rt 201 GN 156 OP 45 LCHO 39
NBA 314 NBC 229
Parent Association
GreenSquare Group Ltd

Westlon HA
○ Charitable HA
TSA Reg ✓ 🕶 🏠
Birnbeck Court, 850 Finchley Road,
Temple Fortune, London,
Greater London, NW11 6BB
T 020 8201 8484
E johnsilverman@btconnect.com
CE Mr John Silverman
Sec Mr John Silverman
Ch Cllr Mrs Joan Ansell
Total Staff 19
Region London
Owned or managed 91
Rt 91 **OP** 91
Tenant Type % Older 100%

Westward Housing Group Ltd
○ Charitable HA
TSA Reg ✓ ◊
Templar House, Collett Way,
Newton Abbot, Devon, TQ12 4PH
T 01803 217500
E joanne.oman@westwardhousing.org.uk
W www.westcountryha.org.uk
CE Mrs Barbara Shaw
Sec Miss Lucy Rickson
Ch Ms Liz Smith
Total Staff 6
Region South West
Subsidiary Association(s) Tarka Housing Ltd; Westcountry HA Ltd

Westway HA Ltd
○ Charitable HA
TSA Reg ✓ 🕶 🏠
1st Floor, Ladbroke Hall, 79 Barlby
Road, London, Greater London,
W10 6AZ
T 020 8964 2323
E enquiries@westwayha.org.uk
W www.westwayha.org.uk
CE Mr Ricky Scipio
Sec Mr Dennis Flanders
Ch Mr David Mark
Total Staff 17
Region London
Owned or managed 574
Rt 574 **GN** 532 **Sup** 42
Tenant Type % Family 57% **Older** 1%
Single 42%

Wherry HA Ltd
■ Non-Charitable HA
TSA Reg ✓ 🔲 🚐 🅿 🔑 ◊
Anglia House, 6 Central Avenue,
St Andrews Business Park,
Thorpe St Andrew, Norwich,
Norfolk, NR7 0HR
T 01603 703500
E info@circle.org.uk
W www.circleanglia.org
CE Ms Sue Stavers
Sec Ms Deborah Upton
Ch Brian Stewart OBE
Total Staff 95
Regions East of England + London, East Midlands
Owned or managed 8007
Rt 6796 **GN** 6014 **Sup** 204 **OP** 578
SO 968 **NSO** 243 **Tot lets** 829
GN bs 5091
Tenant Type % Family 60%
Older 35% **Single** 5%
Development Total 169
NBA 92 **NBC** 77
Parent Association Circle

Whitefriars Housing Group Ltd
○ Charitable HA
TSA Reg ✓
■ 🔲 🚐 🅿 🔑 ♦ 🕶 ◊
9 Little Park Street, Coventry,
West Midlands, CV1 2UR
T 024 7676 7000
E info@whitefriarshousing.co.uk
W www.whitefriarshousing.co.uk
CE Mrs Pat Brandum
Sec Mr Kevin Rodgers
Ch Mr Mick Rawson
Total Staff 649
Region West Midlands
Owned or managed 18306
Rt 16948 **GN** 16238 **OP** 710
SO 12 **NSO** 1346 **Tot lets** 2422
GN bs 15967
Development Total 328
NBA 167 **NBC** 161
Parent Association WM Housing Group

Whitmore Vale HA Ltd
○ Charitable HA
TSA Reg ✗ 🕶
Whitmore Vale House, Churt Road,
Hindhead, Surrey, GU26 6NL
T 01428 604477
E secretary@whitmorevale.co.uk
W www.whitmorevale.co.uk
CE Mr Ryan Kelley
Sec Mr Ryan Kelley
Ch Ms H Delaney Hall
Total Staff 74
Region South East
Tenant Type % Family 2% **Single** 98%

Willesden Green Housing Co-operative Ltd
★ Co-operative Society
TSA Reg ✓
c/o 20 Grosvenor Gardens, London,
Greater London, NW2 4QP
E willesdengreenhc@yahoo.co.uk
Sec Mr Philip Ansell
Ch Miss Mary McCarthy
Total Staff 0
Region London
Owned or managed 18
Rt 18 **GN** 18
Tenant Type % Family 20%
Single 80%

Willow Housing and Care Ltd
○ Charitable HA
TSA Reg ✓ 🅿 🔑 🕶 ◊
Olympic Office Centre, 7th Floor,
8 Fulton Road, Wembley,
Middlesex, HA9 0NU
T 020 8900 0185
E willow@willowhousing.org.uk
W www.willowhousing.org.uk
CE Ms Judy Peaker
Sec Mr Richard Reger
Ch Mrs Charmian Boyd
Total Staff 59
Region London
Owned or managed 970
Rt 968 **OP** 968 **SO** 2 **Tot lets** 61
GN bs 0
Tenant Type % Older 100%
Development Total 20
Rt 40 **OP** 40 **NBC** 20
Parent Association Network Housing Group Ltd

Willow Park Housing Trust
☆ Charitable Company
TSA Reg ✓ 🔲 🚐 🅿 🔑 ♦ ◊
Willow Park House, 8 Poundswick
Lane, Wythenshawe, Manchester,
Lancashire, M22 9TA
T 0161 946 9500
E enquiries@willow-park.co.uk
W www.willow-park.co.uk
CE Mr Joe Doherty
Sec Mr Michael Gerrard
Ch Mr Dennis Finnegan
Total Staff 340
Region North West
Owned or managed 8050
Rt 7849 **GN** 7780 **OP** 69 **SO** 183
NSO 18 **Tot lets** 599 **GN bs** 7780
Tenant Type % Family 52%
Older 45% **Single** 48%
Development Total 174
NBA 110 **NBC** 64
Parent Association Wythenshawe Community Housing Group

Wiltshire Rural HA Ltd
○ Charitable HA
TSA Reg ✓
20 High Street, Bromham,
Chippenham, Wiltshire, SN15 2EX
T 01380 850916
E test@wrha.co.uk
W www.wrha.co.uk
CE Mrs Gillian Shell
Sec Mrs Gillian Shell
Ch Mr Richard Kitson
Total Staff 6
Region South West
Owned or managed 239
Rt 239 GN 239
Tenant Type % Family 71%
Older 12% Single 17%

Winchester Working Mens HS Ltd
○ Charitable HA
TSA Reg ✓
6a Ronald Bowker Court,
Greenhill Road, Winchester,
Hampshire, SO22 5EA
T 01962 733338
E 11lang@tiscali.co.uk
Sec Mr James Digby
Ch Mr R F J Steel
Total Staff 2
Region South East
Owned or managed 92
Rt 92 GN 92
Tenant Type % Family 89%
Older 11%

Windsor and District HA
■ Non-Charitable HA
TSA Reg ✓ 🖥️ 🔒 🔑 🕶️ ◊
Parkside House, 33-39 Sheet Street,
Windsor, Berkshire, SL4 1BY
T 0300 123 1567
E radiandirect@radian.co.uk
W www.radian.co.uk
CE Mr Lindsay Todd
Sec Mr Terry Walker
Ch Mr Peter Coleman
Total Staff 10
Region South East
Owned or managed 4047
Rt 3939 GN 3439 Sup 87 OP 413
SO 101 NSO 7 Tot lets 400
GN bs 3361
Tenant Type % Family 26%
Older 53% Single 21%
Development Total 45
NBA 30 NBC 15
Parent Association
Radian Group Ltd

Wirral Methodist HA Ltd
○ Charitable HA
TSA Reg ✓ 🏠 🔑
Oswald House, 42 Hamilton Street,
Birkenhead, Merseyside, CH41 5AE
T 0151 647 5471
E admin@wmhaltd.org.uk
W www.wmhaltd.org.uk
CE Mr Alun L Hughes, FRICS
Sec Mr Colin Burgess
Ch Mr Mike Howlett
Total Staff 21
Region North West
Owned or managed 767
Rt 749 GN 564 Sup 73 OP 112
SO 18 Tot lets 104 GN bs 546
Tenant Type % Family 37%
Older 31% Single 32%
Development Total 12
Rt 21 GN 8 Sup 13 NBA 4 NBC 8

Wirral Partnership Homes
☆ Charitable Company
TSA Reg ✓
🖥️ 📱 🕶️ 🏠 🔑 🕯️ 🕶️
6 Europa Boulevard, Birkenhead,
Wirral, Merseyside, CH41 4PE
T 0151 666 7001
E feedback@wphomes.org.uk
W www.wphomes.org.uk
CE Mr Brian Simpson
Sec Mr Patrick McCarthy
Ch Mr Gerard Pearson
Total Staff 553
Region North West
Owned or managed 12839
Rt 12396 GN 10599 Sup 23 OP 1774
SO 443 Tot lets 1094 GN bs 10576
Tenant Type % Family 43%
Older 16% Single 41%
Development Total 19
Rt 400 GN 400 NBA 15 NBC 4

Witham HA Ltd
○ Charitable HA
TSA Reg ✓ 🕶️
Podsbrook House, Guithavon Street,
Witham, Essex, CM8 1DR
T 01376 515017
E info@withamhousingassociation.
co.uk
W www.withamhousingassociation.
co.uk
CE Mr Anthony Nye
Sec Mrs Lynne Shea
Ch Mr Anthony Nye
Total Staff 2
Region East of England
Owned or managed 40
Rt 40 OP 40
Tenant Type % Older 100%

WM Housing Group
■ Non-Charitable HA
TSA Reg ✓ 🕶️ ◊
Barnsley Hall, Barnsley Hall Road,
Bromsgrove, Worcestershire,
B61 0TX
T 01527 556400
E info@wmhousing.co.uk
W www.wmhousing.co.uk
CE Mrs Pat Brandum
Sec Miss Zoe Moncrieff
Ch Mr Roger Griffiths
Total Staff 69
Region West Midlands
Subsidiary Association(s) Kemble
Housing Ltd; Nexus (Midlands) HA
(2005) Ltd; Optima Community
Association; West Mercia Homes
Ltd; Whitefriars Housing Group Ltd

Wokingham Area Housing Society Ltd
○ Charitable HA
TSA Reg ✓
c/o 1 Fernhill Cottages, Toutley
Road, Wokingham, RG41 1QJ
T 07816 590537
E wokinghamareahousingsociety@
googlemail.com
W www.wahs.co.uk
Sec Mrs Barbara Hunter
Ch Jean Auty
Total Staff 0
Region South East
Owned or managed 30
Rt 15 GN 15 NSO 15
Tenant Type % Older 100%

Women's Pioneer Housing
○ Charitable HA
TSA Reg ✓ 🏠 🕶️
227 Wood Lane, London,
Greater London, W12 0EX
T 020 8749 7112
E info@womenspioneer.co.uk
W www.womenspioneer.co.uk
CE Ms Janet Davies
Sec Ms Jane Harrison
Ch Ms Leah Hurst
Total Staff 36
Region London
Owned or managed 986
Rt 986 GN 802 Sup 6 OP 178
Tenant Type % Family 20%
Older 25% Single 55%
Development Total 6
Rt 6 GN 5 OP 1 NBC 6

Worcester Community Housing
☆ Charitable Company
TSA Reg ✓ ▢ 🔲 💰 🏠 🔑 🤝
Progress House, Midland Road,
Worcester, Worcestershire,
WR5 1DU
T 01905 670200
E wchtalk@wchnet.co.uk
W www.wchnet.co.uk
CE Mr Stewart Mountfield
Sec Mr Andy Howarth
Ch Mr Chris Almgill
Total Staff 191
Region West Midlands
Owned or managed 5259
Rt 5031 GN 4175 Sup 40 OP 816
SO 228 Tot lets 507 GN bs 3825
Tenant Type % Family 75%
Older 20% Single 5%
Development Total 23
NBA 23

Worth CPT Ltd
TSA Reg ✗
10 Newfoundland Close,
Worth Matravers, Swanage,
Dorset, BH19 3LX
T 01929 439130
W worthcpt.org
Sec Ms Bridget Downton
Ch Mr Bob Kenyon
Total Staff 0
Region South West

Worthing Homes Ltd
☆ Charitable Company
TSA Reg ✓ 💰 🏠 🔑 🤝
Davison House, North Street,
Worthing, West Sussex, BN11 1ER
T 01903 703100
E info@worthing-homes.org.uk
W www.worthing-homes.org.uk
CE Mr Robin King
Sec Mr Robin King
Ch Christopher Polden
Total Staff 95
Region South East
Owned or managed 3413
Rt 3110 GN 2815 Sup 18 OP 277
SO 303 Tot lets 285 GN bs 2663
Tenant Type % Family 24%
Older 46% Single 30%
Development Total 113
Rt 188 GN 188 NBC 113

Wulvern Housing
■ Non-Charitable HA
TSA Reg ✓ ▢ 🔲 💰 🏠 🔑 🤝
Wulvern House, Electra Way, Crewe,
Cheshire, CW1 6GW
T 01270 503500
E enquiries@wulvernhousing.org.uk
W www.wulvernhousing.org.uk
CE Mrs Sue Lock
Sec Mr David Beardmore
Ch Mrs Barbara Shaw
Total Staff 219
Region North West
Owned or managed 5501
Rt 5246 GN 4136 Sup 21 OP 1089
SO 155 NSO 100 Tot lets 939
GN bs 4036
Tenant Type % Family 34%
Older 50% Single 14%
Development Total 127
Rt 103 GN 37 OP 66 LCHO 25
NBA 65 NBC 62

Wyedean HA Ltd
○ Charitable HA
TSA Reg ✓
11 St John Street, Coleford,
Gloucestershire, GL16 8AP
T 01594 838000
E admin@wyedean.fednet.org.uk
W www.wyedean.org
CE Mr Neil Pascoe
Sec Mr Neil Pascoe
Ch Mrs Alison Childs
Total Staff 8
Regions South West +
West Midlands
Owned or managed 446
Rt 446 GN 424 OP 22
Tenant Type % Family 70%
Older 10% Single 20%

Wyndham HA Ltd
○ Charitable HA
TSA Reg ✓ 🔑
Wyndham House, Plantation Road,
Oxford, Oxfordshire, OX2 6JJ
T 01865 511239
E info@wyndhamhousing.org
W www.wyndhamhousing.org
CE Mr Phillip Smithson
Sec Mr Phillip Smithson
Ch Mr Allan Taylor
Total Staff 10
Region South East
Owned or managed 67
Rt 33 OP 33 SO 34 Tot lets 0
GN bs 0
Tenant Type % Older 100%

Wyre Forest Community Housing Ltd
✪ Not-for-Profit Company
TSA Reg ✓ 💰 🏠 🔑 🤝 💧
3 Foley Grove, Foley Business Park,
Stourport Road, Kidderminster,
Worcestershire, DY11 7PT
T 01562 733000
E information@communityhg.com
W www.communityhg.com
CE Mr Ray Brookes
Sec Mr David Knowlton
Ch Mr David Morgan
Total Staff 0
Region West Midlands
Owned or managed 3644
Rt 3528 GN 3325 Sup 6 OP 197
SO 116 Tot lets 291 GN bs 3313
Tenant Type % Family 39%
Older 37% Single 24%
Development Total 123
Rt 296 GN 207 Sup 86 OP 3
LCHO 8 NBA 79 NBC 44
Parent Association
The Community Housing Group

Wyre Forest Sheltered Housing Ltd
○ Charitable HA
TSA Reg ✓ 🤝 💧
3 Foley Grove, Foley Business Park,
Kidderminster, Worcestershire,
DY11 7PT
T 01562 733000
E information@communityhg.com
W www.wfshcare.co.uk
CE Mr Ray Brookes
Sec Mr David Knowlton
Ch Mr J Kelly
Total Staff 0
Region West Midlands
Owned or managed 1944
Rt 1944 GN 43 OP 1901
Tenant Type % Older 100%
Parent Association
The Community Housing Group

Yy

Yarlington Housing Group
○ Charitable HA
TSA Reg ✓
Lupin Way, Alvington, Yeovil,
Somerset, BA22 8WN
T 01935 404500
E corporate@yhg.co.uk
W www.yhg.co.uk
CE Mr Gary Orr
Sec Mrs Caroline Moore
Ch Roger Powell
Total Staff 318
Region South West
Owned or managed 9402
Rt 8673 GN 7051 OP 1622 SO 718
NSO 11 Tot lets 1070 GN bs 7003
Tenant Type % Family 45%
Older 40% Single 15%
Development Total 576
Rt 142 GN 127 OP 15 LCHO 60
NBA 411 NBC 165

Yarrow Housing
○ Charitable HA
TSA Reg ✗
216 Goldhawk Road, London,
Greater London, W12 9NX
T 020 8735 4600
E info@yarrowhousing.org.uk
W www.yarrowhousing.org.uk
CE Mr Tim Hughes
Sec Mr Tim Hughes
Ch Ms Bernadette Kenny
Total Staff 224
Region London
Tenant Type % Family 3% Single 98%

YCH Developments Ltd
○ Charitable HA
TSA Reg ✗ ◊
Brook House, 4 Gladstone Road,
Scarborough, North Yorkshire,
YO12 7BH
T 0845 065 5656
Total Staff 0
Region Yorkshire & Humberside
Parent Association
Yorkshire Coast Homes Ltd

YH Residential Ltd
✪ Not-for-Profit Company
TSA Reg ✗ ◊
Space Property, 44 Call Lane, Leeds,
West Yorkshire, LS1 6DT
T 0113 243 3142
E enquiries@spaceproperty.co.uk
W www.spaceproperty.co.uk
CE Ms Sally Lynch
Sec Ms Grace Dalley
Ch Mr Derek Lawrence
Total Staff 0
Region Yorkshire & Humberside
Parent Association
Yorkshire Housing Ltd

YMCA Derbyshire
☆ Charitable Company
TSA Reg ✓
London Road, Wilmorton, Derby,
Derbyshire, DE24 8UT
T 01332 572076
E operations@derbyymca.org.uk
W www.ymcaderbyshire.org.uk
CE Mrs Gillian Sewell
Sec Ms Jackie Wain
Ch Ms Hilary Disney
Total Staff 119
Region East Midlands
Owned or managed 83
Rt 83 Sup 83
Tenant Type % Single 100%

YMCA Norfolk
❑ Charitable Trust
TSA Reg ✓
48 St Giles Street, Norwich, Norfolk,
NR2 1LP
T 01603 630049
W www.ymca-norfolk.org.uk
CE Mr Tim Sweeting
Sec Mr Tim Sweeting
Ch Mr Richard Pennington
Total Staff 96
Region East of England
Owned or managed 208
Rt 208 Sup 208
Tenant Type % Single 100%

York HA Ltd
○ Charitable HA
TSA Reg ✓
2 Alpha Court, Monks Cross Drive,
Huntington, York, North Yorkshire,
YO32 9WN
T 01904 636061
E info@yorkha.org.uk
W www.yorkha.org.uk
CE Ms Julia Histon
Sec Ms Julia Histon
Ch Mr Jolyon Harrison
Total Staff 50
Region Yorkshire & Humberside
Owned or managed 809

Rt 780 GN 353 Sup 284 OP 143
NSO 29
Tenant Type % Family 24%
Older 20% Single 56%
Development Total 48
Rt 24 GN 12 Sup 12 NBA 21
NBC 27

Yorkshire Coast Homes Ltd
☆ Charitable Company
TSA Reg ✓ ◊
Brook House, 4 Gladstone Road,
Scarborough, North Yorkshire,
YO12 7BH
T 0845 065 5656
E info@ych.org.uk
W www.ych.org.uk
CE Mr Shaun Tymon
Sec Mr Shaun Tymon
Ch Mr Tony Campbell
Total Staff 109
Region Yorkshire & Humberside
Owned or managed 4685
Rt 4489 GN 4293 OP 196 SO 196
Tot lets 433 GN bs 4137
Tenant Type % Family 65%
Older 32% Single 3%
Development Total 127
NBA 67 NBC 60
Subsidiary Association(s)
YCH Developments Ltd

Yorkshire Housing Ltd
○ Charitable HA
TSA Reg ✓
Dysons Chambers, 12-14 Briggate,
Leeds, LS1 6ER
T 0113 825 6000
E enquiries@yorkshirehousing.co.uk
W www.yorkshirehousing.co.uk
CE Mr Mervyn Jones
Sec Ms Gill Baker
Ch Mr James Taylor
Total Staff 748
Regions Yorkshire & Humberside +
North West
Owned or managed 15626
Rt 14740 GN 11166 Sup 548
OP 3026 SO 790 NSO 96
Tot lets 2423 GN bs 10339
Tenant Type % Family 52%
Older 20% Single 28%
Development Total 1097
Rt 641 GN 641 NBA 608 NBC 489
Subsidiary Association(s)
YH Residential Ltd

Yorkshire Ladies Council (Hostels) Ltd
☆ Charitable Company
TSA Reg ✓ 🕶
Forest Hill, 11 Park Crescent, Leeds,
West Yorkshire, LS8 1DH
T 0113 266 7247
W www.foresthill-leeds.org.uk
CE Mrs Elizabeth Thring
Sec Mrs Beverley Hollis
Ch Mrs Elizabeth Thring
Total Staff 6
Region Yorkshire & Humberside
Owned or managed 30
Rt 30 **OP** 30
Tenant Type % Older 100%

You
☆ Charitable Company
TSA Reg ✗ ♦ 🕶
South Wing, Admiral House,
43 High Street, Fareham,
Hampshire, PO16 7BQ
T 01329 825930
E reception@lifeyouwant.org.uk
W www.lifeyouwant.org.uk
CE Ms Nicola Youern
Sec Mr Jonathan Crutchfield
Ch Ms Tessa Short
Total Staff 498
Region South East
Owned or managed 226
Rt 170 **Sup** 170 **NSO** 56
Tenant Type % Single 100%

Zz

Zebra HA Ltd
○ Charitable HA
TSA Reg ✓
5-13 Glendower Place, London,
Greater London, SW7 3DU
T 020 7584 2906
E admin@zebrahousing.com
W www.zebrahousing.com
CE Mr Peter Gray
Sec Mr Peter Gray
Ch Ms Alison Ahearn
Total Staff 11
Region London
Owned or managed 124
NSO 124
Tenant Type % Family 68%
Single 32%

Associates

Associates are local authority departments considering stock transfer as part of a membership. They receive discounts on Federation publications and conferences plus free copies of the quarterly Bulletin. ALMOs are also eligible for associate membership.

A1 Housing Bassetlaw
Executive Department, Carlton Forrest House, Hundred Acre Lane, Worksop, Nottinghamshire, S81 0TS
T 01909 534466
W www.a1housing.co.uk

A1 Housing is a proactive organisation that is leading the way in using ground and air heat source pumps to improve energy efficiency and fuel poverty in the rural areas of Bassetlaw. A1 provides high levels of housing and repair services to tenants in the locality.

Barnet Homes Ltd
Barnet House,
1255 High Road, Whetstone, London, Greater London, N20 0EJ
T 020 8359 4803
W www.barnethomes.org

Set up in 2004 to manage the London Borough of Barnet's housing stock, we have been inspected twice and assessed as a 2 star (good) service with promising prospects. We are on track to complete our £185m programme of Decent Homes improvements in 2011. Our vision is to improve lives and provide quality homes that inspire pride of place and create vibrant and lasting communities.

Cheltenham Borough Homes
Cheltenham House,
Clarence Street, Cheltenham, Gloucestershire, GL50 3JR
T 01242 775310
W www.cheltborohomes.org

Cheltenham Borough Homes is a high performing ALMO, which has been managing and maintaining over 5,000 homes in Cheltenham since 2003. In March 2007 we were assessed as "excellent, with excellent prospects".

Contact Mr Paul Davies

Gloucester City Homes
Railway House, Bruton Way, Gloucester, GL1 1DG
T 0800 408 2000
E customer.services@ gloscityhomes.co.uk
W www.gloscityhomes.co.uk

Gloucester City Homes (GCH) manages and provides housing services for over 4,800 residents' homes in Gloucester.

Homes in Sedgemoor
Bridgwater House, King Square, Bridgwater, Somerset, TA6 3AR
W www.homesinsedgemoor.org

Hounslow Homes
St Catherines House,
2 Hanworth Road, Feltham, Middlesex, TW13 5AB
W www.hounslowhomes.org.uk

Nottingham City Homes Ltd
14 Hounds Gate, Nottingham, Nottinghamshire, NG1 7BA
T 0115 915 7392
E firstname.lastname@ nottinghamcityhomes.org.uk
W www.nottinghamcityhomes. org.uk

Contact Ms Gemma Atkinson

Stevenage Homes
Daneshill House, Danestrete, Stevenage, Hertfordshire, SG1 1HN
T 01438 242666
E deborah.ward@ stevenagehomes.org.uk
W www.stevenagehomes.org.uk

Stevenage Homes Ltd are responsible for the management and maintenance of the Stevenage Borough Council's housing stock of over 8,000 properties. Our vision is to help make life better for the people of Stevenage by providing excellent housing services.

Wolverhampton Homes
Chillington Fields Industrial Estate, Off Hickman Avenue, Wolverhampton, West Midlands, WV1 2BY
T 01902 556789
E homes.direct@ wolverhamptonhomes.org.uk
W www.wolverhamptonhomes. org.uk

Manages the social housing stock for the local authority.

Contact Mrs Ruth Fletcher

The Federation subscriber scheme offers a range of benefits to commercial, public and third sector organisations who wish to support the sector and the wider neighbourhood agenda in which we operate. Further information is available from: www.housing.org.uk.

Charity

Energy Saving Trust
21 Dartmouth Street,
London, SW1H 9BP
T 0207 222 0101
E energy-advice@est.org.uk
W www.energysavingtrust.org.uk

Money Advice Trust
21 Garlick Hill,
London, EC4V 2AU
T 0121 410 6269
E andrew.byrom@moneyadvicetrust.org
W www.moneyadvicetrust.org

Energy

Ebico Ltd
Wittas House, Station Lane, Witney,
Oxfordshire OX28 4BH
T 0199 389 4414
E partners@ebico.co.uk
W www.ebico.co.uk

EDF Energy
329 Portland Road, Hove, BN3 5SU
T 0800 096 9000
E eeprojectsupport@edfenergy.com
W www.edfenergy.com

SSE Energy Solutions
Robert Brown House, Pipers Way,
Thatcham RG19 4AZ
T 0163 527 2191
E energy.solutions@sse.com
W www.sse.com

Finance

LEBC Group
City Tower Piccadilly Plaza,
Manchester, M14BT
T 0161 234 0170
E enquiry@lebc-group.com
W www.lebc-group.com

Moore Stephens
150 Aldersgate Street,
London EC1A 4AB
T 0207 334 9191
E roger.lustig@moorestephens.com
W www.moorestephens.com

Sutherland Global Services Ltd
33rd Floor, 30 St Mary Axe, London,
EC3A 8EP
T 0207 138 0920
E simon.speirs@sutherlandglobal.com
W www.sutherlandglobal.com

thinkmoney
Pennington House, Carolina Way,
South Langworthy Road, Salford
Quays, M50 2ZY
T 0161 605 6005
E ian.williams@thinkmoney.com
W www.thinkmoney.co.uk

Western Provident Association
Rivergate House, Blackbrook Park,
Taunton, Somerset, TA1 2PE
T 0182 362 5110
E nftsupport@wpa.org.uk
W www.wpa.org.uk

Housing

Major HA
431 High Street North, Manor Park,
London, E12 6TJ
T 0207 100 7878
E info@majorha.com
W www.majorhousingassociation.com

TenantID
C/O Callcredit, 1 Park Lane,
Leeds, LS3 1EP
T 0113 244 1555
E tenantid@callcreditgroup.com
W www.tenantid.co.uk

Human resources

Carval Computing
Wrest Park, Silsoe, Bedford,
Bedfordshire, MK45 4HS
T 0152 586 3840
E sales@carval.co.uk
W www.carval.co.uk

Frontier Software plc
1 Crompton Court, Attwood Road,
Burntwood Business Park, Burntwood,
WS7 3GG
T 0845 370 3210
E sales@frontiersoftware.com
W www.frontiersoftware.com

Insurance

Health Matters
4, The Cobalt Centre, Siskin Parkway
East, Middlemarch Business Park,
Coventry, CV3 4PE
T 0247 651 6083
E simon@health-matters.co.uk
W www.health-matters.co.uk

National Housing Federation Insurance Services
Woodlands, Manton Lane,
Bedford, MK41 7LW
T 0800 952 0224
E enquiry@nfhinsurance.co.uk
W www.nhfinsurance.co.uk

R K Harrison Insurance Services
Woodlands, Manton Lane,
Bedford, MK41 7LW
T 0123 430 5555
E enquiry@rkhis.com
W www.rkhis.com

Zurich Municipal
Zurich House, 2 Gladiator Way,
Farnborough, Hants GU14 6GB
T 0870 241 8050
E info@zurichmunicipal.com
W www.zurichmunicipal.co.uk

IT

Bloxx UK Ltd
The Alba Centre,
Livingston, EH54 7EG
T 0150 642 6976
E info@bloxx.com
W www.bloxx.com

CenterTools Software
Elsten House, Rectory Leys, Ofeord
D'arcy, Cambridgeshire, PE19 5SQ
T 0122 365 5236
E sales@centertools.com
W www.drivelock.com

CloudXL
1 Yardley Business Park, Luckyn Lane,
Basildon, Essex, SS14 3GL
T 0207 096 2700
E info@cloudxl.co.uk
W www.cloudxl.co.uk

Destiny Wireless Ltd
Finance house, Park street, Guildford,
Surrey, GU1 4XB
T 0148 373 4050
E sales@destinywireless.com
W www.destinywireless.com

ESRI (UK) Ltd
Millenium House, 65 Walton Street,
Aylesbury, Bucks, HP21 7QG
T 0129 674 5500
E info@esriuk.com
W www.esriuk.com

Housing IT
Queens Court, Wilmslow Road,
Alderley Edge, SK9 7RR
T 0162 558 4850
E info@housingit.eu
W www.housingit.eu

Love Clean Streets
Barham Court, Teston,
Maidstone, Kent ME18 5BZ
T 0173 252 1799
E info@bbits.co.uk
W www.lovecleanstreets.org/Help

Omfax Systems Ltd
21 The Causeway, Bicester,
Oxon OX26 6AN
T 0186 924 2967
E sales@omfax.co.uk
W www.omfax.co.uk

PIMSS Data Systems
10 Woodside Business Park,
Birkenhead, Wirral, CH41 1EL
T 0800 121 8767
E info@pimss.com
W www.pimss.com

Qube Global Software Ltd
Westgate House, Westgate, Sleaford,
Lincolnshire, NG34 7RJ
T 0152 941 3131
E jlavery@qubeglobal.com
W www.qubeglobal.com

Legal

Citation plc
Citation House, 1 Macclesfield Road,
Wilmslow, Cheshire, SK9 1BZ
T 0162 541 5500
E enquires@citation.co.uk
W www.citation.co.uk

Clarke Willmott LLP
10 Furnival Street,
London, EC4A 1YH
T 0845 209 1000
E jonathan.hulley@clarkewillmott.com

Devonshires Solicitors
30 Finsbury Circus,
London, EC2M 7DT
T 0207 628 7576
E info@devonshires.co.uk
W www.devonshires.com

eShare Ltd
New Market House, Market Street,
Newbury, RG14 5DP
T 0845 200 7829
E marketing@eshareuk.com
W www.eshareuk.com

Perrins Solicitors LLP
10 Waterside,
Station Road, Harpenden,
Hertfordshire, AL5 4US
T 0158 246 6157
E f.perrin@perrins-solicitors.co.uk
W www.perrins-solicitors.co.uk

Trowers & Hamlins LLP
3 Bunhill Row, London, EC1Y 8YZ
T 0207 423 8000
E rhughes@trowers.com
W www.trowers.com

Winckworth Sherwood LLP
Minerva House, 5 Montague Close,
London SE1 9BB
T 0207 593 5000
E info@wslaw.co.uk
W www.wslaw.co.uk

Market research

BMG Research
7 Holt Court , Heneage Street West,
Birmingham Science Park Aston,
Birmingham, B7 4AX
T 0121 333 6006
E info@bmgresearch.co.uk
W www.bmgresearch.co.uk

Hometrack Ltd
6th Floor, The Chambers, Chelsea
Harbour, London, SW10 0XF
T 0845 013 2350
E enquiries@hometrack.co.uk
W www.hometrack.co.uk

Telecommunications

Alternative Networks
Chatfield Court, 56 Chatfield Road,
London SW11 3UL
T 0870 167 0105
E dcookson@alternativenetworks.com
W www.alternativenetworks.com

Intratone / Cogelec
Lincoln House, 300 High Holborn,
London, WC1V 7JH
T 0207 092 6665
E aplasse@intratone.fr
W www.intratone.com

Training & consultancy

Campbell Tickell
Ground Floor,
Olympic Office Centre,
8 Fulton Road, Wembley,
Middlesex, HA9 0NU
T 0208 830 6777
E info@campbelltickell.com
W www.campbelltickell.com

Central Consultancy & Training Ltd

28 Pickford Street, Digbeth,
Birmingham, B5 5QH
T 0121 643 4745
E info@centralconsultancy.co.uk
W www.centralconsultancy.co.uk

Commercial Initiatives Ltd

The Mill House, Yoxall Road, Rugeley,
Staffordshire, WS15 3RZ
T 0844 414 6400
E david.leigh@ci-bcp.com
W www.ci-bcp.com

Consult Capital Ltd

Capital Building, Tyndall Street,
Cardiff, CF10 4AZ
T 0333 240 9778
E info@consultcapital.co.uk
W www.consultcapital.co.uk

Encraft

Perseus House,
3 Chapel Court, Holly Walk,
Leamington Spa, CV32 4YS
T 0192 631 2159
E enquiries@encraft.co.uk
W www.encraft.co.uk

IAM Drive & Survive Ltd

IAM House, 510 Chiswick High Road,
London W4 5RG
T 0870 120 2910
E enquiries@iamdriveandsurvive.co.uk
W www.iamdriveandsurvive.co.uk

Liberata

4th Floor, Weston House, 246 High
Holborn, London EC1V 7EX
T 0207 378 3700
E itsolutions@liberata.com
W www.liberata.com

Opal Wave Solutions Ltd

Opal House, Marlow Courtyard,
27 Little Marlow Road,
Marlow, SL7 1HA
T 0162 889 1110
E jonathan.hall@opalwave.com
W www.opalwave.com

Sector – Housing and Consultancy

17 Rochester Row, Westminster,
London, SW1P 1JB
T 0871 664 6800
E mwatkins@sector-group.com
W www.sector-group.com

Shelton Development Services Ltd

Astra House, The Common,
Cranleigh GU6 8RZ
T 0148 327 8444
E admin@s-d-s.co.uk
W www.s-d-s.co.uk

Utilities Connections Management Ltd

Office 3C, Redwither Tower,
Redwither Business Park,
Wrexham, LL13 9XT
T 0197 866 1800
E info@ucml.co.uk
W www.ucml.co.uk

Other

Brixx Solutions Ltd

Chiltern House, 45 Station Road,
Henley-on-Thames, Oxon, RG9 1AT
T 0149 184 5450
E info@brixx.com
W www.brixx.com

Camelot Property Management Ltd

Unit 4, Pegaso, 20 Westland Place,
London, N1 7JR
T 0845 262 2002
E info@camelotproperty.com
W www.camelotproperty.com

Cox Drew Neale LLP

Crawford House, 1A Willow Street,
London, E4 7EG
T 0208 524 3535
E admin@cdnllp.co.uk
W www.cdnllp.co.uk

ERSA

10 Greycoat Place,
London, SW1P 1SB
T 0207 960 6808
E membership@ersa.org.uk
W www.ersa.org.uk

First Actuarial LLP

2nd Floor, The Square, Basing View,
Basingstoke, RG21 4EB
T 0125 634 0070
E peter.shellswell@firstactuarial.co.uk
W www.firstactuarial.co.uk

haysmacintyre

Fairfax House, 15 Fulwood Place,
London, WC1V 6AY
T 0207 969 5500
E marketing@haysmacintyre.com
W www.haysmacintyre.com

Nexia Smith and Williamson Audit Ltd

25 Moorgate, London EC2R 6AY
T 0207 131 4000
E jenny.pool@smith.williamson.co.uk
W www.nexiasmith.williamson.co.uk

Profile Communication

11 Road One, Winsford,
Cheshire, CW7 3PZ
T 0160 688 8111
E nicola@profilecommunication
W www.profilecommunication.com

Prolog Print Media

Unit 1, Meltham Lane,
Chesterfield, S41 7LG
T 0124 654 3000
E sales@prologprintmedia.co.uk
W www.prologprintmedia.co.uk

Skills & Projects

61 Surrenden Crescent,
Brighton, BN1 6WE
T 0845 539 1962
E mark.anderson@skillsprojects.co.uk
W www.skillsprojects.co.uk

Supra UK

24 The Furlong, Berry Hill
Industrial Estate, Droitwich Spa,
Worcestershire, WR9 9AH
T 0190 577 0333
E sales@keysafe.co.uk
W www.keysafe.co.uk

Telecetera Ltd

Carden Close,
Worcester, WR1 2AR
T 0190 561 2220
E cecilia@telecetera.co.uk
W www.telecetera.co.uk

Xmbrace Ltd

CP House,
Otterspool Way, Watford,
Hertfordshire, WD25 8HP
T 0207 953 5043
E info@xmbrace.com
W www.xmbrace.com

Index of advertisers